Concrete progress

Outstanding cement and concrete researchers who visited or worked at the Concrete Research Laboratory (BFL), Karlstrup, Denmark, 1960–76

1	Dr R W Nurse	6	Dr T C Powers
2	Dr B Mather	7	Professor G Wischers *with the*
3	Professor P A Rehbinder		*author,* Dr G M Idorn (8)
4	H H Bache (BFL)	9	Professor St Brunauer
5	P Nepper-Christensen (BFL)	10	B Osbæck (BFL)

Concrete progress

from antiquity to third millenium

Gunnar M. Idorn

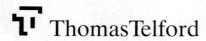

Published by Thomas Telford Publishing, Thomas Telford Services Ltd, 1 Heron Quay, London E14 4J

First published 1997

Distributors for Thomas Telford books are
USA: American Society of Civil Engineers, Publications Sales Department, 345 East 47th Street, New York, NY 10017-2398
Japan: Maruzen Co. Ltd, Book Department, 3–10 Nihonbashi 2-chome, Chuo-ku, Tokyo 103
Australia: DA Books and Journals, 648 Whitehorse Road, Mitcham 3132, Victoria

A catalogue record for this book is available from the British Library

ISBN: 0 7277 2631 5

© G. M. Idorn, 1997

Cover photo: Telegraph Colour Library

Typeset by the Alden Group, Oxford
Printed in Great Britain by Redwood Books, Trowbridge, Wiltshire

Preface

This book deals with the technology that made concrete the most widely used building material in the world in the course of the past hundred years, and the most indispensable for the global socio-economic development in the new millennium. It offers an insight into many people's dedicated, exploratory concrete research, and into strategic planning and management of research and its transfer to engineering practice. It illustrates the role and the consequences of the absence of top-level participative leadership for making the research investments cost effective. It proposes a new paradigm for concrete research to serve the tremendous need for new concrete building and construction in the forthcoming decades.

It was an exciting moment, one evening in 1956, at the petrographic microscope when, in the quest for diagnosing observations on concrete deterioration, the view field caught a 3 mm, triangular flint particle in a thin section of a concrete core from the Oddesund Bridge in north-west Jutland. It revealed irrefutably that alkali-silica gel had exuded out from the swelling cracks in the particle, along their continuations through the adjacent cement paste and had solidified there.

This and numerous subsequent, supporting observations became the "stills" for our mental animation of the cracking and expansion mechanism of harmful alkali-silica reaction in concrete. When that observation proved consistent with the scientists' explanatory perceptions of the conversion of the chemical reaction inside siliceous particles to the mechanical work of fracturing, and with the features of macrocracking and expansion in field concrete, the circle was closed: *we had a holistic concept of alkali-silica reaction in concrete.*

This highlight of imaginative vision and observation methodology in concrete research should be kept in mind when reading in this book about any undertaking for implementation of scientific discoveries in progressive concrete technology and the descriptions of concrete uses in the greater socio-economic developments. The basic foundation for concrete technology progress is indisputably the scientific perception of the material's nature, and the kinetics and thermodynamics of the processes that go on in concrete during production and performance as "geology alive".

On the other hand, serendipity at the petrographic microscope was not considered to override the recognition of damage to field concrete or opportunities for progress in concrete making as the decisive parameters for research strategy decisions by the top-level leaders in the private enterprises and public authorities concerned. For the Danish programme on alkali-silica reaction, the strategy clearly was to assess the nature of the damaging reactions and to find the means to eradicate them. The planning, and the actions for its fulfilment, therefore came to depend on the skills and dedication of the few of us who were employed in the early 1950s and given the opportunity to create a new epoch of concrete research in Denmark. Characteristically, our close interaction with the strategic and funding leaders led to the closure of another circle in the quest for concrete progress: *the creation of consistent alertness towards the cost-benefit issues of concrete research.*

Concurrent with the substantial efforts to ensure the durability of concrete, the situation during the post World War II decades within Denmark and around us incurred exorbitant demands on the rapid growth of concrete production for housing, infrastructure and industrial reconstruction. This engendered high priority for our concrete research to match issues related to mechanization and rationalization of concrete production methods. Our strategy and its breakdown into research priorities which emerged from the multifarious industrial and engineering needs aimed at service for:

☐ high performance service life of field concrete
☐ corresponding new, accelerated production technology and process monitoring methods.

The abrupt discontinuation in 1976 of the progressive concrete research in Denmark, and similar events in other countries in the wake of the oil crisis, offered me the opportunity as a one-man, international consultant to short-cut the common tortuosity of concrete research transfer to engineering practice for clients in the materials industries and engineering and construction practice. The past interactive R&D policy proved then to have built up a prodigious knowledge base for a consultancy service, both regarding investigations of unsatisfactory performance quality of field concrete, and for assistance to new concrete technology development.

Over the years, special commercial/juridical attitudes in some countries directed consulting services towards engagements as experts in litigation. This development is, in principle, depressive because the funding of research and expert studies in litigation cases does not aim at productive progress of technology, but is used in defensive or accusing juridical argumentation, which merely engenders capital transfer between the economic contestants. The expenditure of several hundred million dollars in legal cases in the richer industrial countries during the past decade is an unfortunate paradox in the face of the rising, global demographic evolution. The gist of this perspective is that concrete research needs a profoundly new paradigm for strategy and leadership. My narrative terminates with a proposal for such a renovation.

Seen in this context, it was therefore a rewarding moment one December evening in 1996 when, in a television feature of the production of tunnel elements for the magnificent Øresund Link project, a workman showed thermosensors being mounted on reinforcing bars and explained that they were there to monitor the curing process, i.e. to inhibit thermal cracking of the concrete. This curing technology was conceived at the BFL Karlstrup in 1960–61, when our maturity control from 1953 for winter concreting came into demand for accelerated curing in the new precast industry. After persistent and original research, it was introduced on trial in precast plants in 1971, and was applied on the Sallingsund Bridge project and at the Dansk Eternit-Fabrik in 1975. By subsequent computerization and extension to monitoring the stress development in the early phase of concrete curing, this landmark BFL achievement has become an integral part of the monitoring system control for all major construction projects and precast industries in the Nordic countries, and will now, irresistibly, conquer global concrete production technology.

When the circle is now ineluctably closing for half a century's involvement with concrete progress, readers may ask if, with the telescopic view of hindsight, there are other such recognizable evidences of a philosophy of value for those who will work with concrete research and practice in the third millennium. Well, the book gives its secrets away through reading — but yes, there is one particular issue to be highlighted for younger readers.

In the course of 1945, building and construction commenced in the euphoria of the cessation of destruction, notwithstanding the hopelessly inadequate means at hand, and with the overwhelming national need for concrete in its socio-economic functions clearly visible to any civil engineer, company or public authority. This ubiquitous situation in victorious, defeated and liberated countries made singular dedication a common virtue in the creation of new cement and concrete research within nations, as well as for the renewal of lost, international exchange and cooperation.

Now, on the threshold of the new century, the national identities of cement and concrete production and utilizations are obscured in the industrial countries and also disappearing in many developing ones. The benefits of concrete research and development are, therefore, not recognizable as primarily creating welfare for the homelands' inhabitants; technology, economic trends, and the world demography mean that the beneficiaries of concrete progress will be the people emerging from miserable conditions in the developing world.

Thus, our national challenge in 1945 to work for tangible socio-economic progress year after year for 5 million people on $40\,000\,\mathrm{km}^2$ has changed irreversibly to working for an increasing 4 billion people in continents of 100 million km^2 with no recognizable yardstick for returns on the investments of personal efforts and dedication. In fact, in many situations, economic and political complications may be more easily perceived as barriers against, rather than as realistic opportunities for, concrete progress.

Nevertheless, progress needs to be made where the demands are, not where they have been; and 50 years ago the obstacles also appeared insurmountable — lacking the present day knowledge base, instrumentation, equipment and abundant capital resources. I am therefore confident that, irresistibly, the circle will close around the world, with updated concrete research and practice being developed into a global, cost-effective entity; the indispensable foundation for a concrete world constitution.

Acknowledgements

To recognize benefactors, associates and everyone else who deserve thanks for advice, coopera-
tive assistance, financial support and leadership in the course of about 50 years of joint work
for concrete progress would be an impossible, Sisyphean endeavour. Nevertheless, there are
certain categories of people and individuals who must be mentioned because their intangible
qualities empowered them to influence to a very high degree the events and developments
described in this book.

The management of the Danish company RAMBOLL, consulting engineers, has, since 1992, provided all the necessary facilities and operational assistance which has made it possible to compile the documentation and to write the manuscript of this book and to undertake the required external communications. Interaction with progressive development of the consultants' services to developing countries has been an important asset for my perception of the role of concrete in the further socio-economic rise of the standard of living for their populations. Altogether, the assistance offered by the company has been indispensable in accomplishing the authorship.

Aalborg Portland A/S has offered free access to documentation from the BFL Karlstrup epoch, 1960–1976.

During the first eight years as port and coastal engineer on the remote west Jutland coast, an experience of lasting value was the tutelage in quality concrete making at exposed sites offered by the professional concrete making crews and foremen, the more experienced lone, outposted colleagues up and down the coastline, and, not least, the meticulous documentary reports and records from past concrete construction works and performance inspections by the preceding coastal engineers.

At the DNIBR in Copenhagen from 1953, the emerging group of civil engineers depended for their introduction into the world of concrete research on education by the academic mineralogists and chemists, the late H. Pauly and A. Tovborg Jensen.

During the 1950s, the British Building Research Station, with F. M. Lea's world-famous group of basic and applied cement and concrete researchers, became almost a "joint-venture partner" in the studies of alkali-silica reaction, and long-term close contacts endured with R. W. Nurse and with J. Figg, later at Ove Arup & Partners. During the BFL years, the Cement and Concrete Association, with R. Rowe in charge, became a frequent collaborator, especially through the Cembureau research cooperation, which also made the colleagues at VDZ in Germany a source of fruitful exchange and support. Professor M. Moranville-Regourd offered valuable cooperative training studies of cement chemistry and cement hydration from the advanced French school of applied X-ray crystallography.

Contacts in the USA began with T. C. Powers, G. Verbeck and L. S. Brown at the Portland Cement Association, Kay and B. Mather at the Corps of Engineers, and R. C. Mielenz at USBR during the 1950s, providing a correspondence course education in the physics and chemistry of cement hydration and the properties of hardened cement paste, and in petrography of concrete as a means of diagnosing the causes of distress. Many visits to the USA, beginning with the 4th International Symposium on the Chemistry of Cement in Washington DC and Skokie, Ill., 1960, developed the contacts and joint attendance of conferences. Over the years, ASTM, TRB and ACI offered several annual meetings and committee activities for give-and-take cooperation. When commercial joint-venture studies and consulting services also came into the picture, direct cooperation with J. Skalny, first at Martin Marietta, later W. R. Grace, S. Diamond, Purdue University, and D. M. Roy at Pennsylvania State University came to share exchange and consulting services.

An invited three-week lecture tour in 1982 to Beijing, Nanjing and Shanghai, arranged by Professor Tang Mingshu of the Nanjing Institute of Chemical Technology, was an important eye-opener to the tremendous challenge for concrete researchers in a developing nation comprising one-quarter of the world's population. It also gave me an appreciation for the skill and dedication of the Chinese scientists and engineers.

In Europe, the membership of EIRMA in the 1970s had provided an exceptional insight into the professional methodology for research planning and management in the larger European manufacturing industries. Their systematic approaches for making long-term exploratory research interact with applied research, product development, and market feasibility assessments for overall cost-effectiveness and commercial profitability were awe-inspiring.

The R & D management experience became particularly applicable in consulting service to the American Electric Power Research Institute regarding the uses of fly ash in concrete, the American National Materials Advisory Board regarding the cement and concrete research in the USA, and to the innovative Atlantic Cement, Inc., and Civil & Marine Ltd, in the USA and the UK, respectively. These two companies invested successfully in integrated explanatory and applied research with the objective of advancing production and sales of granulated, ground blast-furnace slag for improvement of Portland cement concrete. The consulting service cooperation with these companies confirmed that cost-effective research and transfer to new technology require interactive, international cooperation under industrial, market-oriented leadership.

Although Part III, about my role as special consultant in legal court trials and arbitration cases, deliberately does not include the services offered by G. M. Idorn Consult A/S after 1986, special acknowledgements are due to W. W. Suojanen, attorney at law, Irvine, California, and R. W. Suderman, Manager of Quality Assurance and Special Projects, LAFARGE CANADA Inc. They were the client's representatives in the major legal conflict about damage to 350 000

Acknowledgements

concrete railway sleepers in the north-east United States, in which I served as co-ordinating expert investigator from late 1989 to 1995. Their consistent requirements to the integrity of the technical-scientific expertise as the documentary basis for the legal operations warranted the winning juridical response to the experts' work and also made the entire investigation a constructive contribution to concrete technology progress in the USA.

Frequent participation in ACI conventions and in ACI committee work, and in conferences in North America and many other countries, consistently updated knowledge about the major trends in cement and concrete technology and research development and offered platforms for personal contributions and contact exchange.

My participation in the moulding of researchers, consultants and industry professionals of different nationalities into teams capable of making tangible concrete technology innovations, gained strength from the international experience, but above all from the professional and collegial teamwork which the staff at the BFL Karlstrup had developed into a first-class performance art through sixteen years of service for concrete progress. When their holistic concept of interactive research and practice becomes broadly adopted in a new mainstream methodology it will be the finest acknowledgement of many other past pioneers on whose works the present day achievements depend.

———

Throughout the work on this book, collegial discussions with and supplementing information from former BFL associates, such as P. Nepper-Christensen, Z. Fördös and H. H. Bache, and former colleagues of RAMBOLL, G. M. Idorn Consult have been very helpful. Mrs Kirsten Toft, RAMBOLL, has, with unending patience, prepared and repeatedly helped to adjust the series of manuscripts and the pertaining correspondence.

———

RAMBOLL supported publication of the book by special pre-publication purchase of 200 copies. F. L. Smidth & Co. A/S and Aalborg Portland made a joint pre-publication purchase of 200 copies. COWI Consulting Engineers A/S and Dansk Beton Institut A/S each made pre-publication purchases of 50 copies.

These expressions of interest in the contents of the work are also highly appreciated.

Contents

Contents

Contents

Contents

Summary

Part I of *Concrete progress* is introduced by retrospectively highlighting the international history of concrete technology and uses. It traces the socio-economic impact of concrete from the magnificent construction epoch of Roman antiquity, to the Industrial Revolution in the nineteenth century, and its continuity between the two World Wars. Then, in more detail, it describes concrete technology progress during the first post World War II decades, which coincided with – and indeed depended on – the demands for concrete to house millions of homeless people and to reconstruct the industrial manufacturing capacity and the infrastructures. I have emphasized the concurrent entrance of scientific concepts and methodology into concrete technology research. In a new generation of dedicated research engineers and scientists, I became involved in the national and international efforts to match the tremendous obligations and the technological innovation opportunities.

I refer to my first eight years' occupation from 1945 as coastal engineer, gaining concrete construction experience, which was an important prelude to my transfer into the emergent Danish concrete technology research in 1953. But the core subject of the review is the record of the sixteen years of teamwork at the Concrete Research Laboratory, Karlstrup, the BFL, from its commencement in 1960, through its development into a cost-effective entity of cement and concrete R & D for the cement industry in Denmark, until its closure in 1976. I describe the reasons for the abrupt cessation of the research funding, which were not merely the consequences of the oil crisis from 1973. There were also more profound changes in the market situations for cement industries, altered commercial investment priorities due to the general welfare growth, and the beginning of the high-technology revolution. In retrospect, it is no surprise that the new hard- and software mass production industries and their sophisticated R & D got the upper hand over our research for a smokestack industry with a still craft-dominated market sector.

The review of concrete research in this epoch in Denmark is, in many ways, illustrative of what happened simultaneously in other, much larger countries. Centres of excellence in basic cement and concrete research disappeared or were gradually choked, and turned into consulting entities or were forced to bid for public project funding to exist. Hence, much of the international basis for further technology progress in concrete production and performance withered away, paradoxically at a time when the need for global acceleration of concrete utilization due to the population explosion in developing countries was just dawning on the horizon.

We have still not seen a renaissance of the past power of concrete research to match the new demands, and I believe, therefore, that the record of our BFL experience is still in many respects a useful model for new innovative enterprises.

Part II is complementary to Part I in the sense that, while that is a broad "inter-country biography" of concrete research and technology development, seen from the perspective of a Danish microcosm towards the greater world, Part II is in fact a unique "vertical" dissection of almost 60 years of international research and transfer investments on one particular subject: alkali-silica reaction (ASR) as a cause of distress in field concrete.

The research in the USA after 1940 engendered complementary research in the UK, Australia and Denmark. I have described how the basic nature of the reaction and its potential global implications were clarified in about 1960. It is – and also seemed to me at the time – an odd paradox, that antagonism within the cement industries prevented further recognition of this cause of distress until the ten international conferences, during 1974–1996, gradually, but with a great deal of resistance in many countries, established that ASR must be considered seriously throughout the world.

In the scrutiny of ASR research, I have drawn on the ten conference proceedings, many other published papers – altogether probably more than 20 000 pages – and my consistent personal engagements. That makes the story of this international research on ASR a "first-hand" account of the rise and decline over six decades of original, science-rooted concrete technology research which gradually, along with the disappearance of participative top-level leadership, became infected by the general reductional philosophy and laboratory empiricism in concrete research. In the concluding state-of-the-art evaluation, I suggest ways and means for establishing final solutions to the remaining outstanding problems of ASR.

Part III describes major research transfer projects in which I became engaged as an independent, international consultant, following the closure of the BFL, until 1986. This review shows that the approaches from clients in many countries were thanks to an established reputation and intense international cooperative investments over the years. The requests for consulting services made my experience with concrete deterioration, industrial concrete processing, the effects of fly ash and ground, granulated blast-furnace slag (GGBS), and also the early years in engineering practice important assets for the clients. The international network of contacts was also very helpful.

The entrance, in the 1970s, of the legal profession into the field of concrete research through litigation cases about field concrete deterioration, appeared to require its own paradigm for investigations and procedures of consulting services, including trial witness capability. The growth of lawsuits, especially in the UK, the USA and Canada, was virtually responsible for the creation of the special "forensic engineering" brand of consulting service. Recent trends in this special field of research transfer make me now appeal for general alertness towards its effects as a hindrance to the renaissance of conceptual, science-based research for worldwide concrete technology progress.

Part IV deals with the needs for concrete to make building and construction investments capable of matching the profound demographic and socio-economic changes of conditions of life for the world's populations in the third millennium. The prevailing concrete research is conspicuously inadequate to serve as support for the required surge of technology development in concrete construction. I consider the challenges further enhanced by adverse financial investment preferences, and because the required growth of cement and concrete uses will threaten exhaustion of materials resources both for cement and for water and aggregates. Cost-effective concrete R & D for resource-saving production technologies and for ensured, long-term performance life of buildings and structures under different conditions, including extreme environmental exposure, ought to be a first priority item of new research strategies.

In the concluding comments I urge, above all, the creation of new international top-level leadership commitments for strategic concrete research planning, under the panoply of what I designate a new Concrete World Constitution.

The professional concrete institutes and organizations operate with many pragmatic issues for broader international validity of structural design, materials standards, test methods, etc. But they are far from presenting an omnipotent, iconoclastic mission in concurrence with the global role of concrete as the indispensable foundation of social and cultural development for the increasing billions[1] of people who have yet to experience the effects of such development.

The primary technical demand is the creation of a corresponding holistic concept of concrete for structural design, materials technology, and research and development. Structural engineers are educated to perceive modelling of structural phenomena and events on a 1:1 or semi-natural scale and, in the past, also to count on the long-term behaviour of field concrete. Concrete technology research has, over the past decades, succumbed to the small-scale modelling empiricism and populistic promotion of transfer to engineering practice through the prevailing communication vehicles. Meanwhile, scientific disciplines such as non-linear, dynamic mechanics' upscaling of elementary phenomena and events, fuzzy-logic and chaos theories, have been made available for seeking answers to the bewildering complexity and holistic nature of our problems and opportunities. The revolutionary advance of computer technology makes it now more urgent than ever that the deadlock of the moribund, fragmentary populism of concrete technology research is broken. Once again, the decisive drive to achieve such a renaissance requires, above all, dedicated and powerful leadership.

It may be prudent to stress that this book is not an encyclopedia of concrete research, neither historically nor in analyses and evaluations of the latter day developments. Its background and focus are what the conditions after 1945 made possible for a small group of civil and chemical engineers and geologists in Denmark to accomplish in terms of concrete technology research in the service of the concurrent innovations in the production and uses of concrete.

The story as the book tells it of the transfer of basic knowledge from abroad into guidance for progressive technology under a consistent drive for cost-effective investment, deems supplementary narratives desirable by researchers in other countries about the many aspects of the research and its basic sciences which our strategic goals and management prevented us from pursuing.

[1] Throughout this book the term "billion" represents 1000 million.

3

Introduction

> *Investments in high-quality research are permanently profitable. They do not depreciate in value in the course of time like buildings and structures or investments in general knowledge and competence. High-quality research achievements are probably the closest we can come to realize the perpetuum mobile concept.*

The changing demography of the world, with continuous growth of populations in the developing regions, presents the primary challenge to concrete technology and production in the new millennium.

The provision of reasonable standards of living for the present, and still increasing, 4 billion new concrete users requires tremendous building and construction programmes which will engender exhausting strains on the available investment capital, the materials resources and the relevant knowledge and skill.

The conventional concrete technology research needs a profound renovation of its scientific basis, and a revival of its classical excellence of interaction with engineering practice in order to ensure the required cost-effectiveness of concrete production to match the challenge of the new conditions.

Technology versus demography

Plain and reinforced concrete acquired its position, during the first four decades of the twentieth century, as indispensable for the development of infrastructure and industrial production, with profound socio-economic impact on people's lives in North America, Europe and Japan.

In the first post World War II decades, concrete also became the predominant building material for reconstruction and industrialization, and acquired an image as the progressive basis for the general advance of social welfare. However, subsequently, high technology industries, rising from systematic applications of basic sciences, have taken over the role as the mainstream feature of commercial growth and social life in the richer regions of the world.

The corresponding changes in priorities for investment of available capital engendered grave reductions in the former commercial and public interest in concrete technology development and research. The consequence appeared, unexpectedly, in the 1970s as widespread, public grievance in many countries about premature dilapidation of concrete structures and buildings. In the Middle East, the appalling, rapid failures of new construction works confirmed that the conventional concrete technology was now left without sufficient support from quality research and updated engineering education corresponding to new processing methods, structural requirements and aggressive exposure conditions.

At the threshold of the third millennium, 4 billion inhabitants of the developing countries are now exposed to industrial commodity consumerism. This brainchild of the enormous productivity of modern, high technology industries, has embarked on powerful, global conquests of new markets by means of the muscle and mobility of international cash-flow capital.

This happens notwithstanding the fact that the primary need for the developing countries is building and construction with concrete of high performance quality and new concrete research which corresponds to the changing conditions of climatic exposure, available resources and educational situations.

The outreach message of *Concrete progress* is both to cement and concrete professions in the developing countries, where the creation of new research and engineering skill still is pristine, and to the hidebound research and practice in the rich, industrialized, technology satiated parts of the world.

It is an essential message in the story that even small countries in critical situations, such as in Europe after World War II, can create strong new professional communities from scratch over brief spans of years, when the socio-economic situation points to advance of cement and concrete production as a high priority, commercial and private investment area.

I have described the story from Denmark in terms of my own experience. Small, elite groups of young, dedicated researchers with civil and chemical engineering and geological/mineralogical backgrounds were able to make new knowledge transferable to concrete engineering innovations, *inter alia* by exchanges with established, high quality research abroad. Our maturity-based curing technology for winter concreting in the early 1950s was a landmark application of new American and British scientific research, and became the precursor for the subsequent monitoring curing technology for concrete hardening at elevated temperatures. Our low-risk policy for alkali-silica reaction in field concrete was another cost-effective accomplishment of a ten-year programme, relying heavily on the extensive, exploratory programmes in the USA and Australia.

The national background behind the consistent public and private enterprise funding of the research was the demand for continuous expansion of cement and concrete production. That encouraged a favourable consensus attitude to innovative, risk-taking technology development, and also directed our new research to support the strategic creation of a scientific knowledge basis and to interact with efforts to contribute to the progress in industry and engineering.

There follows a more gloomy message in my story, related for its educational virtue, of how the continuous rise of our research and development to a state of effective professionalism until the early 1970s, was changed to decline when the markets collapsed.

The background to this downturn was very complex. Initially, the oil embargo and soaring fuel prices made brutal cost reductions in the building and construction enterprises necessary. And, as is common practice in commerce, concrete research was seen as a removable cost factor. Next, the cement manufacturing technology's new burning techniques in dry kilns managed to cut its energy consumption by close to 50%, combined with large increases in the production capacity of new plants. That made cement a global import/export commodity, facing new patterns of tough competition. The mature, industrialized countries, in which the cement industry had been established early, were the hardest hit by these changes, because they had the largest share of smaller, wet-kiln plants, and facilities and capital resources suited to the limited, local markets. They also had the largest share of conventional and science-orientated research, which now saw its source of financial support and the primary national use of its accomplishments crumble, and often also technology educated leaders replaced by external, financial gurus.

Then came the profoundly changing priorities for capital investment and public budgeting preferences towards industries of higher annual returns than the weakening building and construction sectors, and increasing demands on public service sectors with higher political attraction. So cement and concrete also lost its former glory and promising career prospects for top-quality scientists and research engineers.

Unfortunately, during the same period, industrialization of development and production of laboratory instrumentation and auxiliary equipment required much more time to be spent at instruments and in processing of much larger amounts of data than before, both for technicians and research professionals. Correspondingly, less time and fewer opportunities were available for imaginative speculation and visionary contemplation.

The decline of concrete research

The overall effect of these changes in the environment and conditions for concrete research, and the research methodologies themselves, engendered:

- ☐ increasing reliance on empirical modelling experiments and testing
- ☐ increasing ad hoc financing of individual project research, troubleshooting financing and forensic engineering expertise.

Being able to provide "yes or no" answers to presented questions therefore became a measure of researchers' competence to a greater extent than in the past, when the star quality of the researcher was the ability to screen available basic knowledge, discover new opportunities and divine new ways for their exploitation.

The changed conditions also imposed more aggressive marketing and promotion activity on researchers, universities and research institutes, due to the increasing competition for project financing and for special investigations, such as through the EU, the World Bank and national financing agencies.

Even the universities' obligations to be front-line finders of new basic knowledge, in conjunction with the steady updating of academic education, were severely hit by political reductions of the classical, long-term granted financial support.

7

The new trend of ad hoc research financing favoured a remarkable "cosi fan tutti" policy in international concrete research funding. It was easier to produce project applications about issues already under investigation elsewhere, than to conceive and obtain approval for original ideas, hypotheses or methodologies. This trend inadvertently promoted the sharply increasing conference and publication boom, making the addition of data with little or no original value to the knowledge base a common feature in the rising research communication enterprise.

The struggle for survival imposed on many research leaders, concurrent with the weakening markets for their products, contributed to destroying the past interaction with engineering practice for technology innovations. Emphasis began to be placed on the new, sophisticated computerized modelling methodology, neglecting the boundary conditions for transfer to reality in practice. Increasingly, publications of empirical, experimental research appeared to rely merely on correlation data analyses, despite concluding evaluations claiming general applicability.

Concrete construction practice was, in the course of this development, gradually changed to rely primarily on the research as the basis for the slow procedures for long-term consensus adjustments of standard specifications and test methods.

With low profitability in the building and construction professions, it was a consolation that the functional ability and safety of performance of structural concrete relied, in principle, largely on the reinforcement, on the construction economy, and on management and construction effectiveness, rather than on the costs of concrete as a material. Reinforced concrete is, in itself, a marvellous holistic interaction of concrete and reinforcement with prestressing or post-tensioning as further, logical refinements. Hence, structural concrete, made and used under tried and tested circumstances, had achieved an enormous resilience towards failure and deterioration. Especially in a weak economy, the desire not to introduce new materials or technology therefore had a common sense basis.

Spectacular money saving innovations, such as the high range water reducers, were rare, and the conservatism of standard specification systems made it troublesome and risky to introduce novelties such as the Danish curing monitoring system, or to make alkali-silica reaction policy dependent on factors other than the common, empirical test method adjustments.

A further contributing factor in the suppression of new knowledge, was that the specification systems and their incorporation into the larger legislative and societal patterns were different from country to country. Trade barriers, mental attitudes and national pride also created obstacles preventing the rapid spread of new technology methods.

The durability crisis

Severe failure cases, such as those appearing in the course of the 1970s as highway bridge deck damage due to the introduction of de-icing practice, catastrophic early corrosion and concrete deterioration in the Middle East and North Africa, dilapidation of steam cured concrete in multi-storey post World War II habitations in Europe (and the USSR), and harmful alkali-silica reaction in Germany and the UK, awakened concern that new technology had an insufficient basis of updating research. There was an incipient dawning of recognition that new conditions for concrete making, such as (*a*) changed materials and processing technology, and (*b*) altered environmental exposure conditions, deserved more attention.

There followed, in the 1980s, considerable public funding of research, promoted as defensive and preventive of the above mentioned, most widely publicized kinds of unforeseen bad performance quality of field concrete, but without managed international coordination much of this research became exceedingly repetitive. Empirical testing, rather than conceptual contemplation, had become the prevailing requirement in the research communities, and the consequential changes of specifications have largely appeared as adjustments to conventional practice. Some of the adjustments were undoubtedly improvements and, generally, stricter quality control and management was imposed by the building and construction authorities.

The future

The major reason why concrete technology and research now needs to come under the panoply of a greater cause is that the 1990s are the opening decade for a magnificent new challenge: the creation of reasonable standards of living for the 4 billion people in the developing regions of the world, who will increase to 6–8 billion over the next decades, beginning a new chapter in the history of the world. Therefore a new chapter in the annals of concrete technology and research will also begin.

First, because the majority of the said 4 billion people and their increasing descendants populates the tropical and subtropical belt of the world, where the climatic exposure conditions, whether marine, inland humid, or arid, are far more severe testing grounds for field concrete than are the more benign, temperate climates in the northern industrialized regions of Europe and North America. Conventional concrete technology has been developed, and the long-term experience with the performance quality of ordinary field concrete gained, under the latter circumstances.

Secondly, because already, at the end of our century, the resources of aggregates for concrete and, in some regions, also of fresh water, are under pressure of depletion in the industrialized regions. The forthcoming demands for increasing concrete usage in the developing countries, in many of which natural resources are scarce, ought indeed to be considered as a frightening prospect.

Thirdly, any major new investment programme for urbanization of over-populated domestic regions or countries by means of concrete building and construction is certain to impose complex socio-economic changes on people's attitudes and lives. Thorough feasibility analyses are therefore required to ensure the cost-effectiveness of such programmes. This is a pivotal reason why a new conceptual architecture of concrete research and technology is a dire necessity.

Denmark jumping on the bandwagon

The development of concrete technology and research in Denmark after World

War II may, in retrospect, be characterized as a fruitful continuity of the inter-action between development of engineering practice and application of scientific research by a small group of researchers and many younger civil engineers. For myself, the first eight years after 1945 as resident engineer and construction manager along the exposed west coast of Jutland was occupied by reconstruction of the worn-down marine and port works. It was a period of tough apprentice-ship in practical concrete making, with the local foremen and their crews of craftsmen as excellent teachers. They had an experienced cognition of concrete which enabled them to produce high performance quality without access to other than rudimentary quality control measurements.

Our concrete technology education entered its second phase when the Marshall Aid programme, in 1948, offered us new American machinery for aggregate sampling and screening, and for high capacity concrete batching, mixing and placement in large volumes by pumping. American manuals for the operating of the equipment, and concrete technology guide books relying on ACI and ASTM recommendations and requirements, augmented the available textbooks, pointing the way to a new, higher level of concrete engineering skill.

My task was to make these new means for improving the quality of concrete production function as added opportunities in the minds of our experienced craft-trained crews, and at the same time to accomplish the realization of the concrete construction operations at hand. Under these, not always easy, circumstances, trial and error also taught us as a valuable axiom for later research and develop-ment, to take all

☐   characteristics of the materials
☐   features of the new processing technology, and
☐   the harsh coastal/marine climatic environment

into consideration when problems required analyses for operative decisions, and also to consider matters not described in the available guidelines or text-books, which naturally could not relate specifically to our particular situations. The thorough, new mechanization of our site concrete production methods revealed, in particular, that the interactions of the materials characteristics and the successive events in their handling became, ultimately, as decisive as the characteristics themselves. Hence, inadvertent decisions to change the grading of the finest fraction of the sand of the concrete, along with variations of the moisture content in the sand silo, could alter the rheology of the fresh concrete abruptly, make the concrete pump stall and cause expensive, enforced disposal into the sea of all concrete in a pumpline up to 400 m long. Likewise, the casting of up to $700\,\mathrm{m}^3$ volume plain concrete blocks in one operation revealed the mechanism of thermal cracking during early curing, when we measured simultaneous adiabatic and surface temperature rise and decline. This was factual evidence of the effects of heat of hydration in real concrete which had a lasting impact on our subsequent research into curing technology at low tempera-ture for winter concreting, at steam curing's accelerated reactions, and during later investigations of failure cases in hot countries.

The eight years' occupation on the west coast of Jutland also revealed an apparent mystery: concrete groyne and jetty blocks, breakwater slabs and pier walls of identical composition and ages were of performance quality ranging from excellent to severe deterioration, whether they were young or up to 40–50 years of age. This pattern reoccurred at our countrywide field inspections in the 1950s. It suggested that alkali-silica reaction occurred both in harmful and harmless phases and was most frequent in the latter.

My confrontation, from 1953, with applied science in concrete research and development at the new Danish National Institute of Building Research, provided further advanced schooling in the basis for progress of concrete technology for engineering practice. The creators of a new generation of concrete researchers in Denmark, N. M. Plum and P. Nerenst, made acquaintance with the erudite, new basic research abroad into cement chemistry, cement hydration kinetics, and the properties of hardened cement paste, research that would be the indispensable asset for all later concrete progress in Denmark. At first we used that knowledge for the maturity-based curing monitoring to secure frost resistance and delayed load-bearing capability in slabs and columns, etc. during winter concreting. Next followed the use of American literature and contacts for the planning of the, still ongoing, investigations of concrete durability and especially alkali-silica reaction.

The understandable official hesitation in acknowledging the import of such a calamity from the USA made reluctant, but wisely decided, comprehensive field inspections of concrete structures the initial phase of the subsequent ten years of strategic alkali-silica reaction research in Denmark. The field inspections and examination of collected concrete samples gave us a lasting basis of realism for the laboratory work and the scientific studies of the various issues.

As the programme developed, it required thorough, new scientific education in the disciplines of mineralogy, geology, inorganic chemistry and petrographic methodology. With Ervin Poulsen's design of mobile core-taking equipment, and his invention of thin section impregnation, we created the concept of the alkali-silica reaction research:

- field inspections: concrete surface conditions; exposure and concrete materials characterization; coring of samples, etc.
- microscopic examination of cores, thin section preparation
- thin section petrography; thorough description of relevant microscopic features
- experimental studies and testing of laboratory prepared, relevant mortars and concrete
- theoretical studies via foreign research reports, guidance by exchange, etc.
- concluding evaluations and formulation of a Danish policy towards alkali-silica reaction.

The programme included studies of the chemistry of the reaction with and without pozzolans in the concrete. This had as its background material, large amounts of concrete on the west coast of Jutland, made with the Danish moler cement since 1910, and apparently more resistant to alkali-silica reaction than concrete with ordinary Portland cement.

As newcomers, it was self-evident to us that alkali-silica reaction was one and the same thing whether happening in Australia, the USA or Denmark, and that was consistently sustained by our findings and the exchanges with colleagues abroad. Our roots in the field concrete investigations immunized us

11

against exaggerated focus on simplistic laboratory modelling of deleterious reactions in concrete.

We recognized that alkali-silica reaction basically consists of incremental, chemical conversions in siliceous aggregate particles into which the alkali hydroxide pore solution of the cement paste migrated and reacted. We realized that the resulting incremental particle expansions might or might not accumulate to overall cracking through a non-linear dynamic progress. Mortar bar testing by linear expansion measurements was therefore conceived by us as pre-harmonized, averaged measures for convenient assessment of a much more complex course of the reaction in real life. The entropy of the reaction was, so to say, tricked into increasing prematurely in the mortar bar testing procedures.

The Concrete Research Laboratory, Karlstrup (BFL)

Aktieselskabet Aalborg Portland Cement Fabrik had, throughout the 1950s, been the main financial supporter of the alkali-silica reaction programme and of other research undertakings at public institutes.

In 1960, the company decided that as a prominent private enterprise it was obliged to be a leading partner in concrete research for the benefit of its customers. As chosen leader of the new Concrete Research Laboratory, Karlstrup (BFL), I was then, suddenly, confronted by the challenge of participating in the creation of a new chapter in the history of concrete research in Denmark. The job soon proved to include strategic planning and management and the training of a new generation of young researchers and service staff. The purpose of our research was to supply science-based knowledge for cost-effective concrete process and product development, under the drastically changing new conditions: improved cement qualities, rationalization and mechanization of site concrete production, a rapidly growing precast industry involved in a race for production acceleration, and generally increasing alertness towards quality control and updated engineering education.

The 16 years of the BFL research, with a staff rising from 1 to 45 and a budget expanding from 250 000 DKK to 6 million DKK at its closure in 1976, was, for all involved, a persistently demanding and rewarding school in the disciplines of:

☐ operation of an industry-owned research institute with unquestionable and acknowledged integrity

☐ moulding of a continuously increasing staff of young academic researchers, technicians and secretaries to become a single entity, dedicated to its mission

☐ interaction with and learning from advanced cement and concrete research and acknowledged leaders from all over the world

☐ consistent reliance on applicable transfer of scientific knowledge to realistic technology improvements in close cooperation with progressive concrete engineering

☐ application of professional, industrial research planning and management methods through membership of EIRMA.

The BFL was closed in 1976 by a new management of the company, as part of a major overhaul necessitated by the approximately 50% reduction of cement consumption in Denmark. This was an early omen that the ever-increasing building and construction investments since World War II had now peaked. Therefore, also the motivation for the company to supply consumers with new concrete knowledge free of charge, faded and despite the general recognition of the research and contact value of the BFL, no one came forward to secure its continuation.

In the two subsequent years, I functioned in the company as manager of special research projects which were the subject of negotiations with large American corporations, and one with the Icelandic Government, for joint technology innovations. The general economic depression, the special character of the projects and the feeling that neither the potential partners nor the company itself had their hearts in the projects, made me spend as much time as possible in international exchanges, publication of articles and conference participation, etc., realizing that, on the global scale, the need for concrete research and development and the interests in our achievements at the BFL were far from having peaked. The two years therefore became a fruitful interlude of preparation for the subsequent phase of personal, international engagements with concrete research and development.

Consultant for concrete progress, 1978–1986

When I had announced my availability for advisory service, there emerged over the following years sometimes overwhelming requests for assistance from many parts of the world, predominantly for big projects of three kinds:

- investments for promotion of concrete technology improvements, such as by the use of fly ash, granulated blast-furnace slag, and natural pozzolans, low porosity cement, etc.
- investigations to ensure high performance of field concrete, such as prevention of harmful alkali-silica reaction
- diagnosing investigations of concrete failure cases, of which several became the subject of extended litigation in the USA, the UK, and Canada.

Combination of this kind of enterprise with participation in international scientific exchange and contact arrangements was easy, albeit laborious, and comprised a great many invited keynote lectures at conferences.

The gist of this professional life was that my past intensive interaction over many years of research and technology in concrete engineering practice offered a broad basis of holistic experience, which made it easy to see, for instance, the interrelations between temperature elevation during curing of concrete, the effects of pozzolans and GGBS in production and performance, and the relationships of these matters and alkali-silica reaction, sulphate attack and corrosion of reinforcement in hot countries. As a consequence, the service projects also repeatedly revealed the obsolescence of many regulatory requirements and standard specification tests. The conservative reliance on such models in structural design and quality control during construction, engendered increasingly misleading use of the conventional system. The implication hereof was sharply increasing demands on the consultancy service. That sustained what many communications in the consultant's projects suggested, that engineering practice had begun to acknowledge the insufficiency of the prevailing, reductional research for transfer to modern technology.

Towards the third millennium

In the course of 1985, it became clear that the still decreasing international concrete research and the remaining Danish research would continue to give rise to requests for specialized consulting services for cement users in the foreseeable future. I chose to transfer the personal consultancy so as to make it an affiliated company owned by the major Danish consulting engineering company, Rambøll & Hannemann A/S. It is beyond the scope of this story to narrate the now more than ten years' operations of the new company, but there are events and developments in the period which must be referred to as strong indications of perspectives for the future.

The Congress of the United States released, in 1987, as part of a larger Strategic Highway Research Programme (SHRP), 12.5 million US$ for concrete research programmes for improvements of the use of concrete in the highway systems in the USA, which in many States were in deplorable conditions, along with changing priorities for investment capital away from building and construction. The Federal Highway Administration has, after the termination of the programme, received further federal funding for implementation programmes. More recently, a broader association of professional concrete design engineering and construction companies, the American Concrete Institute, the American Society of Civil Engineers, the National Institute of Science and Technology and others, have embarked on a national strategic programme for research on high performance concrete.

Less comprehensive public support for new concrete research has appeared in Europe, with the EU BRITE-EURAM and EUREKA funding agencies. These require participation of private firms and/or public research institutes from more than one member country in the EU. Similar sorts of smaller scale cooperative public research funding programmes have appeared in recent years in several European countries.

Characteristically, no particular landmark innovations have emerged. The attained benefits appear to have been added engineering competence for the participating partners, but very limited outreach effects. Behind the scenes growth of expenses in administration and communications vis-à-vis the accomplishments seems to be an inborn failing in such politically initiated research policies.

Promotional efforts such as those mentioned for substantial increases of investments in concrete research in the industrialized countries are futile as long as they remain programmed for their homelands' conditions, where the development of concrete technology has become irretrievably subordinate to commercially preferable high-technology and consumer-orientated development.

I emphasize at the end of Part IV my conviction that the overriding challenge at the threshold of the third millennium is the creation of a new, holistic concrete research concept, with global leadership commitments and conditions in the developing continents placed up front. Their needs for concrete building and construction as the prerequisite for socio-economic progress, require massive transfer of concrete craft and engineering professionalism, along with thoroughly scrutinized selection of most urgent research investments, depending on the available human, materials and capital resources. In my concluding remarks I have therefore also mentioned the current, major obstacles to making such concrete progress a mainstream issue of the forthcoming, global socio-economic development. One of these is, inevitably, the prevailing fragmentation of concrete research itself, as illustrated in a survey of international concrete research conferences announced for 1997.

The very latest information for the readers of this book is that the European Community is creating a new strategy to support technological developments. In 1997, calls for long-term programmes are issued within the concepts of Large Scale Engineering and Intelligent Manufacturing Systems. The technological and socio-economic philosophy herein corresponds in all essential aspects to the needs for the fundamental changes in concrete research which I stipulate as one outcome of half a century of operations in the field. Thus, the new EC move, although not explicitly referring to concrete and maybe not even implicitly having concrete in mind, does open an avenue offering proper revitalization of the urgently required concrete progress.

FLASHLIGHTS ON HISTORY AND RESEARCH

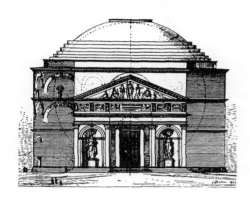

In the ancient Roman empire, concrete was the fundamental basis for the lives of the populations in the big cities, and for the imperial infrastructure and commerce. Limestone and pozzolans for cement production and aggregates were abundantly available, and so were the armies of unskilled "rope-collar" labour who could make concrete with a common performance lifetime of about 2000 years. This was achieved by rigorously imposing a standardized quality of workmanship on concrete making all over the empire.

The axiom of reliance on quality of workmanship was reinvoked when civil engineering made mass concrete with Portland cement a fundamental basis for the Industrial Revolution in the nineteenth century. This reliance is still a prevailing requirement for modern concrete production.

In contrast, Portland cement has, since its trial and error based invention in England in 1824, become an industrial commodity with globally standardized properties. This has been achieved by on-line monitoring control of selection and preparation of source materials and of the subsequent burning, cooling and grinding process, based on knowledge extracted from long-term, consistent investments in cement chemistry research.

Design and construction with reinforced concrete has, in the course of the last hundred years, attained a position as the fundamental basis for industrial production, communication and social life in modern society. The current, profound changes in global demography and industrial potentials are substantially increasing the demands on concrete production capacity – and on the performance quality requirements of concrete. The heritage of reliance on quality of workmanship must be acknowledged in the developing countries, because millions of unskilled, blue-collar workers are required for the predictable housing and construction boom. But this must be accompanied by scientific research into the best means of adapting patterns of workmanship to operate in harmony with the new requirements governing materials, processing and performance under different, unfamiliar conditions.

1

Our heritage of cement and concrete technology

Ancient concrete – pozzolans and workmanship

Numerous books and articles in scientific and technical periodicals have described the usage in the ancient Mediterranean cultures of concrete with lime mortars made hydraulic by means of pozzolans. The Greek knowledge of the use of highly siliceous, volcanic Santorin earth goes back to 500–300 BC.[1] Half a millennium later, Vitruvius had found that: "there is also a kind of powder, which due to its nature gives excellent results". ["Est etiam genus pulveris quod efficit naturaliter res admirandas". *De architectura*. Book II, Chapter VI].[2] He called this powder "pulvis puteolanis", because it was found at the town Puteoli, now Pozzuoli, in the bay of Naples. It is likely that this pozzolan was first used to make hydraulic mortar for marine concrete at Puteoli and Cosa, north of Rome.[3] Its ability to produce concrete of higher strength and durability than pure lime, by the thoroughly regulated workmanship which Vitruvius also described, made Roman concrete the ubiquitous building and construction material for imperial development: from Hadrian's Wall across northern England, over the Rhine and Danube valleys to Turkey, Syria, Israel and Egypt, and further west along the North African coast over to Spain and Southern France, but above all in Rome itself. It is the interior concrete cores of walls, columns, slabs, etc. and brickwork with cementing mortar which have survived to our time, where the cladding facades of marble or stone masonry have disappeared.

The quality of Roman workmanship was achieved by rigorous compliance with "standard regulations", and construction work operated by skilled, professional craftsmen supervising the working crews of slaves, who were in unlimited supply wherever the constructors worked in the Empire. I emphasize the importance of workmanship at this early stage of the history of concrete – incidentally, the quality of Roman tiles and masonry also bears witness to the excellence of their craft skill – because they so cleverly made use of the compressive strength of the materials in their structural system. They had no reinforcement for separate transfer of tensile and flexural stresses, but learned, evidently by trial and error, in a sense to "mould" mass concrete and masonry into magnificent structural shapes and magnitudes.

The Colosseum provides spectacular monumental evidence of the superior engineering competence of the Roman constructors and architects.[4] It was built by the Emperor Vespasian in 72–80 AD over an elliptical base with a 187.77 m long and a 156.64 m short axis. The external wall, even today, reaches a height of 50 m above street level. The foundation consisted of a 6 m thick concrete slab covering the whole area of the building. It was cast on the bottom of the former emperor Nero's lake after excavating to the underlying rocks. A 6 m thick concrete ring which followed the external and internal limits of the superstructure was cast on the bottom slab. The support pilasters for the superstructure were erected on this ring.

The operations to collect the lime, pozzolans, aggregates, and formwork materials for the, approximately, 22 000 m^3 bottom slab and 2000 m^3 ring of mass concrete, and thereafter to mark out, erect formwork, mix, place, compact, level and cure the concrete required superb, one is tempted to say modern, construction management. Also, the genuine architectural and structural innovation required to raise the building vertically with the seating placed amphitheatrically above the constricted arena at ground level is admirable. This design offered the 50–60 000 spectators the best possible views down on the games in the arena.

The intensity with which all views are focused downwards, towards the site of the slaughter, is disturbing. At the opening games in 80 AD, between 5000 and 9000 wild animals were killed as entertainment for the inhabitants of Rome. In the course of the next three centuries munus gladiatori, damnatio ad bestias, damnatia in ludum and venationes[1] involving the deaths of thousands of people and animals took place until the final abolition of the atrocities in 403 AD. Nevertheless, despite the incredible duration of atrocious excesses for populistic pleasure, the Colosseum remains a monument to Roman architecture and engineering skill.

Personally, I have been more pleasantly impressed by the Pantheon, the only imperial building in Rome, which is still used for the purpose for which it was built, divine service, and leaves the visitor in awe of its monumental greatness. It was built by the Emperor Hadrian about 120–125 AD. It is a 6 m thick mass concrete cylinder covered by a concrete dome, the height and diameter of which is 43.3 m. The dome is exactly half of the entire height, and its curve is a perfect sphere, which just touches the paved floor. The weight of the dome is carefully reduced as it travels upwards by diminishing thickness and sectional selection of aggregates, at first travertine and coal, then crushed bricks and finally lightweight pumice in the top section. No other domes of such a large free span were built before the nineteenth century.

The Pantheon was a temple, sacred to the Roman gods, and the building is itself an invocation. The daring dome construction makes its 9 m diameter oculus function like a searchlight from heaven, throwing the ever-changing illumination of the sky downwards as a wandering beam of glittering dust particles through the darkened space. The circular oculus, its position and function, is in superb harmony with the spherical shape and magnitude of the dome. The Roman Emperor invoked this symbol of power, personifying the deities to whom the temple and the people were dedicated.

To me, as a present-day concrete technologist, it is a paradox that the Romans,

[1] Battles between gladiators, convicts set against wild animals, "mutual execution" of convicted criminals and gladiators set against wild animals.

19

who were superb pragmatists as craftsmen, merchants, industrialists, militarists, politicians and mortal entertainers, indulged in the immaterialism of religion as their highest form of government. It rather prevented them from exercising any scientific curiosity and endeavours. Vitruvius was in accordance with this philosophy; he was knowledgeable about what pozzolans can achieve, and how to make the best use of them, but has not a word of speculation about the basic cause of their good effects.

After the decline and fall of the West Roman Empire, the Pantheon was dedicated in 609 AD to Boniface IV by the emperor in Byzans. Thereafter it came into the service of a new authoritarian government which, ever since, has been stronger than the Roman empire, and for more than a millennium ahead would indulge in generously sponsoring its own worshipping arts of architecture, painting and sculpture, but suppress the progress of science and technology to the lowest possible level.

The knowledge of pozzolanic materials for improvement of lime mortar was, for centuries, practically confined to the catholic monks who could read Vitruvius' Latin. Throughout the next millennium the Church, emperors, kings, and feudal chiefs, alternating with or causing anarchy, plagues and devastation, ruled in Europe with limited needs for building materials technology progress. Lime mortars sufficed for most applications, and the inherited knowledge of hydraulic mortars containing pozzolans was good enough for special purposes, such as prestigious buildings for the Church and the rich.

During the twelfth century, the construction of cathedrals flourished.[5] The daring gothic architecture was a formidable structural innovation. There were, however, still no scientific stress-transfer calculations behind the construction, only experience and rigorous quality management. Absolute submission to the dictated creed was the governing philosophy, and at the pragmatic builders' level the guilds appeared in the thirteenth century with the purpose of keeping the masons', carpenters', plumbers' and glassmakers' craft knowledge secret for the associated masters. Hence, kept in poverty for centuries by the governing systems, the European countries were satisfactorily served by conservative preservation of the ancient building materials technology which made experience and workmanship the decisive quality issues.

There was, however, a gradual accumulation of scientific knowledge by brilliant, individual scientists. Copernicus in Poland (1473–1543) found by observations that the earth circled around the sun and the moon around the earth. Tycho Brahe (1546–1601) made far-reaching astronomic observations, but contested Copernicus' interpretations, which Galilei, (1564–1642) confirmed, but was forced to deny by the Roman church. Niels Steensen (1638–1686) made great discoveries in medical anatomy, and regarding geology. He discovered the constancy of crystal angles and taught that "Given a substance possessed of a certain figure and produced according to the laws of nature, to find in the substance itself evidences disclosing the manner of its production".[6]

O. Römer (1644–1710) discovered the velocity of light, and C. Linnaeus (1702–1778) created the botanical classification system. The British physicist Isaac Newton (1642–1727) published *Principia* in 1687. This work opened the door for applications of the natural sciences in the development of manufacturing technology, and many British entrepreneurs became active members of the Royal

Society. James Watt invented the steam engine in 1769, George Stephenson put it on rails as a locomotive in 1814, R. Fulton had used it on water in the first steamship in 1807 in America, where, incidentally, two competing railroads opened between New York and Philadelphia in 1835. J. Wilkinson in England industrialized iron making and constructed iron bridges, and MacAdam invented the crushed stone road pavements.

It was during this epoch that the new philosophy was created which admitted science to be decisive for man's understanding of nature, and subsequently for influence on human life, and provided the means to change that. The chains of ignorant confinement were broken.

There have been other developments since the Middle Ages which worked irresistibly in the same direction. The great explorers following Columbus, such as Gama Vasco, Magelhaes and numerous others, prepared the way for colonization, resulting in tremendous access to new investment capital from the discovered continents and their conquered peoples.

Eventually, the overwhelming power of the new conquests also affected the mundane cementing materials technology, although, until the commencement of the nineteenth century, only by relying heavily on classical knowledge and skill. The flourishing economy and political strength of France in the mid-seventeenth century offered the famous general Vauban of the army engineering corps the opportunity to build both fortresses and ports of concrete,[7] making good use of the excellent pozzolan "Chaux du Teil". Contemporary geology and chemistry were developing in the French state universities and, in 1778, M. Faujas de Saint-Fond published a thorough study of pozzolanic materials, their properties and effects, and referred to concrete works, for instance at the naval port of Toulon.[8] He mentioned the Swedish production of a pozzolan by two-times calcination of an alum schist, and referred to its use in the Troldhättan lock. It is, perhaps, indicative of the limited international interaction of the time, that the French author does not refer to the contemporary English invention by J. Smeaton of a new cement for the Eddystone lighthouse.

He was also unaware that the Danish essayist and playwright L. Holberg in *Denmark's clerical and secular State*, 1749, mentioned that on the island of Bornholm in the Baltic Sea, a coal and cement plant had been built, and that the cement was roughly 10% better than the Dutch cement, and could be had at half the price.[7] The source material for this cement was an argillaceous limestone at the location "Limensgade" (the street of lime), and the cement was, in itself, a true hydraulic lime. Actually, it was a revolutionary innovation, although it did not receive attention as such. (That it was a cement of excellent quality is evident from its continued, esteemed use as "Roman cement" in Denmark throughout the nineteenth century.)

Portland cement enters the picture

In 1824, Joseph Aspdin was granted British Patent No. 5022 for the manufacture of Portland cement. Sixty-eight years earlier, in 1756, his predecessor, John Smeaton, had been commissioned to build the third lighthouse on the Eddystone Skerry in the English Channel off the coast of Plymouth.[9, 10] For the construction, with hewn stones set in mortar, he needed a stronger cement than slaked

*Fig. 1. Eddystone lighthouse on
skerry in the English Channel
at Plymouth, Devon.
Photograph of painting by
Danish artist A. Melbye,
1847, Danish State Museum of
Art, Copenhagen (photo:
G. M. Idorn)*

lime. By experimenting, he obtained the strongest cement by burning an argillaceous limestone and the strongest mortar by mixing this cement with a
pozzolan – which he obtained from Civitavecchia, to the north of Rome. He
claimed to have developed a product as strong and durable as "the best Portland
stone" – the building stone from the island of Portland, which was used extensively in London.

Figure 1 shows a painting of the lighthouse by the Danish marine artist Anton
Melbye in 1847. Although unintentionally, his picture remains as evidence of the
unprecedented service lifetime of the structure, demonstrating what, at that time,
was close to 90 years' resistance to the full power of severe marine exposure.
Actually, the lighthouse was in service until 1876, when it was dismantled and
re-erected on Plymouth Hoe as a monument.[10] It still stands there, a symbol
of the incipient unification of science and technology in the nineteenth century,
which nurtured the Industrial Revolution in the United Kingdom and made the
conquest of overseas positions possible for the Empire. The lighthouse was,
when built, a sort of early signpost for the forthcoming development of
marine infrastructure.

In the wake of Aspdin's invention in 1824, Portland cement became the indispensable material basis for overseas trade by making mass concrete suitable for
large-scale port, dock and marine constructions, and very soon other applications
were also found. J. Aspdin's son, W. Aspdin, used concrete for his house at
Greenwich, Kent, as early as 1843.[11–13]

Meanwhile, the natural sciences began to be employed in the development of
the technology which created the industrial society, and the emergent inorganic
chemistry was applied to explore the nature of the cement calcination process and
the hydration of cement with water. It is not difficult to envisage the benefits of
this kind of research. The economy of producing a uniform quality product at the
lowest cost must have dawned on many of the early Portland cement producers,

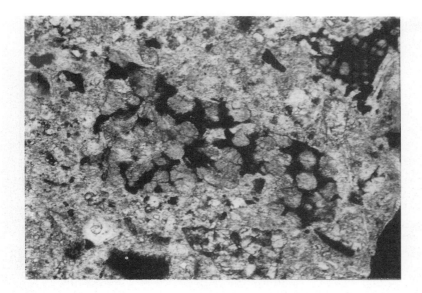

Fig. 2. Large fragment of unhydrated C_2S with interstitial ferrite phase: thin section of W. Aspdin's concrete from 1847 (= N, 160×), from reference [11]

who could envisage a never-ending growth potential for their sales if they complied with the demand on consistent quality.

Figures 2 and 3, which are thin section micrographs of W. Aspdin's concrete from 1847, confirm that his cement possessed the potentials we are familiar with today. They show the existence of the same clinker components in the cement as we have in a modern standard Portland cement, and the 136-year lifetime of the concrete provides excellent quality documentation. But Aspdin did not know about the clinker minerals or how they reacted, and not much about how to attain the same product through batch after batch, in the cement kiln.

The French chemist L. J. Vicat had, as early as 1818, found that lime and silica were the primary reactants and that the mix proportion was essential. The German chemist W. Michaelis studied the hydration reaction. The French chemist H. le Chatelier introduced petrographic examination of cement clinker in 1883, and the Swede A. E. Töernebohm confirmed his observations thirty years later. He introduced, in 1897, the names alite, belite, celite and felite for the four crystalline clinker components which he found in clinker thin sections.[14] Cement chemistry was therefore well prepared for the tremendous developments in the twentieth century.

In contrast to the interaction of scientific research and cement technology development, the usage of cement in concrete still depended on the masons' and carpenters' inherited craft knowledge, but the nature of mass concrete in contrast to masonry made it possible, like in ancient Rome, to produce it using unskilled labour, provided that quality workmanship was rigorously imposed. A British civil engineer, H. Reid, expressed in 1869 the rules for making good concrete in these words:[15]

"The due and thorough incorporation of the cement, sand, and shingle or gravel, with the least amount of water, is the A B C of the process of concrete making, and unless this is rigorously attended to much disappointment will be experienced. The whole of the ingredients

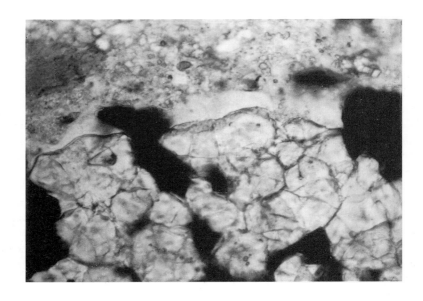

*Fig. 3. Fragment of C_3S
cluster with adherent, secondary
hydrated substance as reaction
rim towards the ambient paste,
and interstitial, amorphous and
dark ferrite phase (× N,
600 ×), from reference [11]*

*should be well mixed first in a dry state, and when this is thoroughly done a quantity of water
added to render the mixture plastic enough to be put into moulds or placed between the boards
used for forming the walls. As a rule the less quantity of water you can use the better. The
concrete should be well rammed in as dry a state as is consistent with the proper requirements
of the material, for too small a quantity of water would be quite as injurious as an excess;
again, that would be materially influenced by the amount of percussion applied by the impin-
gement of the rammer. The rammer should be as heavy as can conveniently be used. Sand,
where a choice exists, should be as rough and coarse as possible. A rotten or friable aggregate
is to be avoided. The sand must fill up the vacuities in the compound. Where practicable,
concrete blocks should be placed for some days or weeks in water. Concrete, when so treated
and carefully and thoroughly mixed will be immensely superior in quality to the ordinary
sloppy and roughly-handled mixture commonly called concrete, only in many cases entitled
to the name because it contains certain proportions of the necessary ingredients".*

This resembles very closely what Vitruvius had written almost two millennia
before, therefore demonstrating that science had not yet made great inroads into
the processing of concrete.

Denmark in the nineteenth century

The absolute monarchy of Denmark declared the nation bankrupt in 1813, as a
consequence of its mismanaged alliance with Napoleon against the victorious
coalition of opposing powers. At that time the only relevant indigenous resource
for fuel had reached a stage of exhaustion, with the forested area reduced to 2%
of the total of some $60\,000\,km^2$. Moreover, overseas trade and agriculture, the
two backbones of the national economy, were destroyed by war and blockades,
and Norway, with its mineral resources, was about to be lost. The sovereign,
Frederik VI, and his state council, comprising progressive, immigrant German
landowners, decided on two primary avenues for restoration:

- advance of any prosperous trade and new industries
- investments in science and scientific education.

The first route was evidently for short-term economic development, the second with expectations of longer term returns.

In the circumstances, both undertakings required the engagement of brilliant young personalities who were dedicated to working for king and country. J. G. Forchhammer, a young geologist, was commissioned to turn the Danish country-side upside down in the search for possible, unknown or unmapped mineral resources, and the physician H. C. Ørsted was granted sponsorship for scientific discoveries.

Forchhammer achieved an excellent, first geological survey of the country. He pinpointed clay and chalk as plentiful resource materials, and was instrumental in the development of "Roman cement" production on the island of Bornholm in the Baltic Sea, where limited amounts of coal were retrievable as fuel. Ørsted discovered electromagnetism in 1820. He saw this accomplishment as evidence of the divine ruling of the universe and of human beings, but could not envisage the applicability of electricity. On the other hand, he was a scientist and realized the basic nature of scientific research:

"The announcement of a new conception is just as much an event as the communication of a new experiment. In fact, this will only gain an impact which may be great or small, through its association with the theatre of ideas".[16]

He also realized the need for scientific education, and in 1829 he was granted royal permission to create the Technical University of Denmark in Copenhagen, of which he became the first director.

The following decades are known today as the "golden age" of Denmark. The first railway came in 1847, the Carlsberg Brewery was founded in the same year, and Tivoli had opened in 1843. A Danish engineer from Ørsteds Technical University, Søren Hjorth, was in 1854 granted the British Patent Nr. 2198 on electrodynamic applications − a forerunner of the dynamo. (He had previously studied G. Stephenson's railway, and was instrumental in the opening of the Copenhagen–Roskilde railway in 1847.) Gradually, cement and concrete also came into demand. Six Roman cement plants were in operation on Bornholm in 1855 and, at that time, the importing of I. C. Johnson's Portland cement from England, and Alsen and Hemmor Portland cement from Germany had also commenced.

Figure 4 shows the first major Danish concrete structure made with Portland cement, the fortress Prøvestenen, constructed 1859–63, for the coastal defence of Copenhagen. Its name, literally translated The Touchstone, was previously the name of one of the navy's warships which had defended Copenhagen against the British fleet in 1801, but implied also that the concrete had been tested in advance and found far more resistant to artillery shelling than the alternative brick construction. Two supplementary fortresses were then also built at Copenhagen.

In 1876, the Danish Board of Maritime Works commenced a major programme for construction of coastal protection works, a few harbours and jetties along the 300 km remote coastline of the west coast of Jutland towards the North Sea.

Fig. 4. The fortress Prøvestenen, Amager at Copenhagen (photo: G. M. Idorn, 1960)

In 1888 reinforced concrete was introduced for the load-bearing structure of a major storehouse building in the Copenhagen Free Harbour. The State Museum of Art was built with reinforced concrete floor decks in 1891, and the famous and elegant "pedestrian bridge" at Langelinie was built in 1894, designed by the young lecturer at the Technical University, A. Ostenfeld. (See front cover picture of reference [17]).

F. L. Smidth & Co. had started to design and manufacture cement producing equipment in 1880. The company adopted and refined the Ransome rotary kiln and was, from 1890, the primary producer for the Danish, and soon also for the Scandinavian cement industry.[18] In this way, the cement industry prepared for the formidable, forthcoming conquest of the building and construction markets by cement and concrete, and for the response by Danish civil engineers and the national cement industry to the international development of concrete technology and research.

Denmark from 1900 until World War II

The commencement in 1876 of the construction of a series of groynes along the west coast of Jutland led to many years of excellence in concrete workmanship and accompanying research and development into the resistance of concrete to severe marine exposure. The Technical University of Copenhagen had, at about the same time, with the later professors A. Ostenfeld and E. Suenson, commenced research and new courses in reinforced concrete design and concrete technology. They trained an outstanding generation of Danish concrete consulting and construction civil engineers. The Danish cement industry installed its first rotary kiln at the Rørdal plant in Aalborg in the year 1900, delivered by F. L. Smidth & Co. A/S.

These unusually compatible engineering and industry investments were nurtured by intensive personal interaction between civil, mechanical and chemical engineers, across the boundaries between the engineers employed in the civil services and those in private firms and industries. The "gap" which developed much later between research and practice did not then exist, and the common dedication to professional progress was further vitalized by frequent communications with those involved in international development, both for the importing of new knowledge and as free intellectual and commercial exports.

There were certain special advantages for Denmark in the quest for front-line concrete positions:

- the raw materials for cement and concrete aggregates were of high, uniform quality, and easy to retrieve
- construction sites and design offices were, to a large extent, also the research laboratories
- the large, public agencies responsible for the infrastructure and other civil services had political back up to participate in short- and long-term research and development
- public and private enterprise leadership had the right visions for the general trend of increasing demands for cement and concrete.

Marine concrete technology

Figure 5 shows groyne No. 59 at Thyborøn, north-west Jutland, in 1896. Between 176 and 214 m from the head of the groyne, construction consisted of 116 test blocks, each 0.6 m^3 which were placed as part of an Inter-Scandinavian Portland Cement Manufacturers Society's research programme into the sea water resistance of concrete. The figures are from the report of the trials, by A. Poulsen.[19] He was the local resident engineer for the Board of Maritime Works, and executive chairman of the cement industry committee. He was

Fig. 5. Groyne 59, Thyborøn on the west coast of Jutland, 1896, showing concrete blocks for field exposure testing by A. Poulsen, from reference [19]

also the author of the report to the International Association for Testing Materials' 5th Congress in Copenhagen, September 1909. Other field test plots for exposure of mortar cubes were carried out at Vardø in Northern Norway with severe freezing/thawing, but negligible chemical activity, at Degerhamn in Sweden at the Baltic Sea coast with freezing/thawing but low salinity of the water, and at Esbjerg, Denmark, with freezing/thawing, North Sea salinity and 1.5 m tide. The report, 27 pages with 21 appendices, was presented in French, German and English editions.

The blocks and mortar cubes comprised concrete made with the different Scandinavian brands of Portland cement, and also blends of pozzolans with cement or with lime. The use of Santorin earth, Neapolitanian and Roman pozzolans, Trass, Chaux du Teil, Danish "infusoria earth" (moler) and blast-furnace slag tells us that the committee members were scholars of the classical, pre-Portland cement technology.

Figure 6 shows that they were also well aware of the implications of "packing" of the sand size fraction of the aggregates. (Other contemporary documents show that A. Poulsen had frequent exchanges with P. Feret in France, the leading expert on the grading of aggregates.) The remark on page 14 of the report: "The blocks were kept moist for four weeks by sprinkling and covering for the sun ..." shows that the engineers were trained in the inherited school of quality concrete workmanship regarding curing.

The field test plot in Thyborøn was laid out in 1896 with extensive recording of local temperature/humidity conditions. Considerable hazardous events were encountered. Many blocks proved to have been made of too lean mixes, and generally the destructive power of the marine exposure, especially on the North Sea coast at Thyborøn and the Barent Sea at Vardø, was underestimated.

The experience gained from this grand scale, experimental programme consists of what the continuous observations by the local resident engineers reported

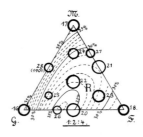

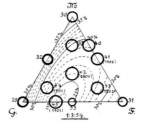

Fig. 6. Packing diagrams for grading of sand, the fine fraction of concrete aggregate, for mass concrete blocks at Thyborøn in field exposure test programme, started 1896, from reference [19]

concerning the durability of the concrete in the groyne at Thyborøn, of pier and jetty structures and mortar cubes at the other harbours, and of the recorded test results with analyses and interpretations of these. The report summarizes, as the primary results, that:

- the chemical action of the sea water is not able to destroy the mortar and concrete made with Portland cement
- the destruction of mortars (as field test cubes) is, for the greatest part, due to the mechanical influence of frost
- the destruction of concrete blocks is also sufficiently explained by the climatic influence
- the mortar mixture 1:3 is too poor for sea water in Scandinavian climates
- the sand used shall be graded
- addition of a finely ground material (trass or even sand) to the cement is advantageous.

The report concludes that the test period had been too short, that the tests would be continued for another ten years, and preferably ought to have been planned to last for a still greater number of years.

A. Poulsen and his colleagues on the west coast of Jutland, especially his successor I. K. Danø, continued their research and incorporated recording and field inspections of the steadily increasing groyne constructions and maintenance with supplementary block castings. Concurrently, they further developed their concrete specifications and site quality control. I updated their work by personal field inspections in 1951–52 with summary and evaluation of their preceding work. [20, 21]

A. Poulsen was granted a patent in 1910 for a sea water resistant moler cement, consisting of an interground blend of 25–30% moler and 75–70% Portland cement. The moler was a tertiary, sedimentary "clay" with a high content of diatomaceous fossils of pure, reactive silica. It was found in the Limfjord area of north-west Jutland. Aktieselskabet Aalborg Portland-Cement-Fabrik manufactured the cement which was specified by the Board of Maritime Works for coastal and port enterprises. The patent was renewed in 1924 with calcined moler as the interground pozzolan. This was waste from the manufacture of lightweight, insulation moler-bricks and, as a blending material, it was of higher reactivity and less water-absorbent than the original, raw moler.

Poulsen found a satisfactory explanation for the value of the moler in its physical and chemical effects in concrete in saline marine exposure, with reference to the century-old explanation brought forward by L. J. Vicat. By reaction with the free lime released in Portland cement paste by cement hydration, the reactive silica created supplementary calcium silica hydrate, which increased the density of the paste and made the calcium ions unavailable for reaction with $MgSO_4$ from the sea water. This was the reaction in marine concrete without pozzolans which formed the "indissoluble salts in such a volume that it may cause the concrete to burst". These "salts" are actually ettringite, calcium alumina sulphate hydrate, CSA, or $3CaO, Al_2O_3, 3CaSO_4, 30-32 H_2O$. This substance was first identified by E. Candlot in 1890, later called the "cement bacillus", and found by Poulsen as white, compact compounds in cavities within concrete blocks which were deteriorating. He had also obtained test results from the Danish State Testing Laboratory showing that mortar specimens with moler cement were more durable than specimens with pure Portland cement, when stored in $MgSO_4$ solutions.

The Danish achievements were presented at the International Association of Navigation Congresses, first in Cairo in 1926,[22] and next in Venice (off the programme) in 1931.[23] The preface to reference [22] mentions that out of 18 authors at the preceding conference in London in 1923, 16 had recommended precautions against deterioration of marine concrete. A majority had recommended the use of pozzolans, while 5 had preferred "extremely careful execution of the concrete work and a large proportion of Portland cement" as sufficient to secure durability.

Figure 7 is a photograph from 1993 of red moler cement concrete cast in 1931 as a protection wall for the South Jetty of Hvide Sande harbour on the west coast of Jutland. The appearance of the concrete, with no other damage than slight surface wear, substantiates Poulsen's belief in his achievements. The Hvide Sande port structures do, however, also contain Portland cement concrete blocks from 1915 which exhibit no damage, although there are also Portland cement blocks of the same age with severe map-cracking and even disintegration. This corresponds to views held by peers of A. Poulsen throughout the many meetings on the subject among Danish civil engineers from about 1900 through the 1930s. Those who contested his views claimed that the $MgSO_4$ concentration in sea water was far too weak to pose any threat to Portland cement concrete, provided that the cement content was sufficient, and the workmanship of high quality.

Seen with hindsight, his many years of construction and maintenance of the marine works along the exposed parts of the west coast of Jutland made Poulsen the leader of an exceptional, integrated research and development effort by a progressive public agency in association with the cement industry.

Fig. 7. Top surface of concrete wall, cast with red moler cement in 1931 at South jetty, Hvide Sande, west coast of Jutland (photo G. M. Idorn, 1993).

Reinforced concrete structures

In the summer of 1902, the dynamic young lecturer A. Ostenfeld at the Technical University in Copenhagen suggested that a newly graduated Danish civil engineer, R. Christiani, who was in Paris, visit the Hennebique firm, a famous developer of reinforced concrete structures. The visit resulted in two years' employment, and, after his return to Denmark, the reinforced concrete design and construction firm Christiani & Nielsen A/S (C&N A/S) was created, with R. Christiani's good friend, captain Aa. Nielsen as partner.[24]

Figure 8 shows their elegant design of a wharf at Assens, Denmark, which they constructed as early as 1906. In this and the following years, they designed and constructed several reinforced concrete arch and beam bridges and proved very competitive, both as innovative structural designers, making full use of the new potentials of reinforced concrete, and as eminently clever construction engineers.

In 1914 they constructed the 40 m diameter reinforced concrete dome of the circus building in Central Copenhagen, still in use today. At that time they had opened offices or affiliated companies in several countries, including Germany, France and England. During the 1920s they ventured further, to South America, South Africa and South-East Asia. They were keen to maintain and develop a major competitive advantage by consistently recruiting the best young civil engineering candidates from the Technical University, then presenting them with tough challenges, not least commercially, and selectively exposing them to different kinds of jobs and environments. They also encouraged personal research efforts within the realm of the company strategy, and gave the qualified engineers substantial freedom – and responsibility – for innovative structural design and site construction methods. The research-minded candidates were even encouraged to write doctoral dissertations as part of their employment.

Table 1 shows that no less than seven outstanding C&N A/S employees became professors at the Technical University – with a richness of experience

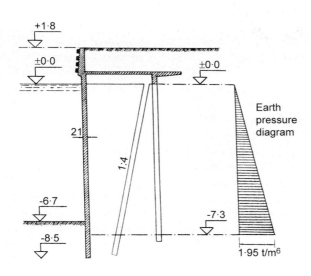

Fig. 8. Wharf in the harbour of Assens, Denmark: design and construction by Christiani and Nielsen A/S, 1906, from reference [21]

31

Table 1. *Professors at the Technical University of Denmark, formerly employees at Christiani & Nielsen A/S*

Professor	Name	Field	DSc year
1931	Chr. Nøkkentved	Statical theory and steel structures	1924
1940	A. E. Bretting	Hydraulic structures	–
1948	A. Efsen	Reinforced concrete and materials technology	1937
1950	H. Lundgren	Port and coastal engineering	1949
1955	J. Brinch Hansen	Geotechnics	1953
1963	T. Brøndum Nielsen	Reinforced concrete	1962
1963	F. A. Engelund	Hydraulic engineering	–

demonstrating the conditions under which the science-based engineering education could be transferred to successful structural design and reinforced concrete construction work. The employment policy also attracted candidates for whom careers as independent creators of new construction firms seemed fascinating. Among these were the founders, K. Højgaard and S. Schultz, of Højgaard and Schultz A/S, E. Thorsen of Monberg and Thorsen A/S, and O. Kierulff and P. Kampmann of the later Kampsax A/S. Also, the later professor M. Westergaard of the University of Urbana and Harvard, USA, commenced his career with Christiani & Nielsen A/S.

Companies like those mentioned above, which based their development on major engineering jobs abroad, provided excellent education for many civil engineers who, without appearing in *Who's who*, made solid and progressive reinforced concrete design and construction development, worldwide and in Denmark. Major bridges such as the Lillebælt and the Storstrøm Bridges and smaller ones, but important in the national economy, such as the Oddesund, Vilsund, Aggersund and Møn Bridges, were constructed in the 1930s as public infrastructure investments by public agencies of high technical competence, and also with the involvement of many engineers returning home from the export-dominated construction firms.

The associated industries complied with demands from customers for product development. F. L. Smidth & Co. and Aktieselskabet Aalborg Portland-Cement-Fabrik marketed, as early as 1924, velo cement, a forerunner of the later rapid-hardening cements. The Dansk Eternit Fabrik A/S was established in 1927, and De Danske Betonfabrikker A/S introduced, in 1929, the first truck-mounted rotary concrete mixer, an invention by the director K. Hindhede.[18] It was the forerunner of the now worldwide ready mixed concrete industry.

Figure 9 shows another Danish innovation of the period, with no national export value, but nonetheless familiar to anyone travelling by air today. The self-educated mechanical talent J. C. Ellehammer (1871–1946) had, entirely alone, constructed an aeroplane with which he flew 42 m at a height of 0.5 m from the ground in 1906, only three years after the Wright Brothers in the USA, whose work and achievements were unknown in Europe until 1908. Be that as it may, for trials of different editions of his "vehicle" and his own invention, the six-cylinder "star-engine", he had constructed what was probably the first airfield concrete pavement in the world in 1906 on the island of Lindholm

Fig. 9. Concrete runway on the Island Lindholm, South Zealand, Denmark. Constructed for J.C. Ellehammer 1906 for experiments with aeroplanes, from reference [25]

off South Zealand.[25] This event is mentioned as a reminder, that new technology more often than not stimulates creative human minds to achievements far beyond what the normalized boundaries ask of them.

Concrete habitations in Europe

Long before prefabrication of concrete elements became the industrial basis for large-scale habitation development in western and eastern Europe in the course of the 1950s, there were European architects who pioneered the use of concrete in house building.

The general housing problems in the 1920s, with deep recession in the European nations, whether victorious or defeated in World War I, drew the attention of young, politically liberal architects towards concrete. It could be made by unskilled, unemployed blue-collar men, it could be moulded in wooden forms, while fresh and workable, to serve a functionalistic architecture. With reinforcement, it provided the freedom to invent new, simple, composite systems of columns, walls and slabs. The general access to the source materials made it possible to design large-scale, low-cost housing projects. Altogether, the nature of concrete and its production methods stirred the intellectual visions of a new architectural style. Previously, esoteric aesthetics "for the few" had been a predominant feature in the history of architecture; in the course of the 1920s, concrete made it possible to give architecture a vision of a social dimension, a mainstream feature of the quality of life for the masses of working people in the industrial societies and the big cities. The German architect Mies van der Rohe said in an interview referred to in reference [26]:

> "It was not until after the war, some time in the twenties, that I realised the importance that technical development was coming to have in everyday life; this was the true driving force of the age, bringing a completely new approach not only to the treatment of materials, but to processes; it turned our traditional conceptions upside down. However, I was

33

convinced of the possibilities of architectural developments thanks to these new means. I could see that it would be possible to harmonise old energies with the new forms. I believed in the virtues of modern civilization, and strove to contribute, through my work, to the refining of the tendencies then emerging".

Another German architect, Walter Gropius, had, in 1919, founded the Bauhaus School in Goethe's hometown, Weimar. He created, along with other liberal intellectuals, a new interactive education in architecture, art and industrial design, and concentrated largely on the exploration of the new potentials for the combined, structural functionalism of concrete and other materials, such as steel and glass, which provided an attractive sort of stern, "naked" functionalism. Also, the functions of houses and buildings with furniture, lighting, sanitation etc. were the subjects of creative studies for new styling which also emphasized simplicity of design and production so as to make them accessible to everyone.[27] In France, the "wildcat" architect Le Corbusier – Charles Edouard Jeanneret – became the visionary designer of spectacular landscaped concrete cities which incorporated the entire functional and social life of people in large communities. Le Corbusier added a philosophical perception of the "raw" simplicity of concrete as the predominating material for the integrated visual forms and load-bearing functions.[28]

Figure 10 shows Le Corbusier's modular figure in the design which is sculpted in relief at the base of the most impressive of his later works, l'Unité d'Habitation in Marseille. The building, with the symbolic relief, is a monument to his philosophy that humanism and rational architectural/engineering design and construction must be conceived as an entity. It is significant that he did not succeed in getting it built earlier than 1946–52.

During the 1930s, neither the Bauhaus School nor Le Corbusier's "social dimension" of functionalism were acceptable to those in political power in Germany and France. The Bauhaus School was at first moved to Dessau in 1926, then on to Berlin in 1932. With Mies van der Rohe as director, the School was closed by the Nazi government when it assumed power in 1933. "Flat roofs were alien to the Nordic race." The Nazi system required pomposity, not social functionalism. Le Corbusier was not accepted as being a fit architect for much other than functionalistic, private concrete houses for wealthy, progressive intellectuals.

In England, the cultural history favoured renewed town planning during the 1920s with separate, one-family and semi-detached houses built with external and partition walls and floor decks of solid concrete. Pioneered by Ebenezer Howard, Welwyn Garden City to the north of London, 1919–20, was a carefully planned, pleasantly green urban environment, in contrast to the pre-war barrack types of low-cost, masonry housing schemes. There was, however, no accompanying, deeper political attempts to comply with the basic sociological problems, and the garden cities in England became little more than pleasant, relatively wealthy suburban developments.

Thus, the initial development of modern concrete architecture for large-scale habitations, infrastructure and cultural activities occurred in Germany and France, through struggles and defeats, until its further development commenced in the 1940s when rebuilding and social reconstruction after the devastation of the war became a dire necessity. It is interesting to note in comparison that

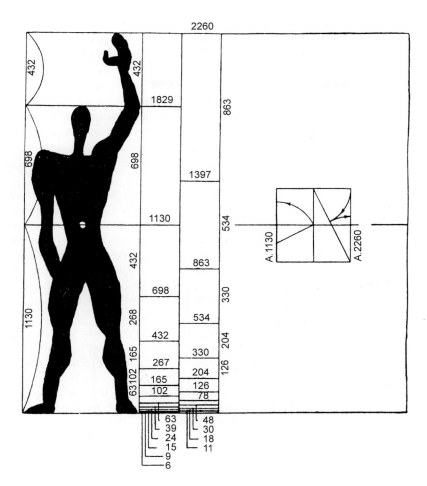

Fig. 10. Modular figure by Le Corbusier, designed as a relief for the base of l'Unité d'Habitation, Marseille, (1946–1952). The architect who pioneered concrete multi-storey buildings is emphasizing the involvement of regard for man and for environmental quality in mass urbanization, to be made possible by industrialization

in the USA, the industrial technology which Ford introduced for streamlined automobile production had a major sociological impact in the 1920s and 1930s. This created demands for concrete pavements for highways and secondary roads, not least in the agricultural States. But timber and steel prevailed in the housing and building sectors, and there were no incentives for comparable capital investments for development of a precast concrete industry with house building based on standard elements. Mass-produced automobiles were readily accepted, but the American home remained a stronghold of individualism.

The first international meetings on the chemistry of cement

The first international conference on the chemistry of cement was what we would today call a workshop for learned colleagues. It was arranged in London, 1918, by the prestigious British Faraday Society, the renowned guardian of the natural sciences and their proper application for technology development.[29] The cement industry had now learnt to manufacture Portland cement of sufficient uniformity to make possible comparisons between the quality of different brands produced at different times and different plants. Basic chemical science had also reached a stage of knowledge which made it realistic to envisage that knowledge of the chemistry of Portland cement and of its hydration could be used to predict the properties of concrete. The demands for such knowledge came hand in hand with the civil engineering development of reinforced concrete, and of regulatory requirements and test methods to control cement quality. Hence, there were good reasons for a scientific state-of-the-art review, and probably also strong desires among the scientists to renew contacts after the separations enforced during the Great War.

The famous French chemist, H. le Chatelier, presented his investigations and hypothesis on the microcrystalline nature of cement hydration products vis-à-vis the perception of these as primarily amorphous gel substances — an issue which would preoccupy researchers for decades to come, because for many years the means of investigation remained too insensitive to make direct microscopic observations of cement paste possible. The conference also reviewed the state of the art of composition and hydration chemistry, and the setting process of Portland cement, and much attention was directed towards the built-up structure of particle aggregations, i.e. the packing of solid particles.

In many ways, it was remarkable that the conference was organized by the British Faraday Society because, until that point, cement research had primarily been advanced on the Continent, especially in France and in Germany, despite the fact that England was the country in which Portland cement was discovered. Perhaps the tremendously profitable, imperial expansions during the nineteenth century had turned scientific research priorities towards other realms, such as, for instance, botany, geography, physics and mechanics. Be that as it may, in 1921 the British Building Research Station began its basic research into the chemistry of cement and cement hydration which was later to prove so influential.

The two decades between the two World Wars made international trade and technology development possible within the framework of economic depressions, grave unemployment crises, and growing political unrest in and among the major power centres of the world. Notwithstanding the waves of economic uncertainty, close association between the cement industry, the plant equipment makers, and industry and public research institutes made possible spectacular advances in basic scientific knowledge and effective transfer to technology. There were, perhaps, three major reasons for the rapid rate of progress.

First, that the wet cement kiln with raw materials preparation and cooling/grinding technology as a simple, one-line production process, was an exceedingly effective 1:1 scale modelling instrument for implementation of research, with continuous interaction between the limited number of cement producers and the very few equipment manufacturers, such as F. L. Smidth & Co., Humboldt and Polysius GmbH, and Allis Chalmers and Fuller Inc. Secondly, that the leaders of the industries were exclusively technologists, educated for development and open to direction from innovative specialists. Thirdly, that the leaders of the public research institutes, such as F. M. Lea, R. H. Bogue and others, were of superb quality, above all science-technology minded, and saw free exchange of important achievements as the basic, executive principle, with unlimited transfer of knowledge to the industries.

As examples of major accomplishments which illustrate the effective transfer of basic research under the given circumstances, it is appropriate to emphasize the exhaustive British studies by wet chemistry of the different reaction systems of the individual and the complex cement oxides' hydration reactions at $+20°C$, and the American development of the "Bogue calculation system" for mineral clinker composition, as derived from the oxide analyses of the raw meal for the cement burning process.

In 1938, a dedicated group of Swedish researchers, counting J. A. Hedvall, silicate chemist, G. Assarson and N. Sundius, geologists and mineralogists, and L. Forséen and S. Giertz-Hedstrøm, chemical physicists, among their number, caused the Swedish Ingeniorvetenskapsakademien and Svenska Cement Föreningen to arrange a Symposium on the Chemistry of Cement, afterwards designated the second.[30] The Swedish group had gained an international reputation for scientific research on cement mineralogy and cement hydration. At this meeting, the global acknowledgement of the "Bogue calculation" from 1931 was settled as a means of cement industry plant monitoring, and for development of cements with special properties, such as setting time, strength, sulphate resistance, etc. In conjunction, optical microscopy was being applied for control of the mineral composition of cement clinker. One could say that about a hundred years of patient, interactive research and transfer on cement chemistry now paid off. Perhaps stoichiometric principles were applied somewhat beyond their validity, but that was a question of subtleties, which were not recognizable in the uses of concrete, and therefore, under the given circumstances, not very important.

There were papers both on the energy-consuming calcination and grinding processes for the making of cement, and on the energy-releasing hydration process of cement and water. Concerning the physical nature of the hydrated cement paste, there was a clear "French–German" controversy with the French favouring the "intergrowth of submicroscopic crystalline theory" against the German preference for "the hydrates as colloid gel". The matter was not yet reconcilable: investigations of the physical properties merited the "gel-concept", while the mineralogical approach favoured the "crystallinity view".

There were visionary contributions concerning the porous structure of cement paste and the pore liquid as a saturated $Ca(OH)_2$ solution; and there were microscopic observations of crystalline $Ca(OH)_2$ and ettringite as secondary components in ordinary cement paste. The new basic research at Portland Cement Association in the USA was presented by reference to a paper by a young researcher, T. C. Powers. Retarders and accelerators as chemical additives to fresh concrete were mentioned in relation to concrete technology, but otherwise concrete was not a major subject of the conference.

Credits and debits in concrete history

Concrete has, ever since its invention in antiquity, been a commodity for the fulfilment of basic requirements for mankind. The demands on its performance quality have therefore always been ineluctably related to governing social systems and their economy.

In ancient Rome, the reverse side of the splendours of imperial life and monumental architecture was, for the common citizen, the frequent, rumbling noise of collapsing insulae, the three to six floor dwelling "boxes" housing the ever-growing multi-ethnical slum proletariat in the city.[31] The insulae, which ran up to 18–20 m in height, were built of concrete or masonry walls of maximum 0.45 m thickness, with timber floor separations, and no amenities whatsoever for the tenants. Quality of materials and workmanship were sacrificed for the builder's capital growth.

During the following "dark centuries" and beyond, the inherited knowledge of hydraulic lime with pozzolans was monopolized by the secular and religious sovereignties. Danish cathedrals and village churches, built from around 1100 AD to the reformation in 1536, stand today as national monuments, not only to early Christianity, but also to imported craftsmanship of high performance quality; and the Danish King Christian IV (1577–1648), a great architect, imported trass (from Dutch merchants) for hydraulic mortars for his palaces and castles. But only primitive building methods and materials were available for the working population in those bygone days.

As I have described above, the nineteenth century changed that. The new natural sciences were gradually applied for the manufacture of Portland cement, and concrete technology resumed the inherited masons' and carpenters' craft as the basis for making the performance of concrete comply with the new demands for quality. Nevertheless, Henry Reid's appeal for quality workmanship, quoted earlier in this chapter, shows that there were powerful economic factors in the new capitalism, which prompted the neglect of quality workmanship. The use of lean and wet, fresh concrete (to save cement), sloppy compaction and curing (to save on labour) had entered the construction sites. In other words, if concrete could be made by unskilled labour, it could also be made inadequately. Presumably, in Mr. Reid's day, brands of Portland cement were sometimes of questionable quality, because knowledge of its correct manufacture was still in its infancy. With the broadening markets for concrete came aspects reminiscent of the shoddy production of the insulae in imperial Rome. These did not manifest themselves in the frequent collapse of buildings, because brickwork, steel and timber still predominated in house building and in structural development, as long as concrete remained unreinforced as mass concrete, where volume, mass and formability in the fresh stage were the decisive, new advantages.

At the turn of the century, the increasing magnitude of public investments, such as for coastal protection, harbour construction, and infrastructure development, required adequate control and delivery of quality materials and work, and this was successfully achieved, for instance by the Danish coastal engineers and their peers abroad. The contemporary introduction of reinforced concrete accentuated this trend, because the load-transfer function brought the safe use of the structures into focus.

Figure 11 is a display, which I have used before in this context, of the reliance of the principles of inherited, classical concrete technology on thorough visual surveillance of the entire concrete making operation at construction sites by

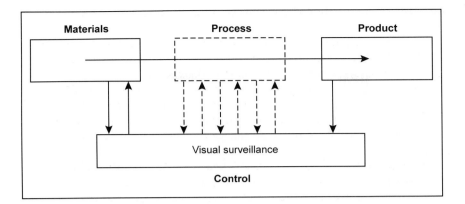

Fig. 11. The basic principle of monitoring process – product quality control: in modern industry by instrumentation which records the transfer of raw materials to final product on the basis of scientific knowledge; in classical concrete technology by visual surveillance based on knowledge by experience with the performance of field concrete

experienced engineers and assistants. Thus, the governing principle was total surveillance control of the concrete materials and the processing phase. This lesson was taught and executed by experienced foremen and site engineers in the disciplinary hierarchy of construction works as part of the heritage from their predecessors.

The system successfully integrated the available hydraulic capability of the early Portland cements, the contemporary performance requirements and design principles for concrete structures, and the polytechnical education of the civil engineers.

Figure 12 shows high performance concrete made in 1915. If quality control had not been common practice, concrete would not, over the decades before the twentieth century, have commenced in earnest to establish its position as superior to masonry structures for versatility in design and construction, to timber for durability, and to steel for cost-effectiveness.

Fig. 12. Mass concrete cast at Hvide Sande, West Jutland in 1915, photograph 1993, completely undamaged despite use of alkali-reactive aggregate and severe exposure to freezing/thawing and splash of sea water

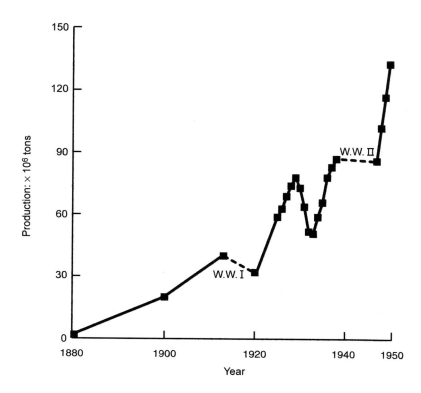

*Fig. 13. World cement
production 1880–1950*

Figure 13 shows the development of the world production of Portland cement
from 1.7 million tonnes in 1880 to 40 million tonnes in 1913, and – with interruptions for the two World Wars – that the further conquest of markets caused
an increase to 135 million tonnes in 1950.

Until 1940, the uses of reinforced concrete had increased, in particular in
western Europe and North America, due to the social and commercial
demands for development of the infrastructure, such as highway and railway
systems, river regulations, port and marine structures and, in mountainous
regions, also hydropower plant construction. Some major defence investments
also relied on concrete. As a consequence, technical, governmental agencies
remained the principal investors in concrete structural design and construction.
This happened concurrently with deep economic and social recessions in most
countries; it coincided also with improvements in cement manufacturing technology, which increased the production capacity, reduced the price of cement,
and increased the strength capability of Portland cement in concrete. The resultant attainable increasing strength of concrete was a basic factor in the development of structural design, with slender structural members and comparable
savings, for instance by the introduction of longer spans in bridges, reduced
use of heavy piles and foundations etc.

This phase of the development of concrete technology was also irreversibly affected by the rationalization and technical refinement of laboratory equipment and working conditions for the testing of concrete materials and concrete. The introduction of laboratory testing made it possible for structural design to obtain quantified values of compressive and tensile strength, of shrinkage and creep, etc., albeit measured on small model samples, which were prepared and tested under homogenized laboratory conditions. Moreover, concrete construction development took place primarily in northern, temperate countries, with field operations restricted to no-frost seasons, and ample time to await the application of live load for about 3–4 weeks. These conditions made the introduction of the standard 28-day compressive strength testing of cubes or cylinders a remarkable, lasting progressive step. Reproducible test data made statical design calculations quantifiable with reasonable safety factors for structural design, because the structural research itself was undertaken using reinforced concrete models of approximately 1:1 scale sizes, or at least of such a scale that model transfer problems were insignificant.

Construction sites were able to use the cube strength test results as a means of establishing rational mix design with given concrete materials, with the water/cement strength relationship as the predominant proportioning parameter. Concurrently, the cement producers could utilize concrete testing in their in-house laboratories for quality control of cement types, and for their customers' service. They also now had available improved means for further development of the hydraulic capability of Portland cements with types and brands of special qualities, such as rapid- and slow-hardening. This related well to the concurrent progress of cement chemistry research, with exploration of the effects of different cement components, and the dependence of the occurrence of these on manufacturing technology.

Thus, for all parties concerned, sample testing of concrete became a simple, reliable means of mutual – and international – communication between research, cement production and engineering practice, effective also for the development of standard specifications for the use of concrete in structural design and construction. The 28-day compressive strength test became the common denominator of this creed of concrete technology, with knowledge extracted from the interpretation of reproducible test data correlation. For a while, it represented a major contribution to the advance of concrete construction and therefore also for social progress in the industrial countries of the world.

In retrospect, the reverse side of this progressive development must also be considered. An accompanying disadvantage was the temptation to use reduced cement contents in the concrete as a trade-off against increasing cement strength. This became widely accepted because the public agencies were under pressure to attain low construction costs. Besides, the high unemployment rates in many countries favoured the use of non-skilled labour. Another effect was the loss of the direct engagement of site engineers and operating crews in day-to-day quality assurance at field concrete production, because the producers and the supervisors became accustomed – and obliged – to consider strength test data, remotely produced in laboratories, as the representative expression of the performance quality of the concrete in their structures. This further promoted the belief within contemporary concrete research, that its laboratories and their sample testing were the superior strongholds of concrete knowledge – even in field usage. This new, simplistic model simulation developed, unfortunately, into long-term misconceptions in concrete research and development.

The slump test, for instance, caused a staggering confusion about the workability of fresh concrete, because the kinetics of the deformation in the test samples went unrecorded. The strength tests could not incorporate the effects of mass, and inherent and external heat versus cooling on the rate of strength development in field concrete, i.e. the kinetics of the chemical hydration reactions. And the complexity of the effects on concrete of deleterious physical or chemical reactions during performance in field structures, could never be properly comprehended by means of the strength tests, and supplementary, mechanical expansion test measurements. Possibly the worst effect of the new creed, for the classical entity of concrete production and supervision on sites, was the transfer of quality assurance to remote laboratory sample testing and certifying test control data documentation. There was a profound loss of vital intellectual input in this separation of actual concrete production and laboratory derived technology.

Nevertheless, it would be wrong to interpret the transition of concrete technology, especially during the 1930s, merely as characterized by the sample testing philosophy. The development was basically multifarious, and in many ways progressive, because investments in concrete constructions were profitable for public and private capital investments, and provided a solution to employment problems. The classical, scientific schools of cement and concrete chemistry created increased and fruitful cooperation between basic academic and institutional research and cement production technology in Germany, France and Great Britain.

In the United States, the Portland Cement Association, sponsored by the powerful national cement companies, commenced a long-term scientific exploration of the nature of hardened cement paste in the mid-1930s. This was coordinated with basic cement chemistry research, with additional funding at the National Bureau of Standards. Universities, closely associated with state highway departments and the builders of dams, port and marine constructions, became concerned about the early heat development during the hardening of mass concrete, and introduced the use of fly ash as a pozzolan. Sulphatic soils in the Western States and in western Canada, and sea water exposure in the warmer coastal States, alerted engineering practice and research to the consequences of sulphate attack with the occurrence of ettringite in the concrete as an acknowledged symptom. In 1940, alkali-silica reaction was identified in highway pavements in California. In these circumstances, the development of testing methods and the authorization of their use flourished, along with fruitful, often seriously argumentative, peer dialogues at conferences, in committees and in publications.

In Europe, high-level emphasis on the development of structural design with reinforced concrete for many different kinds of structure offered remarkable progress in civil engineering design and construction, in challenging competition with steel construction. In Germany, the special political circumstances made the construction of a comprehensive system of concrete highways possible. Exempt from the pressure of cost-savings, inter alia by the compulsory paramilitary "Arbeitsdienst", strong disciplinary management enforced rigorous application of experienced craftsmanship on the construction crews, and attained general concrete quality which was fit for the given purposes.

In all the industrialized countries, civil engineering, the smokestack industries of cement and steel, and technical education and research enjoyed high national reputations and attracted brilliant students for service in academia and in the public and the operating private professions. Therefore, interactive cooperation between research and innovation was also intensive and fruitful, and international exchange was only restricted by the contemporary limitations of communications technology.

World War II made the United States the global powerhouse for all kinds of technology development, while the devastation took place elsewhere, causing tremendous setbacks and interruptions of progress in science, education, and industrial and social developments. Meanwhile, the requirements of the United States' and the allied powers' defence technology had caused a hitherto unknown intensity of application of the natural sciences and mathematics in technology discoveries and innovations, and also public and industrial willingness to accept high investment and research/development risks. Abundant economic resources were made available, academia became involved in high-level decisions and the predominating technical leadership in American industry paid off in dynamic management of technology development. Landmark utilization of theoretical physics, chemistry and electronics demonstrated the merits of the previous long-term investments in strategic basic science and research.

The impact of the overall technology development in the US on the national cement and concrete research and engineering practice was, above all, made remarkable by the intensified application of the natural sciences in exploratory, long-term theoretical studies of the nature and behaviour of cement, cement paste and concrete. It was characteristic of the time and of the industrial environment that the Portland Cement Association assumed a leading position in this development, followed by many universities. The construction boom of the late 1930s had revealed that concrete durability was becoming a matter of economy, and this prompted further intrusion of the physical, chemical and mineralogical sciences into applied research, for instance regarding the resistance of concrete to frost and sulphate attack, and to alkali-aggregate reaction. Besides, the introduction of heavy mechanical equipment, and mass transportation vehicles and systems in concrete construction made the technology applicable to larger scale operations than ever before. Thus, the United States became an arsenal of technical and knowledge resources for the uses of concrete in the tremendous post World War II reconstruction investments abroad, and also for the renovation of concrete technology research.

In western Europe, the heritage of concrete construction and technology from a much more remote period of history than in the United States, proved a potent interactive factor in the post-war reconstruction and subsequent further developments. In the United Kingdom, the basic crystallographic/mineralogical, and cement and cement hydration schools had been actively preserved. In France, complementary cement chemistry, structural innovations and developments of high strength concrete, and visionary concrete architecture were second to none, and France became the seat of the first inter-European materials research association, RILEM. In Switzerland, bridge design reached lasting elegance,

43

and in Spain and Italy thin-shell structural development was outstanding. Austria fostered Graf W. Czernin as an exceptionally talented communicator of new scientific progress in civil engineering education. After some years, the German cement industry reassembled its resources and created the research institute VDZ in Düsseldorf.

Historical concrete balance sheet

The most permanently striking feature of cement and concrete technology in its two millennia history is the social aspect of concrete usage. This is due to the abundance and easy retrieval of the materials and because concrete, from the outset, could be moulded and cast even in very large volumes by a few professionals, overseeing a large labour force. Professionally made concrete has always proven indestructible, but instances or periods of unprofessional disregard of quality requirements have occurred throughout the course of history. The acceleration of the usage of concrete after the first World War and common degradation of concrete production quality in the 1930s made the creation of scientific concrete research necessary in conjunction with the consistently improving qualities of Portland cement. Some concrete technology axioms emerge from this history.

(a) Concrete making is a craft with its roots in ancient engineering experience. Portland cement is an industrial commodity. Its production and properties are controlled on the basis of scientific research.

(b) The introduction of Portland cement made mass concrete a new construction material in the nineteenth century. Surveillance of workmanship was the primary means of guaranteeing performance quality.

(c) The rapid growth of the markets for Portland cement in the nineteenth century stimulated support for adequate production quality control from contemporary chemical science. Cement research adopted the use of modelling laboratory examination and testing as supplementary to the visual surveillance of the manufacturing process procedures. Chemical research led to the Vicat test for setting characteristics, to the Le Chatelier test for volume stability, and to tensile and compressive strength tests by mortar and concrete specimens.

(d) At the beginning of the twentieth century, strong public agencies under civil engineering auspices assumed executive responsibility for major concrete construction programmes in many countries. They were able to undertake and sponsor public concrete technology research, often in association with the Portland cement industry. With the first certification of Portland cement, civil engineering could make concrete of excellent performance quality by rigorously imposed site surveillance, following experience-based production manuals. Sample testing for supplementary site control of concrete was not yet available. Test fields for long-term accumulation of experience regarding the durability of mass concrete under severe exposure were made and used by public agencies in several countries.

(e) The reinforced concrete breakthrough early in the twentieth century introduced laboratory studies with large-scale models of structural elements, such as columns, beams and slabs, for development of cost-effective and safe design methods and specifications. This research required laboratory model testing, especially of the strength and deformation properties of concrete and steel. Concurrently, the versatility of unreinforced and reinforced concrete in building and construction prompted academia and public research institutes to earnestly support free exploratory studies of the chemistry of cement and cement hydration. Also, the chemistry of concrete deterioration under severe exposure conditions, such as for marine concrete, came into focus.

(f) Small-scale specimen testing as a quality control measure on concrete construction sites remained virtually unknown for projects of ordinary magnitudes throughout the first four decades of the twentieth century. Unfortunately, the severe economic crises in the 1920s and 1930s caused common degradation of the classical expectation of excellent site workmanship. Portland cement offered increasing strength capability. Fierce price competitions engendered a reduction of the cement contents in concrete, and a corresponding increase in water contents. Thus, flowable concrete which could not be compacted came into use.

However, as a consequence of a "bad concrete decade" in the 1930s, no wave of structural collapse occurred, as with the insulae in ancient imperial Rome. The reinforcement incorporated warranted adequate stress transfer despite, or even as a response to, cracking of the concrete. The damages caused by negligent engineering practice were initially invisible, or cosmetically hidden, but there appeared, in the course of time, merciless, unanticipated expenses for repair, maintenance or replacement.

2

Field concrete performance – observation and contemplation

Like natural rocks, concrete is subject to inherent changes in its components and performance quality under field exposure conditions. Over more than a century the resistance of concrete to deleterious physical and chemical reactions has been studied, using accumulated experience with field concrete and long-term investigations of the behaviour of selected concrete specimens in field test plots exposed to severe conditions.

The relatively benign, temperate climatic conditions in western Europe initially made the exposure of marine concrete the most difficult problem to address, and made chemical sea water attack a primary candidate as a cause of deterioration.

In North America, high sulphate concentrations in inland soils and severe winter conditions over the greater part of the continent, made chemical sulphate attack and physical freezing/thawing the primary objectives of test plot studies. These studies were concurrent with the development of empirical test and examination studies, and made test plot recording a standardized routine undertaking. This was in accordance with the fact that progressive weakening of the cement paste in non-resistant concrete leads to the same visual appearance of deterioration for both causes of damage. Meanwhile, linear expansion became a standardized measure of both kinds of deterioration in laboratory studies.

The primary visual evidence of alkali-silica reaction was, from its discovery in 1940, observed to be map-cracking in concrete surfaces, but without corresponding weakening of cement paste. Linear expansion of laboratory specimens was also found to be a reasonably quantifiable measure of this reaction. However, alkali-silica reaction did not become an objective of field test studies in North America.

Increasing reliance on standardized laboratory test methods in the 1920s and 1930s turned the attention of the researchers away from the different mechanisms of the deleterious reactions, and the quest for reproducibility of laboratory testing prevented the recognition of the impact of temperature and relative humidity on field concrete deterioration over the North American continent.

The advance of fundamental knowledge on the nature and properties of cement and concrete in the wake of World War II provided a focus for observant researchers on the need for a logical organization of integrating studies into concrete materials, processing, performance quality and field exposure conditions.

The Ikaite story

In August 1962, a small group of Danish geologists examined some white reefs which had been seen "growing" on the bottom of the Ika fjord in south-west Greenland. The reefs were found to be white "columns" of a porous, friable material, rising 10–20 m above the bottom to 0.5 m below sea level. Some were up to 10 m wide. Smaller "pillars" were seen at the feet of the main structures. The water temperature was $+3°C$ at the bottom and $+7°C$ 1 m below the surface. Samples taken by a diver disintegrated to a wet powder, which was found to be calcite, $CaCO_3$. Later, samples were stored in a refrigerator below $+12°C$ and, on analysis, proved to be calcium carbonate hexahydrate, $CaCO_3$, $6H_2O$. This had never before been described as a naturally occurring mineral and was therefore certified as a new mineral and given the name Ikaite.[32, 33] It was confirmed that the material "grew" on the sea bottom as stalagmites in an area with faulted carbonate rock formations. Presumably it precipitated from fissures in the sea bottom which contain supersaturated solutions of calcium carbonate. But the chemistry and mechanism of its formation is still unknown. Might it be crystallization pressure in the fissures which have expelled the excess material, or a supersaturated carbonate solution which precipitates the hexahydrate when mixed with the sea water at the fissure exit?

The gist of this story in a concrete context is that peculiar, "live geology" crystallization processes have been found to occur in sea water at temperatures around $0°C$, and that storage and analyses of the material at standard laboratory "room temperature" levels failed to discover the identity of the material. Hence, in concrete exposed to sea water at low temperatures, there may be unknown phase equilibria systems, differing from those which cement and concrete research have identified as predominating at room temperature.

The story illustrates also that chemical reactions akin to what is known to occur in concrete can happen at considerable rates in the zero Celsius temperature range. More concrete than ever before is exposed to sea water at low temperature and the discovery of Ikaite therefore has great value for turning our attention towards the performance of such concrete.

But the story of this discovery ought also to make us consider that much more concrete is exposed to elevated than to very low temperatures, and to considerable cyclic or irregular, alternating temperature ranges. Moreover, the global trends of economy and demography have already initiated a substantial increase of concrete construction placements in subarctic/arctic regions for the retrieval of raw materials and in subtropical/tropical regions to accommodate population growth. These trends move the hegemony of "room temperature" research down from the position it has held for too long, to a third-rate role. Thus, concrete research ought to recognize the lessons from the Ikaite story: it is vital to take real field exposure conditions as the basis for research into the performance of concrete structures. In fact, this is exactly what our predecessors in concrete research and development did.

Roman concrete

The extent of the remnants of Roman structures and buildings, consisting of concrete or brickwork with hydraulic mortars in many European, Middle

Fig. 14. Top water main, Roman aquaduct, Pont du Gard, Provence, France

Eastern and North African countries has made them almost universal symbols of concrete's long-term durability. This is justified if one also remains conscious of the fact that it is only the durable concrete and brickwork that is left, and that the preservation has been favoured by rather benign climatic exposure conditions.

Figure 14 shows the top water main of the famous Pont du Gard aqueduct in Provence, France. In this case, the vertical sides of the concrete "trough" have been coated by thick layers of hard, durable calcite, actually a limestone modification. The calcite was deposited over the centuries, layer after layer, by the passage of water supersaturated with calcium in the mountains from where the aqueduct brought it down to the Roman city which is Nîmes today. Examinations which I made of samples of concrete from the aqueducts around Nîmes and Arles showed that cavities in the concrete were often filled by secondary calcite, which increased the imperviousness.[7] Other workers have presented complementary observations,[34,35] which confirm that crystallization of secondary calcite in pores or cavities in concrete, in other words a sort of carbonation, may contribute towards making concrete a durable building material under benign climatic exposure.

Middle Age mortar

Figure 15, from reference [36], shows rim corrosion in a dense flint particle in lime mortar from a 600-year old Danish church, i.e. under inland, north-temperate climatic exposure conditions. Presumably, calcium hydroxide in the mortar has attacked the surface of the particle during the course of the centuries. Figure 45 in the same book shows a quartz particle in the mortar with similar rim corrosion. Such surface corrosion reaction is also occurring at an accelerated rate in the

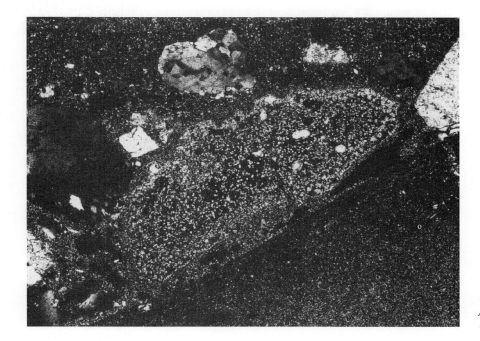

Fig. 15. Rim corrosion in dense flint particle in medieval lime mortar from Danish church (50×)

modern autoclave processing of lightweight cellular concrete, which is made of calcium hydroxide and finely ground quartz sand with alumina powder to create high porosity in the fresh mass. It is reasonable to assume that fundamentally similar, but much weaker, chemical reaction might contribute to strong bond formation in ordinary Portland cement concrete with siliceous aggregates. That might be designated a mild, beneficial mode of alkali-calciumhydroxide silica reaction.

Field exposure test sites in Europe and North America

The field performance of concrete works provided the sole, original trial and error guidance for technology progress, when Portland cement concrete came into common use. Later on, the introduction of systematic field test plot trials demonstrated understanding within the civil engineering and cement industry professions of the need for "natural modelling" studies on the grand scale. Deeper follow-up exploration of the complexity of natural exposure conditions, as related to modern concrete uses have, unfortunately, long been hampered by the hegemony of small-scale, model testing under laboratory conditions.

I have compiled some elementary information relevant to these aspects of concrete research with the aim of illustrating that we are far from having a coherent and consistent progressive knowledge of field concrete performance and that we urgently need a conceptual approach to the dualism of exposure conditions and the mechanisms of deleterious reactions in concrete.

Europe

European research publications on the durability of marine concrete in the nineteenth century show that the resident engineers and the public, technical agencies who were responsible for the works considered the actual structures to be the primary objectives for studies and accumulation of experience. Cement industries took an active interest in, and were often co-sponsors of, such research with particular focus on the development of special, "sea water resistant" cement types and on concrete mix design for durability. In several European countries, large field exposure sites were in operation at the turn of the century, and international exchange and cooperation was intense. In Chapter 1, I have described the work of A. Poulsen and associates with marine concrete on the west coast of Jutland and presented more detailed accounts in references [20] and [21].

There were large contemporary exposure test sites on the North Sea island of Heligoland, Germany, in the Netherlands and Belgium, and in France at Bologna and La Rochelle. The Danish studies,[19] refer also to test sites (primarily for mortar specimens) in northern Norway, the Baltic Sea, Sweden, and Esbjerg, Denmark. During the first decades of the nineteenth century, many small ports were built along the west coast of Norway with mass concrete jetties and slightly reinforced concrete wharves. Their long-term resistance to North Atlantic exposure was described in detail by O. Gjørv.[37]

The magnitude of these undertakings had its background in the growing prosperity of the marine infrastructure and the fishing trades, but it had also much to do with the attitudes of the professional engineers of the time. Those who prevailed as industry leaders were dour people, as were the crews and foremen with whom they worked, and this developed a special kind of site management, with pride in the quality of workmanship. The engineers, working crews, and local populations were also anticipating long-term, if not permanent, benefits from their accomplishments, and the crews and engineers were accustomed to enduring physical hardships on the construction sites which we would not dream of today. The sea was a powerful opponent to the construction programmes, and frequently a deadly one for the fishermen. Hence, it was a general social philosophy that construction, technology and related research were incontrovertibly progressive, and civil engineers were the exponents of progress for people whose lives depended on what the sea gave and took. With this background for the professional work of engaged civil engineers it was self-explanatory that long-term field exposure testing of their products with special, large-scale model tests, was essential for the research on concrete durability.

There was an apparent contrast in the approaches to this research: on one side, the extensive visual field test and actual field structure recording of full-scale behaviour of exposed concrete by civil engineers, without any means for thorough phenomenological analyses of the material on the micro-scale. On the other side, was the chemical science-based progressive research on cement chemistry and the nature of chemical sea water attack on cement paste in concrete. The absence of instrumentation to overcome the apparent gap between these two different approaches was compensated for by imaginative speculations which were enhanced, controlled and contradicted, in other words fruitfully accentuated, by the national and international exchanges. With our present-day hindsight, one is tempted to see this kind of research cooperation as a very special, but now lost, type of cost-effective research planning and management.

The primary objectives of early European marine concrete research and development were:

- improvements in concrete mix composition design, with regard to cement contents, aggregate grading, and workability for compaction "by hand" so as to achieve maximum obtainable imperviousness
- improvements in chemical resistance towards "sea water attack" by development of suitable pozzolanic cements and by the use of blast-furnace slag cements
- improvements in resistance to frost attack by identification and rejection of "frost susceptible", coarse aggregate rock types.

La Rochelle, France

The field exposure test sites at the North Sea and Channel coastlines were destroyed during World War II, whereas the test plot at La Rochelle, France, established by the public "Services des Ponts et Chaussées" in 1902, was preserved. A review of experience extracted from long-term exposed concrete blocks and comparable laboratory specimens was presented in 1975 by M. Regourd.[38] Scanning electron microscopy with microprobe, chemical analysis and X-ray diffractometry were used for the examinations of concrete cast in 1904 and later. The supplementary examinations of mortar bars were carried out with specimens stored in fresh, soft water and synthetic sea water (of 3.53%, i.e. Atlantic Ocean, salinity).

It was found that compact concrete and mortar has good resistance to sea water, irrespective of cement type. Concrete with GGBS in slag cement, and Portland cement with pozzolans showed excellent resistance. Concrete with Portland cement with high C_3A content showed excellent chemical resistance to sea water in some cases – irrespective of the age of the concrete – and inferior resistance in other cases. This was also the experience with cement of low C_3A content. Hence, no conclusive correlation of the C_3A content of cement with concrete durability in sea water was attained. Deterioration of concrete was accompanied by precipitation in cavities in the concrete of secondary calcite, aragonite, gypsum, brucite and ettringite along with devitrified cement paste, i.e. calcium silicate hydrate (C–S–H) and calcium hydroxide. M. Regourd designated the observed ettringite as *expansive*, although her observations did not explicitly show that the visible secondary crystalline ettringite formations had exerted any fracture-causing pressure.

The photographs, Figures 1 to 4 of M. Regourd's paper, of exposed blocks in the test plot illustrated that the primary evidence of damage had been wear and tear causing gradual abrasion of concrete from the surfaces inwards. The basic mechanism of this form of deterioration is a gradual crumbling of the cement paste due to micro-disruption in the wake of chemical weakening by sea water attack, and/or physical weakening by freezing/thawing, with subsequent alternate wetting and drying shrinkage. The weakening eliminates the bonding between cement paste and aggregates.

Danish test plot experience

The earliest Danish field test site at Thyborøn, see Figure 5 in Chapter 1, was overbuilt or replaced in the 1920s due to the extensions and maintenance of the groyne which became the southern lee-jetty for the entrance to the Thyborøn harbour. In the meantime, the number of groynes along the coast was increased and they were periodically renovated. Extensive records of the concrete behaviour were made at two comprehensive field inspections, in 1910 and 1924, and a third which I carried out in 1952.[21] The information from these inspections was then used in the 1953–1960 series of general field investigations, involving core taking and macro- and microscopic examinations.[39–43]

The large number of reasonably comparable concrete blocks under the same exposure conditions made the assembly of groynes an exceptional field test plot; almost as if one had made a large series of laboratory concrete prisms and placed them under field exposure conditions. My training in interpreting the visual evidence of damage helped to clarify the limitations of what one could conclude about the causality of deterioration mechanisms by this method. It was evident at an early stage that there was an apparently haphazard distribution of durable, well-preserved concrete blocks among more or less severely deteriorating ones and that the predominant visual evidence of damage was map-cracking rather than crumbling, such as was observed at the French La Rochelle test plots. It was also evident that map-cracking was rare in blocks cast with the pozzolanic moler cement, which were more prone to have suffered wear and tear.[21]

The thin section examination of concrete from cores taken from these blocks, and of comparable concrete from northern Jutland highway bridge piers, revealed the occurrence of the same secondary crystalline compounds in damaged concrete as was observed in the concrete from La Rochelle, as referred to above. But we had also, in disintegrated concrete from the Copenhagen harbour, observed secondary crystallization of hydrocalumite ($C_4A\,H_{12}$).[44]

The special feature of the concrete groyne blocks was, however, that fractures associated with reacted aggregate particles provided conspicuous macro/micro-evidence of deterioration in cores and thin sections, wherever map-cracking in concrete surfaces was the conspicuous field evidence of damage. We did not identify features of the crystalline secondary compounds, including ettringite, indicating that expansive pressure as a mechanism of cracking had been exerted during the crystallization process. Consequently, from our studies of the visual field features and the internal macro- and microstructure of the concrete, we concluded that the secondary crystalline compounds were the results of the deleterious reactivity, but that alkali-silica reaction was the primary cause of observed cracking. This conceptual approach became the basis for the diagnosing system which I presented later.[36]

Table 2. Thirteen field test sites in the USA operating around 1950, reproduced from reference [45]

Region	State	Localities	Test objective
East	MA	Cape Cod Canal	Sea water, cold
	NY	Saugertie	Fresh water
	NY	Wellsville	Test road
	SC	Greenville	Test road
	GA	Perry	Test plot
	FL	St. Augustine	Sea water, warm
Central	ILL	Naperville	Freeze/thaw
	MO	Mexico	Test plot
	CO	Green Mountain Dam	Dam
	KA	Topeka	Test road
West	CAL	Sacramento	Sulphate soils
	CAL	Florence	Dam
	CAL	Newport Beach	Sea water, warm

North America

The growth of concrete construction in the USA and Canada made many institutions and federal and state research groups aware of the possible benefits of long-term experience with experimental field test plots.

Table 2 is an early survey, reproduced from reference [45], of 13 such field observation sites which were operating in the USA around 1950. Three stations operated special test sites for concrete in sea water, one was chosen for a cold environment, and two for warm environments; one at the Atlantic and the other at the Pacific coast. The impact of the use of the automobile by the ordinary civilian in the USA, which occurred much earlier than in Europe, had advanced concrete highway construction in the 1930s. This development had prompted the building of four test roads, i.e. pavements, to be used for the recording of resistance to traffic and environmental exposure. Three concrete dams were apparently also studied for performance quality. Finally, there was a special test site in Sacramento, California, for the study of concrete exposed to the aggressive sulphatic soils found in the west.

The distribution of the 13 test sites over the wide range of climatic conditions in the USA was presumably not the result of a joint research strategy, but rather an expression of the absence of federal centralization in the fields of concrete construction and research. It was, however, also an expression of the genuine concern within the many professional communities about the durability of concrete under severe exposure conditions, which made field concrete an indispensable target of the research.

During my first visit to the USA, in 1960, the following six operating field test sites were described to me:

☐ Treat Island, Maine – with beams, blocks, cubes etc. of concrete exposed on the beach to cyclic wetting/drying and severe freezing/thawing in the tidal zone

□ Cape Cod, Massachusetts – with blocks for study of the effects of air entrainment on concrete in cold sea water
□ St. Augustine, Florida – with piles of concrete vertically placed in the tidal/surf zone for study of sulphate resistance of concrete with different cements in a warm coastal climate, with oceanic salinity of the sea water and alternate wetting/drying dependent on the weather
□ Naperville, Illinois – with beams and blocks of concrete exposed to severe freezing/thawing during winters and warm, humid summer seasons. The primary objective of the tests at this site was the effects of freezing and thawing on concrete of different compositions, with and without air entrainment
□ Sacramento, California – with concrete beams exposed to alkaline sulphatic soils with partial saturation and evaporation
□ Los Angeles Harbour, California – with blocks of concrete with different cement types, mix-compositions, and sizes and forms exposed to cyclic wetting and drying in the warm, Pacific coastal climate.

The Treat Island site was established by the US Army Corps of Engineers in 1936. The St. Augustine site was established in 1939 and taken over by the Corps of Engineers in 1946. Subsequently, the Portland Cement Association had built a supplementary test site adjacent to the former. The Association established the Sacramento site in 1941, the Cape Cod and the Naperville stations in 1948, and the Los Angeles harbour station in 1959.

I visited the sites at St. Augustine, Los Angeles and Sacramento. At the first, some of the piles appeared to have exudations of alkali-silica gel on the surfaces, longitudinal cracking and rust coloration in the cracks. At Sacramento, the primary evidence of deterioration of the prismatic concrete specimens was crumbling, advancing to disintegration of the most severely affected members, and the deterioration became far more advanced in concrete above, rather than below, ground level.

The performance of the St. Augustine test specimens was analysed in 1968 by B. Mather (the Corps of Engineers site)[46] and G. Verbeck (the Portland Cement Association site).[47] Both authors seem, a priori, to have made their analyses on the basis of the classical perception of sea water attack and to have sought correlations between the C_3A content of the cement and the resistance to the sulphatic aggressivity of the warm sea water. Verbeck correlated further the resistance with the degree of longitudinal cracking in the reinforced piles, which was judged to be caused by chloride-induced reinforcement corrosion. Mather referred the C_3A content to measurements by microscopic examination of cement clinker samples, whereas Verbeck referred to the Bogue calculation of the C_3A content.

Neither author examined the permeability of the concrete, or its microstructure, for evidence of chemical conversions in the cement paste or, for instance, of alkali-silica reaction. Moreover, data for the concrete compositions, such as aggregate grading and water/cement, are scarce and there is no information in the articles about the concrete production circumstances.

The behaviour of test specimens in the Los Angeles harbour was examined in the 1960s by P. K. Mehta,[48] who found blocks with 14–15% C_3A Portland cement (calculated) in excellent condition after 67 years of exposure.

54

The experience with concrete specimens at the Sacramento test plot was described by Verbeck.[47] The objective was to study the resistance to sulphate solutions (with 10% Na_2SO_4) in the local soils of concrete made with different Portland cement types, different mix proportions, different pozzolans etc. Verbeck observed a considerable spread of rates of deterioration by measurements of strength and dynamic modulus of elasticity at intervals. Four different modes of determination of the C_3A content of the cements contributed to making the observations inconclusive.

D. Stark reviewed, in 1982,[49] eleven years of performance data for concrete beams stored in the sulphatic soils of the Sacramento test plot. The beams were exposed to six to eight annual cycles of flooding and top-half drying while the bottom half was kept embedded in the sulphatic soil. The degree of deterioration was evaluated visually every other year by a rating scheme of 1.0 (representing no deterioration) to 6.0 (representing failure). Tests with different ASTM types of Portland cement were found to reaffirm that resistance increased with increasing cement content and decreasing C_3A content in the cements. Blends of 40% high alumina blast-furnace slag or fly ash with Portland cement were found to enhance deterioration. Steam curing and air entrainment were found to be beneficial "to varying degrees". The paper has no information about the temperature and relative humidity interaction with the cyclic exposure changes, or on the concrete production procedures, except for the steam cured specimens. Neither are there data about the properties of the used slag and fly ash. The mechanism of the deterioration is illustrated by Figure 2 of the paper which shows crumbling of the beam surfaces progressing to complete disintegration, but there is no description of the mechanism and chemistry of the deleterious reaction. Hence, neither freezing/thawing nor alkali-silica reaction are mentioned as being eliminated as possible contributing factors to the deterioration.

E. M. Harboe described briefly, in 1982,[50] experience from 1951–71 from a test plot at Fort Collins, Colorado, with concrete test specimens, such as cylinders and pipes, which had been kept buried in the local sulphatic soils, albeit primarily contaminated by calcium sulphates rather than the more dreaded sodium sulphates found in the western States and western Canada. In conjunction with laboratory testing of the sulphate resistance of different concrete compositions, the experience was judged to uphold the superior resistance of concrete with low C_3A cements. Public works in the State of Colorado had experienced severe sulphate attack from water in soils and streams on pipelines, dams, etc. Illustrations in the paper show severe disintegration of such exposed field concrete, albeit without explanatory petrographic or chemical examinations or characterizations of the climatic exposure conditions.

E. G. Swenson and C. J. Mackenzie reported in 1968[51] that sulphate attack in field concrete exposed to sulphatic soils had been observed in western Canada as early as 1908. Subsequent reports on actual attack of sulphatic solutions in soils or free-flowing water on concrete structures in western Canada by G. C. Price and R. Petersen[52], W. D. Hurst,[53] J. J. Hamilton and G. O. Handegord,[54] illustrate consistently the mechanism of the deterioration as crumbling of concrete surfaces advancing to general disintegration. None of these papers, which all refer to cases in climatic exposure with severe winters, presents supporting petrographic examination and chemical analysis for identification of the nature of the deleterious reaction, although "weathering" is mentioned as an additional deleterious factor.

The Treat Island station has been, and is still, used for long-term durability studies of a large number of different series of concrete specimens belonging to different research programmes. H. T. Thornton Jr described the exposure conditions in reference [55]. The salt content of the Atlantic Ocean sea water was stated to be 35.28‰. The tidal range is from 4−8.5 m. Specimens were installed at mean tide elevation, giving twice-daily immersion and drying in cold air. In the winter seasons, thawing at $+3°C$ (immersion) alternates with freezing at temperatures down to $-23°C$. On average, 100 cycles are attained per winter. The summer seasons are of northern temperature levels, i.e. of low chemical activation energy for sea water attack.

The behaviour of exposed specimens is inspected visually at different intervals for the Corps of Engineers programmes along with weekly time/temperature records. Annual inspections with visual ratings, resonance frequency and pulse velocity measurements and photographic recordings are undertaken during summer seasons. A 50% reduction of E_{dyn} is used as failure criterion. The performance is updated in annual reports. The paper shows photographs of prismatic blocks at various stages of deterioration. Scaling, crumbling of surfaces and disintegration are the characteristic visual evidence of the deterioration.

Based on comparisons between laboratory tests with mortar bars (of different compositions) in warm sea water, corresponding to the St. Augustine exposure, and the field test specimens of Treat Island, K. Mather[56] suggested that deterioration at Treat Island was caused by a "complex series of interactions among the constituents of cements, aggregates and sea water not previously appreciated". The suggestion of complex interactions was based on statistical correlations, but without accompanying microstructural studies of the various types of deleterious reaction.

E. F. O'Neil[57] studied the performance of reinforced concrete beams at the Treat Island test plot with regard to corrosion of the reinforcement and freezing/thawing. An exposure study spanning 27 years substantiated general knowledge about the essential parameters for corrosion of reinforcement in concrete exposed to cold sea water and freezing/thawing, including the merits of air entrainment.

M. Schupack[58] investigated the resistance to the Treat Island exposure of twenty post-tensioned I-beams and found that, with adequate design and concrete composition, the beams endured more than eleven years' exposure. Details of the concrete composition, production characteristics and microstructure before and after exposure were not presented.

V. M. Malhotra, G. G. Carette and T. W. Bremner[59] investigated the durability of concrete containing GGBS, fly ash, "or both" in the Treat Island exposure test plot. Concrete prisms and cylinders of different compositions, with and without the slag and fly ash, were installed at the site in 1978 for visual inspection and non-destructive measurements at yearly intervals. No conclusive results were attained.

J. F. Lamond and M. K. Lee[60] briefly summarized the extensive programmes. Different organizations were referred to as having operated at the Treat Island test site for studies into the impact of the local exposure, in particular the severe freezing/thawing on concrete made with different source materials, etc. About 1700 specimens had been installed over the years. No basic data are included in the paper. It is mentioned that the prevailing investigation methodology is by ratings of the visual degree of degradation, supplemented by pulse-velocity and resonant frequency measurements, whereas more detailed examinations of the mechanism of deterioration do not appear to have been undertaken.

V. M. Malhotra, G. G. Carette and T. W. Bremner[61] described 14 years of investigations carried out on concrete specimens at the Treat Island test plot. The article comprises descriptions of the different concrete compositions, the production of the concrete specimens and one winter's freezing/thawing exposure conditions. The performance of the specimens was characterized by a visual rating system and ultrasonic pulse velocity measurements. The rating system identifies ten grades of performance from 0, characterized by less than 15 aggregate particles exposed, to 10 for disintegrated specimen. The ratings 0 to 5 are illustrated by sketches showing increasing exposure of aggregates in the concrete surface (presumably the top surface of the specimen). This grading illustrates that weakening and removal of the cement paste, the weakest component of the concrete, is the mechanism of the deterioration. The ratings 6 to 10 are characterized by disappearance of increasing parts of the specimens. There are no further detailed examinations of the partial breaking away of the specimens, of whether the non-destructive measurements are expressions of macrocracking through the concrete mass, or microcracking in the cement paste. Neither are there data on possible chemical conversions in the cement paste, such as carbonation, ettringite formation etc.

Climatic exposure

The development of concrete technology took place in the northern temperate belt of the world until World War II. In western Europe the climate is benign in terms of summer and winter temperatures and relative humidity. Hence, the situation in the nineteenth century made the assumed chemical sulphate attack on concrete exposed to sea water a naturally high-priority candidate for research when durability problems appeared in marine structures. In North America it was the colder regions, rather than the Sunbelt States, which became the site of the Industrial Revolution. In the twentieth century, concrete highways and hydropower structures in the mountains directed attention to freezing/thawing as the primary cause of deterioration, with considerably more severe climatic conditions during the winter than occurred in Europe, and over much larger areas.

The commitment to maintenance and renewal of the European coastal test plots decreased considerably in the course of the twentieth century. There were several reasons for this. There were so many major marine and port concrete structures, suitable as objectives for realistic evaluations of the parameters governing durability. Besides, it was found at an early stage that concrete with ordinary Portland cement could be made to possess excellent durability, even in severe marine exposure. There was ancient, hereditary experience that pozzolanic cements offered good resistance and, along the northern continental coastlines, concrete with slag cements won high reputations for sea water

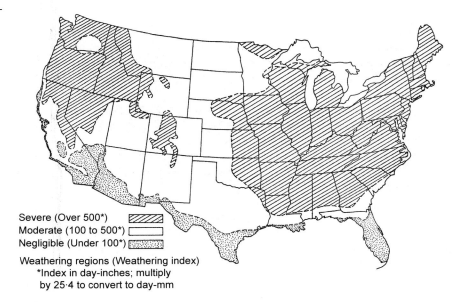

Severe (Over 500*) ⬛
Moderate (100 to 500*) ☐
Negligible (Under 100*) ▦

Weathering regions (Weathering index)
*Index in day-inches; multiply
   by 25·4 to convert to day-mm

*Fig. 16. Weathering regions in
the USA*

resistance. Moreover, the Portland cement manufacturers learned, through
chemical research and laboratory testing, that low C_3A cements offered higher
resistance to sulphate solutions than did ordinary Portland cement types.

In North America the development of empirical laboratory specimen testing
made the generally accepted test methods the primary control measure for the
effectiveness of preventive measures and, as a logical consequence, also in the
course of time the preferred objectives of the research. The field test plots
were preserved and used, one might say, more as a correlation basis for the
test methods and their acceptance criteria, than as the primary objectives of the
durability research. Hence, also at the test plots, empirical measurements, such
as the non-destructive methods, became the data suppliers, and the visual
ratings were largely evaluated as such, rather than as points of departure for
studies of the mechanisms which caused the visual evidence of damage.

Figure 16,[62] from the ASTM standard specification C33 for coarse concrete
aggregates, is an expression of the quest for uniformity (and simplicity) in the
regulatory requirements for insurance of concrete durability in the USA.

The applied weathering index is the product of average, annual numbers of
freezing cycle days, and the average annual winter rainfall. For actual construction work planning, the user is referred to local weather bureaux for more
detailed local information. Although the specification concerns coarse aggregates,
it refers to the use of the aggregates in concrete: in other words, its purpose is to
ensure the durability of concrete, not of the aggregate while kept in stockpiles.
There is no equivalent or similar guide by ASTM for the resistance of concrete
to weathering. This may be because the specification writers count on the general
use of air entrainment in the cement paste for resistance to freezing and thawing,
and do not consider any weakness towards weathering of the fine aggregates in
concrete.

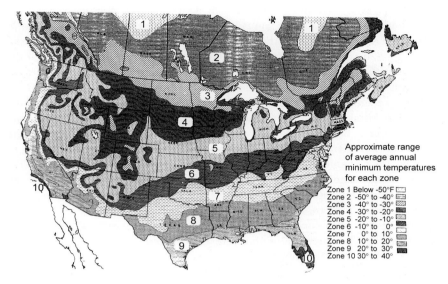

Approximate range
of average annual
minimum temperatures
for each zone

Zone 1 Below -50°F
Zone 2 -50° to -40°
Zone 3 -40° to -30°
Zone 4 -30° to -20°
Zone 5 -20° to -10°
Zone 6 -10° to 0°
Zone 7 0° to 10°
Zone 8 10° to 20°
Zone 9 20° to 30°
Zone 10 30° to 40°

Fig. 17. Hardiness regions for agriculture in the USA

Figure 17,[63] shows climatic grading of zones related to the hardiness of vegetation in the USA. This map, issued by the federal agricultural department, demonstrates the emphasis on annual output and profitability of agricultural production. In contrast, Figure 16 may imply that the durability of concrete is not generally considered a production and safety cost or profit issue in comparison with agriculture. The simplicity of the figure is in accordance with the researchers' habit of presenting very limited data on climatic exposure at investigations of field concrete durability. It also concurs with the standardization of laboratory test conditions to represent overall comparability and reproducibility rather than realistic simulation data for the representation of real exposure characteristics.

The two papers referred to above regarding the Sacramento test plot experience,[47, 49] contain no information about the annual temperature and relative humidity history. D. Duvall,[64] mentions for south-central Wyoming that "winters are long, and during the short summers, temperatures can reach ninety-five degrees [35°C] during the day, and fall to forty-five degrees [7.2°C] during the nights. Rainfall is barely twelve inches [300 mm] a year". This means that relative humidity is low, except during nights after precipitation and when snow thawing is intensive. Within the States, other extreme and complex climatic inland conditions occur, almost representative of what may be encountered in all other parts of the world – but only rudimentarily applied in concrete durability research.

The test plots at Treat Island, St. Augustine and Los Angeles are special in the sense that they represent marine exposure conditions which are much more uniform worldwide than are inland climates; data are available both from concrete research papers and general statistical surveys.

In the polar seas, surface temperatures of about −1.5°C are common. In hot regions like the Arabian Gulf, about +24°C is the average, rising to about

+30°C in shallow coastal waters. The daily temperature changes in sea water are nowhere more than 5°C. The annual temperature ranges are highest in the cold-temperate regions, such as in the seas around Denmark, where the range is from −1°C to +20°C, whereas the maximum difference between high and low for the oceanic surface waters is less than 5°C. Deeper than 200 m, the temperatures are constant and, from about 2000 m depth, close to +4°C.

The average salt concentration in the oceanic seas is 36‰. It is about 35‰ in polar seas, rising to 37‰ in the tropics due to more intense surface evaporation. In sea water in hot climates, such as at the Arabian Gulf coastline, where there are no outlets of fresh water from big rivers, the salt concentration may rise to above 50‰ during days with +50°C maximum temperatures, relative humidity < 20% and windy weather. For coastal concrete construction under such circumstances one must be aware that the evaporated water is salt-free, but that airborne drops of sea water rapidly dry up to fine particles of solid salt. These precipitate on concrete structures, soil, etc. even 20–30 km inland. As a consequence, condensation of moisture on concrete surfaces during nightly cooling leaves concentrated brine solutions to penetrate into them through cracks or pores, thus aggravating corrosion processes during the daily heating which may raise concrete surface temperatures to above +50°C.

In more benign, temperate climates, such as in the seas around Denmark, where the sea water is diluted by fresh water from rivers and rain, salt concentrations of 20–25‰ are common, reducing away from the oceans to less than 10‰, such as in the Baltic Sea. However, cold bottom currents may carry heavy, salt-enriched water high up into brackish parts of such inland seas, and cause corrosion problems for concrete above the water surface of partly submerged concrete structures.

The content of sodium in oceanic waters is about 11‰, leaving about 24‰ to the anions of magnesium, calcium and potassium and the cations of chloride and sulphates. The proportional composition of sea water is constant, independent of the concentrations.

For marine and coastal structures, the splashing of sea water and wetting/drying due to tidal cycles may represent much more severe exposure and rates of deterioration than is usual for inland structures, due to the intensive wetting/drying combined with heating/cooling effects. In hot, marine exposure this means aggravation of chemical reactivity, in the colder regions aggravation of freezing and thawing.

Communications during the past decades about concrete durability in hot countries have supplied information, although still scanty, about different marine exposure conditions. Along the coastlines of the Arab Emirates, for instance, the annual rainfall is somewhere about 10–20 mm, falling in one or two showers. The relative humidity may correspondingly decrease to 10–20% RH during daytime, rising to close to 100% during nightly cooling and condensation. Along the north-eastern Australian – tropical – coasts, annual rainfall of about 2000 mm has been reported. This amount of rain falls during the six-month winter season, whereas there is very little rain during the summer seasons, but still a daily RH of 50% or more. Unconfirmed journalistic information has mentioned 10 000 mm rainfall throughout the year over smaller islands off the tropical West African coast.

Effects of climatic exposure

The climatic exposure map of the USA, Figure 16, may be considered as a memorial to the past when concrete generally was considered as durable as the Danish concrete block from 1915, Figure 12. The changes in technology and usage of concrete after World War II engendered a different story. The two reports issued by the National Materials Advisory Board under the National Engineering Academy in 1980 and 1987,[65, 66] revealed grave concern about the serious deterioration of American concrete structures and insufficient knowledge of the impact of severe environmental exposure conditions. The catastrophic, early failures of numerous new structures on the Arabian peninsula, Libya and other oil-producing countries with hot climates during the 1970s and 1980s disclosed the profound inability of consultants and contractors to cope with the hot, saline environmental exposure conditions. They were obviously unaware that northern, temperate specifications, production procedures, and test methods were not applicable to these conditions.

The impact of these events, and contemporary comprehensive deterioration of precast high-rise buildings in western European countries, has shown that even relatively benign climatic exposure must be taken into account in design and production of modern concrete. As implied above, the available data banks for systematic utilization in concrete engineering practice are scarce.

Nevertheless, there had, in fact, been earlier attempts to bring these issues into focus. At the RILEM winter concreting conference in Copenhagen in 1956, E. G. Swenson[67] reported on winter weather conditions in Canada, and the protective means for making winter concreting possible. H. A. Vinberg[68] reported on examinations of winter temperature characteristics in Sweden for the planning of laboratory testing conditions. Data about the number of "frost days" and freezing-point passages were accumulated. J. Jessing[69] described the influence of weather factors on heat energy levels in a concrete body, resulting from loss of heat by condensation, convection and radiation, vis-à-vis supply of heat energy by sun radiation. He proposed testing of the extensive calculations by globoscope measurements on actual concrete structures. No follow-up research with such experiments is known to the author. What happened instead was that research and testing laboratories in western Europe, North America, Japan, and the USSR, became equipped with increasingly sophisticated instrumentation. Such investments made it important to produce corresponding amounts of comparable data about the behaviour of standardized laboratory specimens, exposed to reproducible and amplified, aggressive impact. The motivation for studies with reliable laboratory modelling of field concrete disappeared. Even the impact of the inherent heat of hydration development during the curing of concrete was ignored. Concurrently, the major public agencies and cement industries, which had accumulated long-term field experience with patience and enthusiasm, lost large shares of the concrete market to the private housing and construction sectors. Hence, the formerly close ties between the sponsoring agencies and the operating research groups were loosened or disappeared. Concurrently, long-term field test plots became easy victims. A few test sites, such as la Rochelle in France and Treat Island, Maine, in the USA have been kept operational but, as described above, with only modest interest in managed creation of essential new knowledge about the environmental impact on field concrete performance.

As a consequence of the ascension of laboratory-confined research, no systematic field concrete "climate encyclopedia" exists today.

Mechanisms of deleterious reactions

Descriptions of field concrete and test plot specimen deterioration, as referred to above, may identify the failure mechanisms as crumbling with increasingly protruding aggregate particles and eventual disintegration, when the causes of failure are either sulphate attack with chemical degradation of the cement paste, or freezing/thawing with physical ice formation in the pore system of the cement paste. These observations are, in principle, not compatible with the utilization of linear expansion of mortar bars in laboratory studies as complementary evidence of the two mechanisms.

The contrast is, nevertheless, merely apparent. Both in the field and in test specimens the expansive reactions take place in the hardened cement paste, whereas the aggregate particles do not expand. In field concrete it is the additional weathering, etc. which causes removal of the weakened cement paste and eventually also of loosened aggregate particles. (At testing, advanced deterioration of specimens might similarly cause disintegration.)

The studies of concrete in test plots and field structures in North America and western Europe do not seem to have been concerned with the mechanisms, or the particular characteristics of the deleterious reactions, but seem rather to have accepted indirect, empirical measurements of a non-destructive nature as satisfactory for the comparability analyses by which the experimental studies have usually been evaluated.

When alkali-silica reaction became involved, it was observed that it was the reacting aggregate particles which were at the root of the expansion and cracking, whereas the cement paste remained unaffected except by the imposed cracking.

Table 3, from reference [70], was presented at the international RILEM conference in Copenhagen on winter concreting, 1956, as our first guide to interpretation of the visual evidence of deterioration in field concrete; in other words, to the diagnosing of field concrete failure cases. Our basis for the table comprised many photographs of field concrete deterioration in the USA, and also of severely disintegrated concrete in sulphatic soils. This tutorial information was extended by our own, extensive field inspections in Denmark, and the further theoretical studies of the chemical and physical deleterious reactions.

The American introduction of air entrainment,[71] was presented at the conference as a means of securing resistance to freezing and thawing of hardened concrete, whether cast in winter seasons or in more benign temperature ranges. Danish contributions illustrated the evidence of damage by freezing of immature concrete, due to ice-lens formation in the young, "green" cement paste.[72]

Hence, at this conference, a landmark initiative towards realistic interpretations of field concrete deterioration was taken to characterize the mechanisms of the reacting processes:

- *alkali-silica reaction* is a chemical reaction in aggregate particles, which causes them to crack by swelling, and extend the cracking into the cement paste
- *frost attack* is a physical reaction in cement paste which delaminates the paste

Table 3. Combinations of visual field evidence and some potential causes, from reference [70]

Visual field evidence of deterioration		Causes of deterioration		
		Alternate freezing and thawing	Sea water action	Alkali-aggregate reaction
Structural expansion		Exceptional	Exceptional	+
Fracturing	Off-scaling	+	+	−
	Pattern cracking	Exceptional	Exceptional	−
Pop-outs in connection with:	Reactive aggregates	Where porous	+	+
	Inactive porous aggregates	+	−	−
	Gel	−	−	+
Gel exudations		−	−	+

and loosens the bond between aggregate particles and paste (in concrete with frost-susceptible aggregate particles these may swell and crack like alkali-reacting particles)

□   *sulphate reaction* is a chemical reaction which disintegrates cement paste and loosens the bond between aggregate particles and the paste.

We were aware that sole reliance on the visible surface evidence of damage to field concrete might be misleading for diagnosing interpretations, and we had, in 1956, commenced supplementary studies, by means of drilled cores and thin sections, of the macro- and microscopic effects of the deleterious reactions. Ervin Poulsen's construction of a transportable coring machine, and his invention of epoxy impregnation for thin section manufacture,[73] were indispensable for these further studies.

The combination of the issues which were presented at the conference:

□   *monitored processing technology* to provide
□   *prescribed performance quality*, including resistance to
□   *measurable effects of aggressive exposure conditions*

was, albeit unwittingly, a prescient view of the holistic concept of concrete

research for engineering practice which was to have a profound influence on our
further research work in Denmark.

Field performance feedback to research

The planning and management of the field exposure test plots for marine
concrete in western Europe during the late nineteenth and the early twentieth
centuries had involved a formidable development of international exchange
and cooperation for improvement of field concrete performance. The research
was run by outstanding personalities in the national cement industries, universities and public marine construction agencies. The interaction between the various
groups representing different approaches to the cooperative efforts was superb.
The overall strategic goal was to achieve satisfactory field performance. The
primary importance of long-term realistic assessments of the behaviour of concrete under actual field service over a range of different exposure conditions
was mutually acknowledged, as was the progressive application of scientific
achievements.

Later on, and especially after World War II, concrete construction with much
higher performance requirements than previously spread to larger parts of the
world. The further spread in the forthcoming decades will present investors
and engineers with exposure conditions of all existing ranges, combinations,
and short- and long-term variations of climatic aggressivity towards concrete.
The demographic changes and the ongoing quest for more natural resources
mean that the most aggressive, cold and warm exposure conditions will come
to predominate over northern-temperate, benign circumstances. This perspective
calls for international top-level leadership requests for cooperative programmes
to develop in depth characterization of climatic exposure conditions which are
relevant for concrete construction projects, and for investigations of field
concrete failure cases.

International development of such a system would make standard specifications and durability research globally complementary and be a strong incitement
to rationalize national laboratory testing in accordance with the relevant field
experience.

A new era of concrete research

The general belief in the synonymy of technology development and social progress in the industrial world before World War II, was shattered by the terror and devastation which the military applications of science and technology caused. The first demands on concrete after the war were for reconstruction of housing with urban facilities, infrastructure, and constructions for industrial production where the war machines had rolled over. The magnitude of the destruction was so overwhelming that mechanization of concrete production was applied wherever suitable machinery could be made available, and elsewhere a profusion of unemployed people was at hand to make concrete, but without any training in the technology. Even the rubble from destroyed cities was put to use as aggregates. The supplier of construction equipment and capital for the reconstruction in western Europe and Asia was the USA, where industrial capacity had increased and technology had developed to extents which made surplus production available for the large-scale export policy required.

Denmark had passed the years of the 1940 to 1945 deluge without major catastrophic destruction. There had been no compulsory military war participation, and the universities had, throughout the years of occupation, produced almost the usual number of MSc graduates. A new generation of civil engineers was therefore eager to be engaged in construction and building programmes in 1945, and wanting to be acquainted with and make use of the new scientific and technological developments in the allied countries, especially the USA.

Concrete Marshall Aid

I was confronted by the profound mechanization of concrete production on construction sites which came to western Europe, including Denmark, with the American Marshall Aid programme from 1947–48, when I was in government service as resident engineer for the western jetty reconstruction at Hanstholm, north-west Jutland, 1948–52. The pre-World War II commencement of a fishing and trade harbour had progressed only as far as construction of this jetty. The work had been discontinued during the 1940–45 occupation, when the location became the site of a German Atlantic West Wall fortification, with a 12 000 man occupation force. Meanwhile, the ocean waves and wear and tear had destroyed the serviceability of the, only partially completed, jetty.

Marshall Aid gave the Hanstholm job a bulldozer and scraper for retrieval of beach sand and gravel, a screening plant for the aggregate processing, a batch plant tower with silos for aggregate, cement and fresh water, weight-batching, and an $0.8\,m^3$ Ransome mixer delivering 3–6″ slump concrete to a remixer above a Rex concrete pump which discharged through a pipeline assembled of 3 m long 8″ steel pipes. The construction company, Monberg & Thorsen A/S, was awarded the contract on a payment for all costs plus 10% overheads basis. As the resident engineer, my task was to assure the department that the works were carried out in accordance with the valid specifications, i.e. in the best traditions of many years' concrete works on the severely exposed west coast of Jutland.

Notwithstanding this heritage, we were forced to recognize that the new equipment introduced a technology for concrete making, placement and hardening which, in many respects, was different from the old way of doing things. The *Rex Pumpcrete Practice book*,[74] from the Chainbelt Company, Milwaukee, therefore became an indispensable textbook and guidebook for the local concrete testing laboratory on the site, which I had erected for sieve analyses of aggregates, slump, air content and mix compositions, (but not for compressive strength tests, as I could not obtain consent to acquire such expensive equipment). The quality of the, approximately, $20\,000\,m^3$ concrete made and placed in the course of 1948–1952 is documented in reference [20].

The exposure of the site, with up to 5 m high North Sea waves during frequent storms, meant that there were not more than about 70 days a year on which operations on the jetty were possible. This gave time between operations for studies and analyses of experience, and necessitated protracted casting of concrete when the weather permitted, sometimes of more than 48 hours' duration. This presented unusual opportunities for assembling documentary control data, and making observations by eye and hand on the properties and qualities of the concrete materials and concrete. Hence, these four years provided fundamental empirical and construction site based insight into the requirements imposed by modern mechanized concrete production on the technology, in order to attain or exceed the quality of hardened concrete which we knew could be obtained by traditional workmanship of "hand and shovel".

Initially, the revelation in the Pumpcrete book of the advanced state of American concrete technology was like being admitted to a new engineering post-graduate course. The book, tables for transfer to the metric system and the dictionary were my basic information for many hours of self-education during dark winter and light summer nights, and the periods of calm weather were our opportunities for implementation of the new knowledge. The contacts and help from the chemical engineers of Aktieselskabet Aalborg Portland-Cement-Fabrik was also important. The cement company had changed the classical moler cement to the new "marine" cement, consisting of a low C_3A Portland cement clinker interground with 12% calcined moler. The Hanstholm reconstruction works pioneered the use of this cement type, and the first delivery in Denmark of bulk cement by truck was of this cement to Hanstholm. The cement company further assisted with general information on concrete technology. Their customer service, CtO, made our compressive strength testing of concrete cubes for quality control.

The pumping method required special attention to the properties of the fresh concrete. The horizontal length of the pipeline reached about 400 m, and at the end the concrete was placed underwater in large sections at up to 8 m depth in continuous casting, with final top level about 3 m above sea level. These conditions made the rheology of the fresh concrete a matter of combined workability (in the pump) and cohesion (first in the pipeline, then at underwater placing). Trial and error experience showed that the local beach sand and gravel could not comply with these demands without the addition of about 10% of a special, clayish "fine sand" found in a fluvio-glacial sandpit some 20 km away.

Recording of the hydraulic pressure within the fresh concrete during its passage through the pipeline proved helpful, first for finding a suitable mix composition with regard to the rheology, and secondly as a control measure for maintaining the optimum rheology during long-term continuous castings. The moler in the cement was also found to be advantageous for the rheology. The air entrainment added cohesion at the casting site, where it was required for the submerged placement, but had no rheological effect under compression in the pipeline.

Figure 18, from reference [20], shows a series of measurements of the magnitude of the pressure at the concrete pump piston, depending on the length of the concrete "sausage" in the pipeline. As one can see, there is a considerable scatter which reflects the impact of variations of the mix composition – water content, sand grading – on the rheology of the concrete.

During the summer periods, when most castings took place, some of the larger sections of 400–700 m^3 mass concrete developed long surface cracks during curing. (Wet curing was either accomplished by sprinkling or inadvertently, by splashing from the waves.) This caused us to measure the temperatures of the concrete during its curing at various depths in the large masses, along with simultaneously recording the temperatures of the ambient air and sea water.

Figure 19, from reference [20], shows a series of these measurements. In the interior of the mass concrete block there were adiabatic conditions and a temperature rise to +40°C, determined by the specific heat of hydration of the marine cement and the concrete mix composition. At 25 cm depth in the mass (from the surface) the dissemination of heat to the colder environment causes shrinkage, relative to the simultaneous expansion in the interior mass. The rather slow rise of the interior temperature to the moderate rise +40°C – due to the low-heat cement, low cement content of the concrete, and the cool environment – and the later apparent closing of the surface cracks as the concrete mass cooled, alerted us to the heat development and dissemination during the curing of field concrete, in contrast to the isothermic laboratory curing/storage conditions prevalent in most concrete quality control, and in concrete research, even to the present time. In other words: my perception of the "room temperature syndrome" initiated here.

In periods of stormy weather there was also time to make observations about the durability of concrete from the 1912–15 construction of a "lee-jetty", a few groynes, made with Portland cement in the 1920s, and moler cement concrete from the 1930s in the jetty being renovated. Much of the older Portland cement concrete showed intensive map-cracking. A visit in 1951 by P. Nerenst, who had discovered alkali-silica reaction in the Vildsund Bridge, revealed that the map-cracking might be considered as evidence of alkali-silica reaction. This

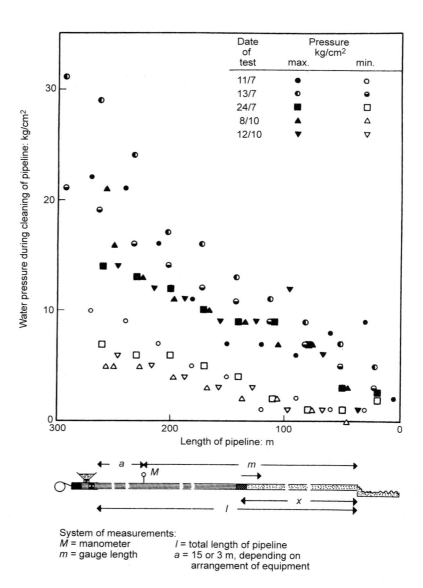

Fig. 18. Measurements of the
hydraulic pressure in the
pipeline of the REX concrete
pump at five castings for repair
work on the jetty at Hanstholm,
1951

System of measurements:
M = manometer   *l* = total length of pipeline
m = gauge length   *a* = 15 or 3 m, depending on
                             arrangement of equipment

was the starting point of my subsequent long-term preoccupation with concrete
durability and deterioration.

   The last feature worthy of mention about the "research-apprentice" years at
Hanstholm is that the entire activity of concrete making and quality control
was made possible and fruitful by the dedicated cooperation of engineers and
work crews on both sides – the contractor's and the resident engineer's. This
was important both for the work and concrete quality and for the educational
output, because on the west coast of Jutland the principle still prevailed that
the quality of concrete workmanship depended on daily, participative sharing

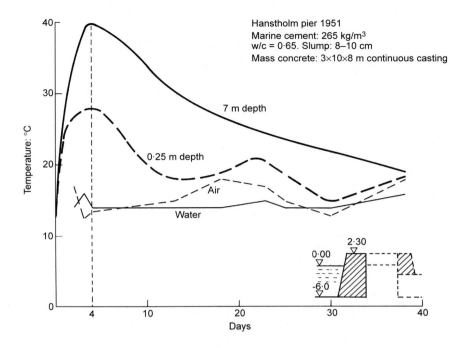

Hanstholm pier 1951
Marine cement: 265 kg/m^3
w/c = 0·65. Slump: 8–10 cm
Mass concrete: 3×10×8 m continuous casting

Fig. 19. Measurements of concrete temperatures during hardening of section S.V. 12, the jetty at Hanstholm, June 1951

of experience and visual surveillance. The development of a positive attitude towards research through these means was a lasting benefit.

Some readers may wonder that these years of pre-research engineering practice did not comprise any work with structural issues or development. However, that was due to the circumstances. The concrete was large mass-sections, walls and heavy slabs of several metres' thickness, and the structural integrity of the jetty was not an issue, except occasionally when waves generated by a gale hit a casting operation before sectional completion. Under these circumstances, the live load exposure was, however, not calculable, and could only be managed by careful planning and execution of the operations on the jetty – and by accepting the inevitability of some loss of materials and subsequent repair costs.

New concrete technology research in Denmark

The liberation of Denmark had left the country with a reasonably preserved infrastructure, but a serious housing shortage and a high unemployment rate. Traditional house building in Denmark was in masonry and timber, and production virtually ceased during the winter seasons.

In 1947, the Ministry of Housing founded the Danish National Institute of Building Research (DNIBR) with a large department for architectural studies and a smaller one for materials technology, with emphasis on concrete. The magnitude of the national problems gave rise to the growth of private firms in the building sector, which invested in the development of building systems with precast concrete in modular designed walls, slabs and columns. In order to comply with the demands, new kinds of engineering – architectural interactions had to be established, along with innovative developments of precast concrete technology, thorough mechanization of construction, erection on site of precast concrete elements, and appropriate project planning and management methods.

The confrontations between the typical, analytical engineering and the conceptual architectural approaches became, under the given circumstances, very educational and helped to accomplish the overall mission and to make concrete the indispensable building material for the solution of major social habitation problems.

The Danish academic architects had a high regard for the social engagements and functionalism of the former Bauhaus School in Germany, and also for Le Corbusier's visionary concrete city design developments in France. They were also profoundly attached to the quality of classical craftsmanship and design. This professional standpoint was eminently suited to the tasks at hand, and contagious for the cooperating civil engineers. Hence, a significant part of the older city slum habitations in Denmark was, concurrent with the baby boom, replaced by new urbanization programmes, consisting of precast multi-storey apartment buildings in green surroundings in the course of the late 1950s and the 1960s.

The situation created the opportunity for the development of a new concrete research as the major occupation of the materials research department of the DNIBR, for which the late N. M. Plum was appointed director. His previous concrete technology research and advisory service with Christiani & Nielsen A/S had prepared him to comprehend the overriding importance of concrete research for updating past technology to ensure compliance with the new conditions of increasing demands for accelerated production capacity and concrete making. He established personal contacts with prominent concrete research workers abroad, such as T. C. Powers in the USA, and research directors such as F. M. Lea in the UK, and himself contributed, among other things, the application of statistical methods for evaluation of analytical test results in concrete research and site quality control.

In a review, in 1956,[75] of the history of concrete construction development in Denmark, containing a discussion of general aspects of concrete research, Plum presented the following views on research methodology and management:

"*Before entering on a new project, practice, or research, much time and money will nearly always be saved if the following suggestions are adopted.*

(1)   Read the literature – it will save repeating previous mistakes, and enable a much more accurate aiming at the target. It is quite fantastic to see the amount of repetition of the same tests that has taken place because of an ignorance of what has been already done.

(2)   Think before starting actual experiments. From existing knowledge, it is frequently possible, by calculation of the physical and chemical processes, to reach the goal without tests, or to get so near to the truth that tests are needed merely to verify or to state arithmetically what is conceived by the mind.

(3)   If and when tests are necessary, simulate the actual conditions of exposure in practice as closely as possible, even if this entails considerable complications, and record as many test conditions and test results as possible. The number of accelerated standard test procedures that are poorly correlated with actual conditions in practice is

overwhelming, and presents a problem of high importance to national economy. Economic conditions must mainly be based on the degree of safety under service conditions, but at present this degree of safety has little connection with the results of accelerated tests. Further, a valuation of test results will be frequently complicated by lack of data which at the outset are considered irrelevant, and some extra data will often, when kept on record, render many later tests superfluous".

When I joined the DNIBR at new year, 1953, this tutorial advice was a helpful introduction to future work with concrete research and development.

Close contact with advanced, scientific concrete research had already been established while I was working in Hanstholm, with both the American basic studies of the physical properties of hardened cement paste and the protective effects against freezing of air entrainment,[71, 76] and the British research into cement chemistry and time-temperature interdependence of cement hydration with the Saul maturity function.[77]

During the summer of 1953, my colleagues P. Nerenst and E. Rastrup invented a pioneering system approach to winter concreting. An adjusted maturity function by Rastrup[78] was combined with application of the Fourier equation for heat dissemination through solid masses in a calculation system which made it possible:

- in planning of winter concreting, to estimate the need for the use of warm concrete, insulation and required time before form removal
- at building sites, to determine precautions for prevention of early freezing, and of required time before form removal − by measurements of the temperature in the hardening concrete and calculation of the corresponding maturity, referred to 28-day compressive strength at 20°C.

The new methodology was presented in the DNIBR recommendation No. 17 *Betonstøbning om vinteren*[79] with tables for pre-design of the procedures under different site conditions and environmental temperatures, and with a method for determination of the actual maturity during early curing of concrete. The philosophy was that science-based control of the delayed development at low temperatures of the performance quality of concrete − durability and strength − made it possible to advance building and construction projects during large parts of typical Danish winters. The pioneering research philosophy was that we considered the actual concrete property development under variable site conditions to be the focal issue, and that we applied cement hydration kinetics as a quality assessment tool instead of relying on arbitrary room-temperature specimen testing. The recommendation was widely sold and used, and followed up by governmental requirements for compliance with the recommended practice on subventioned building projects (which comprised the majority of those carried out), and with training courses, record forms, etc.

In my opinion, the unpredicted long-term effects were what made this first comprehensive Danish concrete technology research programme singularly profitable.

- It won broad engineering approbation for our emphasis on establishing contacts with basic research overseas, for transfer to new engineering technology at home.

□ It substantiated past experience that the actual field concrete is the primary objective for realistic implementation of theoretical research.

□ It confirmed past experience of environmental, climatic impact on the behaviour of concrete and made heat evolution during concrete curing a monitoring parameter. It therefore ensured that the concrete production phase became an important objective for forthcoming research.

□ It illustrated fundamental aspects of the mechanisms of frost attack on concrete and thereby connected research on concrete production technology with the research on durability.

□ It presented the new Danish concrete research team not only as "takers", but also as "givers" in the emergent post-war international concrete research community.

Table 4 shows the origins of delegates at the RILEM Symposium on Winter Concreting, in February 1956 (the first major international concrete conference arranged by the organization).[80] It was held in Copenhagen as recognition of the research work done in Denmark during the preceding years, and, as the table shows, it attracted delegates from many countries. T. C. Powers was the delegate for the USA, and he was impressed by our implementation of his basic, exploratory studies of the physical properties of hardened cement paste.[81, 82] In connection with his own, first international presentation of the long-term scientific research at the Portland Cement Association in Skokie, USA,[83] he commented on our application of his results in the DNIBR winter concreting guideline:

"Before speaking on the subject assigned to me, I should like to comment on the paper from The Danish National Institute of Building Research presented in Session C.

The work of Mr. Nerenst and his associates is, in my opinion, outstanding and very valuable. These young scientists have applied methods of analyses that we could hardly have attempted. I believe the results they are obtaining are exceedingly valuable, and we are very, very much interested in them.

However, I should like to add that although I think the analytical approach is valuable and should be continued, in this case I was a bit dismayed when I first came in contact with it. I had considered the equations we had developed as being not much more than expressions of ideas, expressions of relationships that identified variable factors and gave something of the relationships between them. When I found them being used almost literally, I was taken aback. But now having observed the results, I must acknowledge that these men had more courage than I. The equations seem to be working better than I thought they could.

Nevertheless, I surmise that finally we shall have to rely to a considerable degree on the empirical method. Perhaps the greatest value of the kind of studies I have been reporting lies in the help they give us when we are interpreting empirical tests or field observations.

I hope Mr. Nerenst and others of the Scandinavian group who are approaching these questions in such a thoroughgoing way will continue the work, and will demonstrate that my pessimism is quite unjustified".

Unwittingly, T. C. Powers had touched upon basic issues of the barriers against transfer of research to technology innovation. This was subsequently illustrated by the many years' delay in the USA's acceptance of the maturity concept and heat transmission calculation methods for monitoring of the concrete curing process.

Table 4. Origin and numbers of delegates at the RILEM Symposium on Winter Concreting, Copenhagen, February 1956

Region	Country	Number of delegates	
Nordic countries	Denmark	49	
	Finland	18	
	Iceland	2	
	Norway	13	
	Sweden	22	
			104
Western Europe	Great Britain	13	
	France	12	
	Germany	27	
	Austria	18	
	The Netherlands	25	
	Belgium	11	
	Saarland	1	
	Switzerland	7	
	Italy	1	
			115
Eastern Europe USSR	Czechoslovakia	4	
	Poland	9	
	USSR	12	
			25
North America	Canada	1	
	USA	1	
			2
Asia	Japan	6	
	China	9	
			15
Total		261	

Notwithstanding the concentration on the exploration of the basic nature of hardened Portland cement paste, the symposium programme also deserves acknowledgement because it not only presented the research, but also, in two sessions, emphasized the special problems facing engineering practice in concrete construction jobs during winter. It therefore promoted integration of the two aspects of concrete technology development. The pioneering contributions regarding the issues of winter concreting in practice came from the East European delegations, and the USSR delegation represented the creation of a formidable, precast concrete element industry, which moved the manufacture of standardized, storey-assembling concrete elements inside industrial production plants, in which accelerated hardening was arranged, e.g. by electrical heating or steam curing. This was a way of preventing interruption of house construction during the severe Soviet winters, desperately needed after the tremendous devastation of the war.

Within these retrospective comments about the symposium, it should be noted that neither the American achievements with air entrainment as an effective preventive measure against frost damage to field concrete, nor the Danish maturity-based monitoring of concrete curing won acceptance in the majority of European countries at that time. Moreover, the application of external heating of concrete during early curing, such as was introduced in the nascent precast industries, was made without knowledge of the potential risks of elevating the temperature much beyond that which the hydration of cement itself produced.

The Concrete Research Laboratory – Karlstrup

The concrete research laboratory at Karlstrup, some 20 km south-west of Copenhagen, was established in 1960 by the major Danish cement company Aktieselskabet Aalborg Portland-Cement-Fabrik, which was under the same family ownership as the cement machinery manufacturing company F. L. Smidth & Co. I was in charge of the research from 1 April 1960 until 1 April 1976.

The buildings for the research laboratory with the Danish name Betonforskningslaboratoriet Karlstrup (BFL) were erected in the course of 1960 and the first half of 1961. The 2000 m^2 facility was designed with sections for physical and chemical studies, including thin section preparation and optical microscopy, a small workshop, and a large hall for concrete making and testing, etc. with climate-controlled storage rooms.

From mid-1961 the laboratory staff comprised: two MScs, (one civil engineer, one chemical engineer), one technical engineer, one technician (instrument maker), one photographer, one foreman and one workman, two secretaries and myself, MSc, CEng, 40 years old, as the leader.

Of the nine employees, of an average age of 34 years, the technical engineer and I were the only two with some background knowledge in concrete and research, and my experience with the practical work and operation of laboratory research was confined to petrographic examination and thin section preparation.

When my position as the director of the company's R & D (from 1972) ceased in 1976, shortly before the research operations were confined to projects for company uses, the staff comprised 45 people – of about the same average age as in 1960 – and the laboratory had issued 419 reports on research programmes, 91 reprints of published articles and many published, but not reprinted papers.

The work of the staff had won an undisputed national and international reputation for science-based research and innovations in concrete technology. The most far-reaching technological accomplishments, which had an effect far beyond the BFL itself, were the following:

- A general formula was developed for the w/c – concrete age – concrete cylinder compressive strength development with typical Danish Portland cement types. This considerably reduced the need for trial testing during concrete mix design in practice.
- General relationships were established between the porosity and strength of cement paste in concrete, the porosity (and strength) of aggregates and the overall strength of concrete,

and of the fracture mechanisms of concrete as related to the relative strength of aggregates and cement paste.

☐ *Monitoring of simultaneous, static pressure and controlled, high frequency vibration of fresh concrete was discovered to lead to doubling of the strength of the hardened concrete in comparison with ordinary vibratory compaction.*

☐ *Application of the low porosity cement (LPC) approach made it possible to produce prestressed concrete I-shaped profile beams with the same load-bearing capability as steel beams of the same height and weight.*

☐ *Epoxy and sulphur impregnation of hardened concrete was shown to produce strength gains of the same order of magnitude as reached with the LPC approach.*

☐ *The Arrhenius equation was introduced as the indispensable basis for the development of curing monitoring technology. The maturity computer was developed as the corresponding data logger for engineering practice.*

☐ *My diagnostic system for investigation of deterioration of field concrete was established and served as the initial knowledge basis for further studies of the effects of deleterious reactions in concrete.*

☐ *The BFL maintained, throughout its existence, a high intensity of national and international interactions which proved to have lasting beneficial "side-effects", such as:*

— *personal career development for staff members*
— *creation of a progressive attitude among Danish engineers to qualified, science-based concrete technology research*
— *development of international contacts, with visits by prominent academic and industrial professionals from all over the world*
— *indirect marketing, and openings for export marketing, of Danish cement and concrete enterprises*
— *impact on the international development of concrete research*
— *contributions by fellowship arrangements for students and professionals for the general advancement of concrete technology knowledge*
— *communications regarding experience with management and planning of concrete technology research.*

The closure of the BFL in 1976 was the inevitable consequence of plummeting cement consumption in Denmark and abroad in the wake of the oil crisis. But there was also a general trend towards transferring capital investment interests away from the "smokestack" industries towards the electronic, chemical and service industries, which were more profitable in the short term. This development had already diluted American cement and concrete research during the 1960s. The BFL was one of the first victims in Europe, and a precursor of a long-term degradation of institutional cement and concrete research in many European countries.

The creation of the BFL

Concrete research at the DNIBR in the 1950s played a decisive role in the creation of general appreciation within Danish engineering practice of the importance of science-based cement and concrete research for technology development. Aktieselskabet Aalborg Portland-Cement-Fabrik (APCF) was the major sponsor of the ten-year research programme on concrete deterioration at the DNIBR, and the company participated in and co-sponsored much of the other DNIBR concrete research and educational course programmes for civil engineers, technicians and manual workers. The technical advisory services department of APCF, the CtO, was the active partner in the cooperation. It had already, in the 1930s, established a small laboratory for mix proportioning with standard concrete testing as a free service for the cement users.

F. L. Smidth & Co. (FLS) and APCF became acquainted with new cement industry investments in cement and concrete research abroad, such as, for instance, that launched by the Verein der Deutsche Zementindustrie (VDZ) in Germany, the Cement and Concrete Association (C&CA) in England and the Portland Cement Association in the USA.

FLS had a well-equipped R & D laboratory for investigations related to the design and construction of cement plants and customer service, and also for development of its cement manufacturing machinery. The market situation required that all the R & D capacity be reserved for these tasks of service to the sales department. Additional undertaking of concrete research was therefore not desirable for the company.

The APCF wanted support for the continuing growth of cement consumption from more concrete technology research than the public investments at the DNIBR could supply. The company had, like several cement industries in Europe, the opportunity to cover the concrete research expenses through price agreements with the governmental monopoly council, and they were tax-exempt as research investments. Hence, the boards of the APCF and FLS decided to establish the BFL for concrete technology research under ownership and management of APCF. The company declared that it would welcome any additional public concrete research activity.

Policy and strategy for the BFL research

When I was appointed chief of the new laboratory, shown in Figure 20, the president of APCF issued instructions for the forthcoming work. We were to create and acquire knowledge for improvements of concrete technology and offer our information, free of charge, to the Danish concrete engineering professions. We were to cooperate closely with the CtO for implementation of the research accomplishments, inter alia by training course and publication programmes, but we could not undertake special implementation projects with individual engineering companies, and we could not charge customers consultancy fees, whether contact was made through the CtO, or directly. We were to work with absolute integrity in open, external communication and exchange. Consequently, we would not be involved in cement production research, or sales policy, although we might be asked to undertake projects concerning the properties of special cements, such as marine and white cement types, in concrete. A long-term strategy for the research had not been formulated by the company. It was envisaged that one would emerge from our work in the course of the first years. I was to refer to a laboratory committee consisting of the vice president for the APCF technical operations, the leader of the CtO, and the director of FLS R & D.

Personal approach to the leadership

The 1945–52 period as resident port and coastal engineer in West Jutland had given me valuable experience with new concrete processing technology and

Fig. 20. The Concrete Research Laboratory, Karlstrup (BFL); 1961–1976

the performance of concrete under severe exposure conditions. The 1953–60 period as research engineer at DNIBR had provided group and programme leadership experience, and a new personal field of specialized research and investigation methodology. The concurrent work on winter concreting, quality control, air entrainment, etc. had also provided an entrance to personal studies, to contacts with contemporary scientific cement and concrete technology, and to research abroad. The special DNIBR environment had also offered extensive contact with collegial consulting engineers, contractors and architects, and close association with their pioneering efforts to create a Danish precast concrete industry.

I had written several articles on new concrete technology in Danish periodicals and was the primary workhorse for the general report *Chemical reactions involving aggregate* for the 4th International Symposium on the Chemistry of Cement in Washington DC, September 1960. As lecturer in materials technology at the new Danish Academy of Civil Engineers (DIAB), I had written a 158-page textbook on cement, in 1958; the first ever issued in Denmark.

The directions I was given for the research policy of the new BFL suited me very well, and were also something of a relief. I had never before been in the service of a private company, and the FLS-APCF corporation was one of the biggest industry enterprises in Denmark, with a reputation as a rather closely run family operation, with a strong patriarchal management style.

I was also aware that the APCF and FLS management hierarchies primarily considered concrete research to be a matter of concrete cylinder strength testing, mortar bar expansion, and shrinkage measurements: in other words, the common empirical correlation-based research. My previous exchange experience had taught me that the prominent international cement and concrete research institutes in England and the USA now emphasized theoretical physico/ chemical studies for the understanding of chemical processes and their physico/ mechanical effects on the properties of cement paste and concrete. I had also seen a clear tendency, in the academic research abroad, to engage science-trained physicists, chemists and mineralogists/geologists in concrete research in addition to civil engineers, and to invest in the use of sophisticated, new analytical instrumentation.

This kind of experience made me determined to engage chemical engineers from the outset and to accept considerable investments in scientific education of the engineers, including myself, by subscribing to and reading the leading cement and concrete research periodicals, and by attending conferences. And to disregard an 8 am to 4 pm working day policy.

We would also need to publish, and learn from readers' responses, and to be open-minded regarding exchanges with researchers abroad, because we would be the party to gain the most in give and take situations.

I was against the proposal that we should take up research subjects which featured on programmes elsewhere. I realized that what the bigger institutes abroad chose to work on, might also appeal to the sponsors as "safe" or worthwhile for us to undertake. My philosophy was that we should, instead, find relevant problems to solve which nobody else had yet recognized.

Much of these concerns could not be shared with my new associates or the steering committee. On the other hand, their positive attitude to the work was indisputably essential, not least to make the Danish engineering profession feel confident that we would produce new, useful information. And yet, for some time it would be uncertain whether our fledgling team would become a competent research group in possession of the necessary, but rare, combination of visionary curiosity, pragmatic diligence, and integrity. This uncertainty was further exacerbated by the concurrent employment boom for civil and chemical engineers and the decision by the company president that I could not engage professionals who were already employed in engineering practice.

Preparations for the commencement of the BFL research

During the erection of the laboratory and installation of its equipment, the two first engaged professionals and myself worked out a proposal for an opening research programme. This comprised 27 individual projects, distributed among the subject areas:

(*a*)   curing of concrete
(*b*)   functional properties of concrete
(*c*)   durability of concrete
(*d*)   property measurement methods
(*e*)   environmental exposure conditions
(*f*)   sundries.

We realized that the programme (with a few more proposals which were added subsequently) was far too comprehensive. Therefore, a working group, representing the steering committee and myself, was appointed to propose a selection of the most desirable projects to start with, considering the given operational conditions. During four months' intensive work we developed and used an original screening procedure with estimated, 1–4 "suitability" ratings of the collection of proposals following five criteria.

1. *The general need for the project in engineering practice and the consequences of its accomplishments.*
    We considered whether a project was desired from an external viewpoint, was educational, relevant for exchanges abroad, and provided continuation of current research. We also estimated its duration, and finally whether it might preferably be left to outside research.
2. *The inherent compatibility (the "holism") of the collection of projects.*
    We cross-referenced the interrelationships among the projects in order to classify to which extents they indicated mutually supportive characteristics, especially regarding the theoretical background, and whether other projects might be definite "loners", but possibly thereby have special merits.
3. *The reliance on available equipment.*
    We considered whether the projects could be carried out with the given equipment and staff capability, or would need to be deferred to a future opportunity.
4. *The primary external recipients.*
    We considered the different "customers":

    □ aggregate producers
    □ concrete and cement product producers, pipe manufacturers
    □ lightweight block manufacturers
    □ precast industry
    □ contractors
    □ ready-mix companies
    □ consulting engineers
    □ building owners
    □ public and technical agencies
       (state railways, highway departments, marine engineering)
    □ universities and technical colleges.

5. *The primary recipients in the corporation.*
    We rated the interest in the project by the APCF sales production and technical information departments, and by FLS, the Dansk Eternit Fabrik A/S and the Siporex company.

The series of five ratings was then displayed in five tables, once we had attained consensus evaluations. These served as the basis of our final agreement for selection of eleven projects as the most desirable for the commencement of operations at the BFL.

The eleven selected projects

Table 5 shows the titles of the selected projects. These represented compromises into which there was also room to incorporate our personal ideas and fields of interest besides the analytical evaluations. They were also flexible in the sense that the elaboration of operational project descriptions was left to the further work of the BFL staff. The future development showed that they served well as a balanced combination of strategy and pragmatism, and as a suitable outset for subsequent reviews and revisions of the research programme.

Table 5. Selected research projects for the commencement of sixteen years of operation of the Betonforskning-slaboratoriet Karlstrup, BFL, in 1961

Project	
Number	Title
1.	Hardening of concrete
2.	Shrinkage of precast concrete elements
3.	Bond between cement paste and aggregate particles
4.	Mechanisms of chemical reactions in concrete
5.	Sulphate resistance of concrete
6.	Failure of concrete of a pier in a North Jutland harbour
7.	Brownish stains on surfaces of concrete made with white cement
8.	Effects of tidal exposure on entrained air in concrete
9.	Failure of a concrete brine container
10.	Concrete strength – w/c relationship
11.	Measurements of entrained air in fresh concrete

Project No. 1, hardening of concrete had the objective of describing "typical" hardening processes, first in cement paste, and next in concrete. The designation "typical" referred to the conditions of concrete making in ordinary practice, i.e. not as with standard laboratory room temperature and 100% RH. Characteristic heat and strength development courses were to be established for Danish cement types and concrete with such cements. The influence on the hardening process of low and elevated temperatures, respectively, and of low and high RH, would be investigated.

Project No. 2, shrinkage of precast concrete elements, referred to problems with joints between assembled precast wall and column elements in the new precast house building constructions. It was stipulated that if the major fraction of a "total shrinkage" of elements could be made to happen before assemby, i.e. during storage after casting, then the "residual shrinkage" could be designed to be insignificant. The project was to establish the acceptable magnitude of the residual shrinkage, and ways to manipulate it, for instance by prolonged storage before mounting. More fundamental studies into the nature of shrinkage in concrete were envisaged for longer term research.

Project No. 3, bond between cement paste and aggregate particles in concrete, was actually a transfer of unsolved problems from the DNIBR programme on concrete deterioration. We had observed that cracking in concrete of good quality usually went through aggregate particles, and, in cases of alkali-silica reactions, always happened in and radiated from reacting aggregate particles. But we had also seen that in cases of frost attack and sulphate attack the cracking passed around aggregate particles. In other words, some fracturing mechanisms demonstrated solid bond between cement paste and aggregates, while others apparently caused the destruction of the bond. We had contradictory observations and hypothesis from abroad, which left much uncertainty about the possible influence on the bond strength of concrete with the most frequent rock types in Denmark, flint, granite and limestone. Hence, we were to attempt to identify the nature and strength influencing effects of bond under favourable and disadvantageous circumstances.

Project No. 4, mechanisms of chemical reactions between rock types and cement paste in concrete, was also a follow-up to the public concrete deterioration programme, which was now terminating. Although we had numerous observations of how alkali-silica reaction affected concrete, made by the advanced petrographic methodology, and with several thousand measurements of linear expansions caused by the reaction in mortar bars, we did not know how the chemical reaction caused the observed mechanical effects. The project was to comprise a combination of "strain gauge" monitoring of mortar bar expansions and microscopic observations of concurrent rupture mechanisms. The methodology was envisaged to be made applicable also for freeze/thaw studies and for the project No. 2 investigations.

Project No. 5, the sulphate resistance of concrete, was also a continuation of the previous research at DNIBR, and desirable as guidance for the choice of cement types for major marine and fisheries port projects, which the Danish government was planning. FLS was interested in providing services to many customers abroad, because there was general international uncertainty about the influence of the C_3A, the C_3S and the constitution of C_3A in cement clinkers, depending on the kiln operation situations. Also, the aggressivity characterization of marine conditions was to be considered.

Project No. 6, failure of a concrete pier in a North Jutland harbour, was actually a case of consulting investigation which the CtO had accepted in the city where the largest APCF cement plant was located. For the BFL it was also an educational project for the new research associates.

Project No. 7, brownish stains on surfaces of concrete made with white cement, was prompted by complaints from users of white cement. We were to seek the identity of the rock types with components which were susceptible to dissolution by the pore liquid of the cement paste, and to environmental moisture. Criteria for rejection of aggregates with such materials were to be described for advisory service by the CtO and the APCF export marketing function.

Project No. 8, effect of tidal exposure on entrained air in concrete, was based on previous observations by thin section examinations of deteriorated marine concrete. In such thin sections, air bubbles were frequently found wholly or partly filled by secondary, crystalline calcium hydroxide, or ettringite. The experience was entirely with concrete which was too old to be air entrained. The increasing use of this new technology alerted us to the concern that the intended frost resistance attained by the air entrainment might be lost during longer time exposure, if the entrained air bubbles were filled by secondary solids. The past observations made tidal exposure a likely basis for the research, but we thought that other performance circumstances might also require attention.

Project No. 9, failure of a concrete brine container, was a consultancy case handed over from the CtO. There had been claims from industry companies that concrete containers for brine solutions had shown rapid deterioration, whereas in other cases such containers had shown excellent durability. The project was to aim at discovering the reasons for the different resistance.

Project No. 10, concrete strength – w/c relationships, was primarily seen as an updating of the basic values of the strength characteristics of the Danish cement types. These data, for the ordinary mix-design rules in accordance with the conventional formulae, had not been revised for many years. Meanwhile, cement types had been refined by changed clinker compositions (with higher C_3S contents) and finer grinding.

Project No. 11, measurements of entrained air in fresh concrete, was proposed because the existing American and Danish methods measured the total air content in the fresh concrete. But it was the distribution and bubble size characteristics in the air entrained hardened concrete which granted the beneficial effect for frost resistance.

The first years of the BFL research

The activity of the new research group commenced in 1960, several months before the project proposals for the research programme were worked out. In August, we made a thorough field inspection of concrete piers in the harbour in North Jutland, which figures in project No. 6 above. We also prepared a literature review on this type of deterioration.

I issued reports about an eight-week study journey to cement and concrete research institutes across the USA, which I had undertaken in continuation of the 4th International Symposium on the Chemistry of Cement in Washington DC and Skokie, Illinois. This tour became an indispensable basis for the building-up of contacts for the BFL work with the American research communities, and gave me an impression of the challenges we were up against.

The American research had, since the late 1930s, created a completely new school of basic physico/chemical studies of the nature of hardened cement paste and of the deleterious processes in hardened concrete. Concurrently, there was a powerful wave of development of standard test and examination methods, with ASTM as the executive consensus operating institution. The magnitude of equipment and staff at the major research institutes and the high level of the leading researchers' scientific knowledge was, in some ways, almost as frightening as their attitudes to free exchange and collegial support were welcome. There was also some basis for confidence in our status. We were definitely ahead on petrographic thin section studies of deleterious reactions in concrete, and our perception of the mechanisms of physico/chemical deterioration. Likewise, our approach to monitoring of concrete curing by application of the maturity concept was a novelty for most of our American colleagues. In engineering practice, it was apparent that the structural development in the USA with precast and prestressed concrete was less advanced than in Europe. Field inspections in California showed me bridges of 30–40 years' age (Monterey County and Los Angeles) which, despite severe cracking due to alkali-silica reaction, performed satisfactorily under far more intensive traffic loading than originally envisaged. A visit with C. Wakemann to Los Angeles harbour also showed me that sea water, i.e. sulphate, attack was negligible on high quality concrete of 30–50 years of age, despite C_3A contents above 10% in the cement used.

1961 was the first year spent in the new laboratory. Much time was devoted to development of the research programme, installation and checking of equipment, operational training and organization. Besides this, I wrote three Progress Reports, N2, N3 and N4, left over from the previous DNIBR long-term programme, and three papers on concrete durability for a RILEM conference in Prague. We conducted three investigations into aggregates from Danish gravel and sand pits, and one field and laboratory investigation of failure of concrete footings at a plant for sulphuric acid.

At a public, technical hearing I presented a tentative strategy for the BFL. We would take up studies of the effects of mechanization and acceleration of the processing of concrete in its fresh state and during curing, as influenced by the development of cement production technology and new concrete production conditions, such as the use of steam curing and new chemical admixtures. We would create a basis of scientific knowledge for the work, and also build thereon for further studies of concrete durability, which in our opinion would depend heavily on the applied processing methods for new concrete production.

My attendance of an OECD seminar on research management, organized by the Academy of Technical Sciences (ATV), proved to be the strategic and educational event of the year. During three days of informal discussions the attending groups of 41 directors from European (and a few American) public and industrial research establishments revealed a wealth of leading-edge knowledge about how to manage research. I was the only representative of research for the building and construction sector. Some of the research directors from multinational corporations, with R & D staffs of a thousand or more people, claimed that management was merely about hiring the most sophisticated, young scientists. The company would thereby be nourished for continuous technology innovations. Other directors preferred more conventional management systems and hierarchical organizations over-bridging to research implementation in process and product development.

A last day summary of the exchanges emphasized the following.

"A research policy is needed for fundamental research. A research programme is necessary for applied research.

Programmes are useful for obtaining external support.

Programmes are internal guidance, not bookkeeping. Keep it flexible.

10–15% fundamental research is necessary for any laboratory. It is useful to do urgent applied work.

Sales departments look 6 months ahead.

Production departments look 1–2 years ahead.

Research must look 10 years ahead.

The research man must have the final say inside his laboratory, but must coordinate with outside agencies.

The research manager must be at equal level with the top management.

The answer to new problems is not: why should we do it, but rather – why should we not do it.

A nuclear problem is: how do we gain wisdom."

The general emphasis was on two avenues of technological research management:

☐ high level material science and scientists are the incontrovertible basis for successful materials technology research, whether at university or industry corporation levels

□ the European industrial development needed renovation by improvement of the basic science–technology interaction.

In retrospect, one must be aware that European industries and universities were just about to recover from the aftermath of World War II. Concurrently, the capital flow to building and construction was increasing, and the general public, media, politicians, and industry leaders looked towards new R & D as the means of profitable growth. Financing was therefore not a problem: the uncertainties concerned the ways in which the investments in R & D could be made to give the most satisfactory returns. For me, the visits to the USA and the workshop confirmed that our initial research programme was a reasonable, long-term perspective of interactive studies combined with educational, pragmatic troubleshooting projects for the CtO. I had also learned that serious applications of modern materials science in concrete research would primarily rely on engagement of the right kind of new associates. I would have my hands full, in addition to my own specialization, as the generalist and outreach contact developer.

At the end of the first year I was also confident that the predictable further increase in cement production and sales would make increases of our work capacity possible, if the company were satisfied with our accomplishments.

A ten-year cost-benefit review

In 1970, the company management agreed to my proposal to prepare a ten-year review of our work as the basis for updating the philosophy of the R & D situation in the company. I prepared a comprehensive analysis in five internal reports, which suggested more direct implementation investments in joint ventures with selected clients, and more effective use of our capabilities by the different companies of the FLS corporation. The series of reports actually motivated the promotion two years later of the BFL to the official R & D function of the company, available as such for the corporate companies.

As part of the review, I was asked to prepare an estimate of the economic output of the ten years of BFL research: the return on the company investment, so to say. Initially, this seemed to be a suicidal assignment, since we consistently had to operate without charging for our services. Moreover, we were unable to claim that any fraction of the steady increase of the cement consumption in Denmark in the past decade was a result of the BFL research accomplishments. We were well aware that the governmental subvention policy for housing and infrastructure was the primary reason for the booming cement sales, and for the willingness on the part of the company to let our research grow over the period. Nevertheless, the BFL was not accustomed to eschew impossible tasks.

We explained that the benefits for the company fell into eight categories of activity:

□ research projects
□ educational services
□ lecturing
□ service investigations for the CtO

☐   special publications
☐   public services – Denmark
☐   public services – abroad
☐   investments for future work.

For the first three categories, we assumed as a yardstick for estimation of an income, albeit fictitious, what we could have charged clients per research project or "unit" of services if we had operated as a commercial contract research and training course institute. With this method of estimation applied to our records, we came to the following value of the efforts, accumulated over the ten years:

☐   research projects – 25 million DKK
☐   education – 0.5 million DKK
☐   lecturing – 2.5 million DKK.

The services to CtO were similarly estimated to represent a value of 1.0 million DKK.

The special publications comprised my dissertation and two particularly response-intensive articles:

☐   *Strength of structural lightweight aggregate concrete* by H. H. Bache.
☐   *Hydration of Portland cement paste at high temperature under atmospheric pressure* by G. M. Idorn.

We knew that these publications (and several others) were widely read, and prompted many people to approach us, regarding both the scientific contents and advice about applications. We knew that the costs of these publications were about 2 million DKK, and found that the corresponding "company value" could reasonably be suggested to be:

☐   special publications – 20 million DKK.

Our public services in Denmark comprised participation in work for the Academy of Technical Sciences (to which I was elected in 1965), The Danish Concrete Association (in which we usually held positions on the board) and different public committees, such as in the Danish Civil Engineering Society. We knew that the time spent in these services amounted to an average of about 200 000 DKK. One benefit of this participation was substantial influence on decisions about general technical and public development; it also created confidence in the company's services to the public and cement consumers. Hence, we estimated the value at ten times the cost, or:

☐   public services, DK – 20 million DKK.

Our public services abroad comprised memberships and cooperative work in the Nordic Concrete Association, RILEM, Cembureau, Highway Research Board, USA, ASTM, ACI etc. From the outset in 1960, I expanded the contacts and services in these organizations to include my new colleagues. By these means we also ensured important return of information to the companies in the FLS corporation, and to the Danish concrete enterprises.

The costs of these external service efforts were about 750 000 DKK for the ten-year period. The value could only be estimated satisfactorily with a corporate yardstick, because Aalborg Portland[1] itself was only an international player in the field of white cement. Failing a corporate yardstick, we claimed a theoretical value equal to ten times the expenses, in other words:

☐   public services abroad – 7.5 million DKK.

Our value estimate of the above categories of the BFL service, altogether close to 75 million DKK (in 1969 kroner) for the ten years was definitely not accepted literally by the company management, as the realistic counterpart of the accounted under 2 million DKK net expenses over the same years. Nevertheless, despite the fact that modesty with regard to judgement of our own performance was not our best known quality, it was acknowledged that we contributed a new multifarious picture of the R & D function; in other words we had a clear concept of what we had spent the investments on with a visible, growing consistency. We did demonstrate solid convictions of the quality of our efforts, but this was also repeatedly sustained by the obvious goodwill in Denmark and abroad, of which the management had ample evidence. It was also clear that, in a reconnoitring capacity, we traced many indications of the likely trends in future technological development, and that our interaction with the Danish concrete engineering community was an asset which supplemented the R & D services excellently.

Implicitly, our review disclosed that we did not have effective pathways for implementation of our research accomplishments in concrete production, whether on sites or in precast plants. The review became helpful in the subsequent debates about this change of the R & D policy, which we pursued vigorously from the BFL's side, with the advantage of the EIRMA experience to back us up, and with most of the Cembureau member companies as remarkably conservative counterparts.

There was, of course, one aspect of the R & D value estimate which we underestimated, because our focus was aimed at what we had accomplished over the passed decade. In its entirety, it could all justifiably be considered as an investment for the company and its customers, to bring them into international front-line positions in technology development. To attain that position required the companies to supplement the BFL research with sufficient investments in technology innovations. The promotion of that investment became a major BFL activity in the forthcoming years.

The BFL situation in 1975

1975 was the last entire year during which I functioned as the leader of the BFL and, since 1972, as director of the new R & D function of the company. The following survey of BFL work over the years shows how far the sixteen years of uninterrupted progressive development had brought us.

The background to our work had been the continuing inflationary, national economic boom, which had resulted in an accompanying steady growth of national cement production, from 1.4 million tonnes in 1960 to 2.9 million tons in the peak year 1973. This corresponded to a cement consumption increase in Denmark from 266 kg to 510 kg per capita.

[1] Aktieselskabet Aalborg Portland-Cement-Fabrik changed its name to Aalborg Portland in 1972.

It was the skyrocketing oil prices in the late summer of 1973, which suddenly signalled a gloomier future than we had been accustomed to count on, while we, blindfolded by the apparently automatic progress year after year, had worked under constant pressure to comply with the accelerating cement and concrete technology development. The BFL had, in fact, concurrent with its promotion in 1972 when it became the seat of the company's R & D function, changed its policy and given cost-effectiveness high priority in order to match the company and corporation development needs without sacrificing our underlying, long-term research programmes.

In 1975 the thumb was beginning to turn downwards for our research. It was dawning on the shareholders of Aalborg Portland that the ever-rising energy prices, combined with dwindling sales, predicted a profound recession for building and construction, with plummeting earnings, and large, superfluous cement production capacity and manpower. The big brother company, FLS, saw the same writing on the wall. The company was on the point of scrapping its conventional preference for the wet kiln cement plant system, and developing a powerful marketing campaign for its new pre-calciner, dry kiln systems, when the global cement plant market also collapsed. Moreover, import of foreign cement to the hitherto protected national market areas could be envisaged, as surplus cement plant capacity became a multinational problem for cement industries.

The BFL had, since 1972, experienced an increase in the number of requests for its services, also within the corporate companies. In several studies in the course of 1975, we supplied analyses with memoranda showing that, at least without capital interests and depreciation to pay, we were a profitable, economic department of the company. This stage of development had its basis in the intensive work during the preceding 15 years, and, in our view, provided strong indications that our research establishment could be more effectively utilized. Our studies comprised both commented surveys of the historic development of the research, and budgeted planning for further development of the BFL as a self-sustaining unit within the corporate framework.

The major evidence of the consistent progress of our work was the reprints of published papers, and the internal progress reports on the research activity.

Reprints

Table 6 surveys the number of reprints of articles published by the BFL personnel in cement and concrete periodicals and conference proceedings, etc. since 1960. The reprints are categorized in the topical fields:

- management
- laboratory research methods
- processing and performance
- durability
- sundries.

The reprints of papers about management of research were contributions to public debates about concrete research, including the role of the BFL therein, and served also to secure BFL's position as a leading national vehicle

Table 6. Survey of categories of reprinted articles published by the BFL, 1960–1976

BFL reprints	
Subject areas	*Number issued*
MANAGEMENT	33
Research strategy	
Concrete	8
Building	2
Industry	7
Public relations	
Presentation of the BFL	9
Visits abroad	2
University CEng education	5
LABORATORY METHODS	13
Testing	
Cement	2
Aggregates	1
Concrete	3
Optical microscopy	3
SEMEX	2
Library	2
PROCESSING AND PERFORMANCE	24
Processing phase	
Fresh	1
Compaction	1
Hydration	3
Steam curing	4
Performance phase	
Shrinkage–swelling	5
Hardened concrete	4
Contact phase	2
Impregnation	
Sulphur	2
Epoxy	2
DURABILITY	14
Sea and groundwater	4
Alkali-silica reaction	5
Freezing/thawing	3
General	2
CEMENT	3
Belite in OPC	1
C_3A	2
Sundries	4

for progressive development of the civil engineering capability for design and construction with concrete. Positions in the Academy of Technical Science and the governmental research council also allowed me to participate in the general debate on technological development in trade and industry.

In the field of laboratory methods, we published articles about special BFL developments of methodology, such as combined compressive strength/E_{dyn} equipment to mount on concrete cylinder test specimens, thin section manufacture, etc.

Reprints of papers for rationalization of the processing of concrete and for improvements of the properties of hardened concrete were prepared to disseminate the results of our research programmes. In the field of concrete durability, our reprints reflected the continuing work to update knowledge of deleterious reactions in field concrete. The reprints of articles about cement and sundries represent work in the 1970s, influenced by our function as the R & D operation.

Most of the reprints on management and public relation subjects were in Danish, whereas those representing our factual research activity were primarily in English. Both categories were distributed free of charge to relevant national and international contacts, the first-mentioned in order to gain influence on progressive policies, the second to create the foundations for mutual exchange.

Table 7 is a list of seven BFL papers representing invited contributions to major international conferences on cement and concrete research. Reprint No. 6 was a general report (of which I had been the author of the major part), No. 49 and the paper to the 6th ICCC, Moscow 1974, were principal papers. Still in Aalborg Portland employment I was, in 1977, invited to be a member of the international scientific programme committee and author of the general report on cement-aggregate bond and durability for the 7th ICCC in Paris 1980.

Reprint No. 37 was for the symposium in honour of T. C. Powers in 1965, and reprint No. 77 was the keynote address at the 25th anniversary of *der Forschungsinstitut des Vereins des Österreichischen Zementfabrikanten*.

The invited papers illustrate the international goodwill we attained over the years, and circulation of these and other reprints in to an ever-growing mailing list, and to visitors, was an effective way of disseminating our knowledge and views.

Internal reports

Table 8 shows the number of progress reports which served as the primary documentation for the work at the BFL from commencement to closure. A total of 419 such reports was issued, and many of them were distributed to a large group of contacts for information or exchange. They are separated into the three main categories:

- □ management
- □ consulting service
- □ research

with some of the reports figuring in more than one category.

At first glance, it may appear strange that a modern concrete research laboratory,

Table 7. *Examples of invited papers for international conferences 1960–1976*

BFL reprint number	Authors, titles and publication identifications
6	Bredsdorff, P., Idorn, G. M., Kjær, A., Plum, N. M., Poulsen, E.: Chemical reactions involving aggregates. With discussions. *Proceedings IV ISCC*, Washington, 1960, Secs. VI, Paper VII. Washington DC, 1962
37	Bache, H. H., Idorn, G. M., Nepper-Christensen, P, Nielsen, J.: Morphology of calcium hydroxide in cement paste. pp. 154–174. *Highway Research Board Special Report 90* (Symposium in honour of T. C. Powers), 1965
49	Idorn, G. M.: Hydration of Portland cement paste at high temperature under atmospheric pressure. pp. 411–435. *Proceedings V ISCC*. Session III–4A. Tokyo, 1970
58	Idorn, G. M.: Conditions for using concrete as a constructional material in Arctic harbours. pp. 1334–1342. *Proceedings 1st International Conference on Port and Ocean Engineering in Arctic Conditions*. Vol. II. NTH Trondheim, 1971
–	Idorn, G. M. and Fördös, Z.: Cement-polymer materials. *Proceedings VI ICCC*. Section 3, Topic 3-3. Moscow 1974, Reprint. Il Cemento. Vol. 72. pp. 73–108. 1975
77	Idorn, G. M.: Von der Krise zum Fortschritt, von der Forschung zur Entwicklung. *Sonderdruck aus Zement und Beton*, pp. 45–52, Heft 2. 1976

over the course of sixteen years, issued in total 182 internal reports on management. The breakdown into the five management sub-groups shown in Table 8 holds the key to the explanation. In the first place, as a laboratory operating for the customers of the owner company's products, without charge for its services, we were asked, from time to time, by the company management to estimate the value of our services in relation to the invested means. Secondly, in the course of 1968, I prepared a study for a thorough revision of the strategy, policy and organization of the research. I wanted to do that because the interaction with concrete engineering practice for implementation of our research results was, in our experience, ineffective without our own engagement in implementation projects for the end-using precast and construction companies. There was also a growing awareness that some of the companies within the Aalborg Portland–FLS corporation could benefit from consultant services, due to the advanced stage of knowledge and instrumentation at the BFL. This function was settled by the BFL's appointment as the R & D function in 1972.

Then, in 1974, came the signals that we might succumb to the depressive trends of cement consumption. That required further analyses of the potential benefits of our existence, although in the end it was to no avail.

Table 8. Survey of categories of internal reports issued by BFL, 1960–1976

Operative category	Numbers issued
Management	182
Strategy and planning	27
Education and contacts	96
Internal service	23
Public relations	28
Specials	8
Consultant service	77
Field concrete – failure cases	13
Aggregate examination	7
External testing service	9
Cement	24
Noise	2
Roofing tile processing	10
Eternit processing	6
Curing – field concrete	4
Sundries	2
Research	185
Modelling of concrete	21
Compaction – fresh concrete	25
Hydration – curing	23
Deformation – hardened concrete	14
Strength	7
Lightweight concrete	19
Impregnation	6
Low porosity cement	8
Fibre reinforcement	6
Durability	25
Sundries	31

I also prepared several reports on the planning and management of industrial research to transfer the new insight I had acquired through the educational appointment in 1970 as the company delegate to the European Industrial Research Management Association (EIRMA), and as a member of the Board of Directors in the Association. The participation with EIRMA in the accumulation of experience with R & D management within about 150–180 large, European industrial companies was a major source of inspiration, which helped to make our management effective and innovative.

The second group of internal management reports were requested records concerning the events and effects of educational, external visits abroad by the personnel. This was our way of advancing the professional and scientific education of the research staff, including myself. We felt a great need for acquaintance with what we considered to be outstanding cement and concrete research abroad. The third group of reports concerned the quality assurance for instrumentation and its use, and the public relation reports were draft manuscripts of publicity statements, and included our widely circulated annual reports. The special reports refer to my personal progress reports, left over from the forner DNIBR/ATV programme on concrete disintegration, and to manuscripts for my doctorate dissertation, 1967.

From 1972, as the company R & D force, we were intensively involved in consulting services, with noise measurements in cement plant grinding departments, for improvement of the processing procedures at a concrete roofing tile company, with curing monitoring and fibre reinforcing studies for the Dansk Eternit Fabrik A/S, and with the introduction of our new maturity-based curing monitoring technology at three new, major Danish bridge construction jobs the Sallingsund, the Vejle Fjord and the Alssund Bridges where our specialists were called in due to severe thermal cracking early during the curing of sections of these structures. Adaptation of this methodology prevented cracking during the subsequent castings. These consulting services determined approval for use of the methodology in the Public Danish Highway Directorate for all bridge projects under their authority.

The internal research reports were the bread and butter documentation for the longer term research projects of the BFL. They are in such an order that the logical, holistic "structure" of the research is visible. The modelling of concrete comprised physico/mathematical descriptions of the nature of packing and rheology of fresh concrete, and the interdependence of strength, density and fracture mechanics. The compaction of fresh concrete was studied theoretically over several spans of years. Studies of cement hydration also lasted several years before the routes became visible for definite approaches towards monitoring technology for curing of concrete at elevated temperatures, i.e. with high yielding cements, high cement contents in concrete, and with external heat in precast concrete, as well as with unpredictable temperature differences at construction sites. Shrinkage and swelling of precast concrete elements were an important research subject during the first 4–5 years of our work.

Research on the strength development and strength levels of concrete under different conditions was a key issue in nearly all other topical problem areas, such as the properties of lightweight concrete made with expanded clay aggregates. It was also related to our investigations of technology for obtaining high levels of strength, durability and ductility by special technology, such as impregnation of the cement paste with polymers or sulphur, low porosity cement, and fibre reinforcement of the cement paste.

Studies of concrete durability were, in the first years, primarily concerned with sulphate attack and freezing/thawing, partly as contributions to a Nordic concrete research cooperation, and later for the initiation of new research on alkali-silica reaction.

The category of sundry research projects in Table 8 covers a variety of different, smaller projects initiated by personal interest, support to university studies, visitors' programmes, etc.

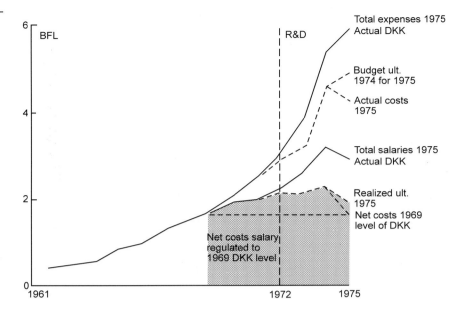

Fig. 21. Operation costs for the BFL 1961–1975 and earnings since 1969

Economic development

Figure 21 shows the operation costs of the BFL research from its commencement in 1961 to 1975 (minus the original building and installations and therefore also without depreciation).

Total expenditure and salaries are shown in the two full-line curves in actual DKK, and in the punctuated curve with inflation adjustment after 1969. The earnings from 1971 show charges for company and external R & D project services. The figure shows that in 1975 we spent no more than in 1969 in real expenses, whereas our earnings were steadily increasing. These earnings illustrate the increasing use of our service capability during the last four years of operation – in fulfilment of our forecasts when this kind of operation was accepted in 1971. Until then the total funding had been spent "in bulk" on the BFL research programmes and on our own development projects, to a large extent as we ourselves wanted.

Figure 22 shows the remarkable response by the BFL to the opportunity for service projects financed by sources other than Aalborg Portland in 1971.

Table 9 shows the financial situation for 1975. The company funding of our long-term programme and internal R & D projects was reduced to 50% of the total spending, while the project services for company, corporate companies and external clients amounted to 25.6, 14.7 and 9.8%, respectively, together also 50%. This new development for deliberate implementation of our special knowledge was charged without added overhead expenses, and the expenses were tax exempt for the clients.

Table 10 is a breakdown of the management elements of the operations for the period 1973–75, when we were increasingly involved in a determined fight for the survival of the laboratory. It is evident that we achieved an intense internal

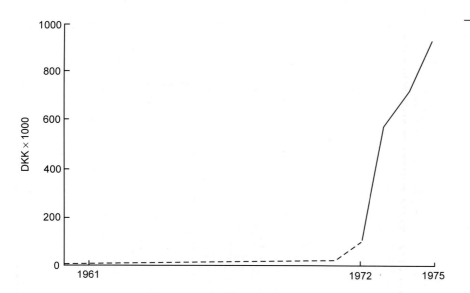

Fig. 22. The increase of BFL's earnings 1971–1975 from sources other than Aalborg Portland

rationalization. The cost of administration was reduced from 25 to 20% of the total expenditure in the course of the three years.

Research and service projects, 1975

We responded to the discouraging threat of approaching economic downturns with determined efforts to make the cost-effectiveness of our work irresistibly visible to the company, the corporation and the public and private customers, who indirectly financed the research.

Table 11 illustrates, by selected examples, the complexity of research projects and services we were now able to undertake and offer to our "market" within the six categories:

(i) concrete processing
(ii) hardened concrete, including durability

Table 9. Operating revenues for the BFL in 1975, comprising basic funding and charged project services

	DKK	
Operating revenues	Income	Expenses
Aalborg Portland basic funding		
BFL long-term research	1 567 985	
BFL R & D projects	1 482 275 3 050 260	
BFL project services		
Company	1 535 725	
Corporate companies	890 905	
External clients	598 110 3 024 740	
Balance	6 075 000	6 075 000

95

*Table 10. Proportional distribution of the time spent at the BFL in 1973, 1974 and 1975 on R & D
project services, and on different categories of the "bulk" financed research activities*

Operation	Recorded time spent: %		
	Nov. 1973	Oct./Nov. 1974	Oct./Nov. 1975
R & D service, external and company	19	28	34
Basis			
Long-term research	4	4	3
R & D at the BFL	14	10	12
Training of staff	4	5	1
Travelling	4	5	5
Literature studies	7	6	5
Sundries	10	8	9
Absentees etc.	13	12	11
Administration	25	22	20
Total	100	100	100

(iii) cement
(iv) fibre reinforcement
(v) product and process innovations
(vi) instrumentation and special services.

Many service projects were undertaken or offered because our physico/
chemical instrument equipment and staff expertise had reached a very high
level of complex effectiveness.

Political trade-off for Aalborg Portland

At no time during the existence of the BFL had there appeared consistent efforts
on the part of the cement users or public organizations to establish an alternative
or complementary concrete technology research in Denmark. Hence, Aalborg
Portland had, through its willingness to carry the investments, and thanks to
the acknowledged integrity of the BFL research, won national confidence for
its effective service in the general development of concrete technology. The
BFL services regarding kiln operations in cooperation with FLS, and joint
training courses, conference arrangements etc. were additional assets. The introduction by the BFL of professional, industrial R & D management was a novelty
within the corporation, and placed the company, internationally, as a progressive,
front-line member of the cement industry. Generally, these kinds of benefit could
not be quantified in the accounting records. In one respect, however, the
company management estimated a calculable profit of our work and existence:
our knowledgeable position regarding alkali-silica reaction was useful in avoiding
the production of several hundred thousand tonnes of low alkali cement for
special production and service operations. This amounted to an estimated 10
million DKK annually, or a total of 160 million DKK over the years of BFL's
existence.

Table 11.1. Survey of service and research projects performed by the BFL in 1975

Concrete processing
Precast technology. This cooperative project with two precast concrete companies from 1971 was carried out with implementation of compaction and curing technology theory and newly invented monitoring systems. The two companies calculated 1.5 million DKK savings for the production of $50\,000^3$ precast concrete products. New plants were designed for incorporation of the innovative technology.
Concrete roofing tiles. After thorough studies of existing production technology, new design of the concrete-mixing procedure and the steam curing chamber methods was developed.
Eternit plant. Scrutiny of the processing technology for asbestos-cement roofing tiles helped to improve reduction of peak curing temperatures and improved control of water escape during the early, hot curing phase.
Greenland marine concrete. The curing technology was redesigned for use under arctic conditions with development of a special software programme and pilot testing for the processing of a large, prismatic concrete column.
Danish state railways. The temperature distribution in concrete during the curing of 3000 tonne tunnel elements was measured and found to be in accordance with the precalculated data based on our maturity and heat transmission models.
Chemical admixtures. Investigations were made for comparison of the effects of different new HRWR-admixtures for Aalborg Portland's evaluation of marketing interests.
Ready-mix computer monitoring. Analyses and proposals for online batching and mixing control were made for a corporate company.
Accelerated cement test method. An accelerated cement test method was developed for prediction of 28-day strength by a method involving approximately 1 day's special cement-hydration.

Table 11.2. Survey of service and research projects performed by the BFL in 1975

Hardened concrete, including durability
Concepts of concrete strength. Theoretical studies of the nature of the strength and fracture mechanics of hardened concrete at a modest level were the maintained investments in 1975 of background research.
Durability case studies – Denmark. The BFL occasionally assisted the CtO with special investigations for diagnosing field cases of concrete deterioration and contributed thereby to counteracting the populistic campaigns "against concrete".
Durability study – Iceland. The occurrence of alkali-silica reaction was diagnosed in concrete from a marine structure.
Concrete damage to tops of smokestacks. Cracking and crumbling of concrete in top sections of chimneys for cement kilns were diagnosed to be caused mainly by sulphuric acid attack.

Table 11.3. Survey of service and research projects performed by the BFL in 1975

Cement
Cement production. The BFL analytical instrumentation and expertise were applied jointly with the technical expertise of the Aalborg Portland plant professionals and FLS expertise to update the processing technology with new kiln types and requirements for cement quality.
Fly ash in blends with cement. Fly ash types from Danish power plants were examined for suitability as supplementary cement material and for energy saving in cement production.
Low porosity cement for high strength concrete. Vigorous efforts were invested in the development of real high strength concrete by means of the American LP cement. The introductory research became a joint venture with Westvaco Corporation USA and the Dansk Spændbeton A/S.
Sand–chalk cement. The BFL participated in pilot investigations which confirmed that the new cement type, made without clay as conventional source material, would be suitable for elevated temperature curing.

Table 11.4. Survey of service and research projects performed by the BFL in 1975

Fibre reinforcement
Fire-resistant wall boards. Intensive search was made for new suitable fibre materials for replacement of asbestos fibre, which was to be banned for industrial application.
Alkali-resistant glass fibre. Different investigations were undertaken for development of processing technology and products with glass fibres as reinforcement. Emphasis was on long-term resistance to the pore-liquid of cement paste in concrete.
International fibre reinforcement cooperation. By invitation, the BFL provided service to RILEM and Nordforsk for international progress on the uses of fibre reinforcement.

The architecture of the BFL research

We adopted an overall architecture for the BFL research as a guiding framework for strategy, project selection and implementation of the results of the work.

Figure 23 is a display which I made in the mid-1960s, because I felt a need to communicate our underlying concept of the integration of basic chemistry, physics, and mechanics knowledge behind the research projects on materials, processing, and performance of concrete. The figure was also a guide to the interactive use of external knowledge, and it emerged from my previous experience, first in practice with production of concrete, and then in research with comprehensive studies of field concrete performance. The figure also reflects that our research was developing concurrently with a tremendous commercial development of new analytical instrumentation such as X-ray diffractometry, scanning microscopy and microchemical analyses.

Figure 24 represents the apparent adoption, some years later, of the strategic

Table 11.5. Survey of service and research projects performed by the BFL in 1975

New product and process innovations
Sulphur impregnation of concrete. Investigations of sulphur impregnation of hardened concrete were undertaken as a supplementary innovation to LPC concrete and epoxy impregnation. Pilot castings were technically convincing.
Sulphur impregnation of gypsum. Preliminary studies were made for a project concerning the possible advantages of the strengthening of gypsum boards by impregnation of the board product with sulphur.
Lightweight concrete. "Heavy–lightweight" aggregates were investigated for suitability as coarse aggregate in lightweight prestressed concrete bridge decks.
Perlite. Investigations were commenced on a feasibility study for possible import of perlite from Iceland for expanding and sale in Denmark.

Table 11.6. Survey of in-house development of instrumentation and of special services which the BFL performed in 1975

Instrumentation and special services
Concrete process monitoring instruments. Associated with the major precast concrete innovation programme, pilot editions of monitoring instruments were developed and put on trial: ☐ maturity computer for on-line recording of time/temperature development as "maturity time" during the curing of site and precast concrete ☐ robust adiabatic calorimeter for site determination of the heat of hydration of cement (in concrete samples) ☐ temperature-regulated storage container for concrete specimens, capable of simulating calculated or measured temperature developments in actual site or plant concrete during the early curing phase ☐ device for rapid analysis of the content of water in fresh concrete ☐ on-line workability recording instrument for installation in concrete mixers.
Defective prestress steel delivery. Scanning microscopy of a prestressed steel delivery to a Danish construction company. Our micrographs made rejection of the delivered sample possible.
Foreign aggregates. Aggregate materials from the Orient and Africa were examined by petrography and physico-chemical analysis, including alkali reactivity tests. The examinations were made for Danish engineering firms who were aware of the risk inherent in materials and environments different from ours.
Suspended dust. Analytical methods for examination of suspended dust in polluted air were developed jointly with the environmental technology group of FLS.
Control service of testing equipment. Annual control visits and check-lists were made on local laboratory equipment for the cement plants and corporate concrete producers.
Noise levels in processing plants. Special noise-level instruments were used for site improvements to Aalborg Portland and corporate and external companies requiring such services.

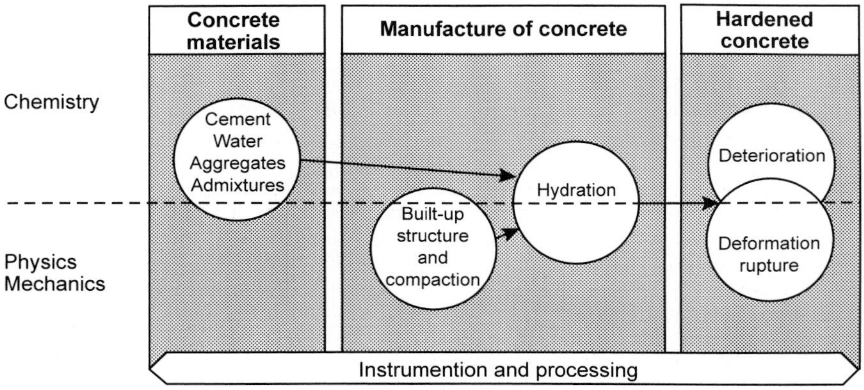

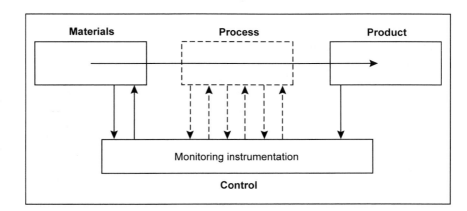

Fig. 23. *Display of the holistic "architecture" of the BFL research as an illustration of our research strategy for internal and external communication*

framework which identifies concrete making as an industrial flow process. The quality assessment relies on monitoring of the operations which alter the mixture of ingredients to the final product. This perception of concrete production emerged from my interaction with R & D directors in major European industry corporations, who convened and cooperated in EIRMA to advance their skill as cost-effective research managers. The display reflects the increasing mechanization of concrete production, requiring model-true, monitoring recording of the progressive changes from fresh to hardened concrete through the phases of batching, mixing, transport and placing, and curing. (It is not accidental that the figure is identical with Figure 11, with the exception that the visual surveillance of the past is now replaceable by monitoring instrumentation.)

Figures 23 and 24 highlight our efforts to make the BFL the Danish headquarters for progressive R & D, with a sufficient basis of external and in-house scientific knowledge. Such a philosophy was exceptional, if not unique, in contemporary concrete technology research. Much of the foreign, academic and public, institutional research became caught up in the boom of high-power data-processing instruments, which tied the workers to bench work and overwhelming data processing and, at times, very specific interpretations.

Fig. 24. *"Management model" of concrete production, with classical "visual surveillance" for quality assessment (cf. Fig. 11) replaced by "monitoring instrumentation", hence emphasizing primary goals of our research*

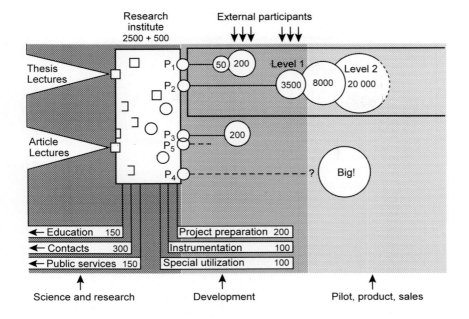

Fig. 25. Display illustrating the BFL's integrated approach to the complexity of long-term explanatory research, implementation by joint development projects and general dissemination (DKK ×1000)

Simultaneously, emphasis was being put on the standardization of sample preparations and testing procedures. This created an unfortunate disregard for reliable modelling of the circumstances for the making and behaviour of real concrete in laboratory-confined research, in contrast to the production of field concrete.

Figure 25 is another display of the structure and ways of operation of the BFL as the seat of R & D from 1972, when we had begun to undertake joint technology development projects within the corporation and with external precast concrete producers. The rectangular "BFL-body" opens up towards the left, with its output of publications and contributions to education (fellowships), contacts (visits and visitors) and general services (committee work, etc.). To the right is shown the outreach of development projects at various stages. It is deliberately implied that the transfer from new BFL discoveries to new technology in concrete production and usage may require considerable investment beyond the costs of the initial research. (The two marked-up projects P_1 and P_2 were at that time in progress with Danish industry partners.)

Figure 26 symbolizes the long-term realizations of our conceptual framework for innovation of concrete technology by means of the interaction of basic and applied research. The fundamental exploration of the properties of hardened cement paste had commenced in 1934 at the Portland Cement Association in the USA. The studies were in publication from about 1947, and were supported by basic studies of cement hydration, especially in the USA and Great Britain. The applications in Denmark were commenced by the DNIBR in the 1950s, and at the BFL we turned the focus towards the new conditions for concrete processing in the emergent precast industry. By about 1970, we possessed sufficient basic knowledge for the creation of cooperative projects with external companies for development of:

Flashlights on history and research

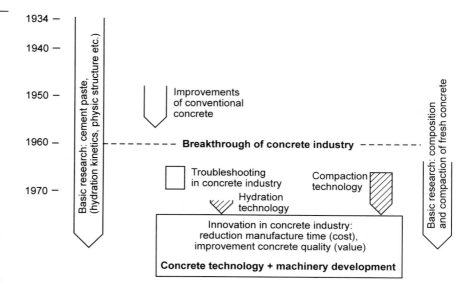

Fig. 26. Depiction of the BFL's emphasis on integrated research for precast concrete to improve the cost-effectiveness of industrial manufacturing flow by teamworking with outstanding professionals abroad

☐ maturity-based curing monitoring technology
☐ a combined static pressure and vibratory compaction technique which enabled considerable cost-savings and quality improvements for the production of precast concrete.

It was an unexpected twist of fate, that these achievements had just been made ready for broad marketing when the profound recession in building and construction in Denmark and abroad emerged and swept the BFL overboard.

Major R & D programmes

The display in Figure 26 of two major accomplishments of the BFL research did not represent the consequence of a particular selection of the two projects with initially predicted concrete goals and clarified methodologies. The tortuous routes from initiation of the programmes to the development phases passed through a number of different research projects, involving along the way internal education, periods of apparent defeat, stimulation through contact with famous research personalities from abroad, and consistent interaction with the concrete producing industries about pragmatic, short-term troubleshooting service through the CtO.

"Nepper's formula" for the relationships between the compressive cylinder strength of concrete and its cement content, w/c and age for different types of Danish Portland cement:[84]

$$f_c(M_{20}) = \exp\left[\frac{A_1}{\sqrt{a}} + \left(A_2 + \frac{A_3}{\sqrt{a}}\right) \cdot \frac{w}{c} + A_4\right]$$

in which f_c = compressive strength, a = equivalent maturity age at 20°C.

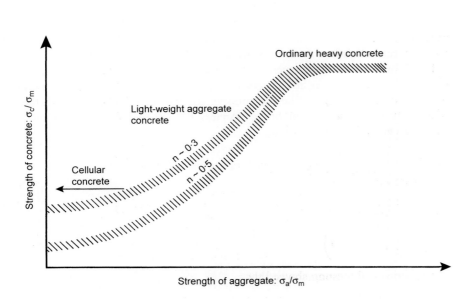

Fig. 27. Strength of concrete σ_c (linear scale) versus strength of aggregate σ_a (log scale) for different volume concentrations of aggregates n. The depiction is shown dimensionless through division by the strength of the mortar σ_m, after display by H. H. Bache

A_1, A_2, A_3, A_4 are constants, dependent upon the types of cement and of aggregates.

For concrete with ordinary and rapid hardening cement, the relationship after 3, 7, 28 and 91 maturity days can be reduced to:

1. Ordinary Portland cement:
$f_c 3 = \exp{(4.4 - 2.6 \, w/c)}$
$f_c 7 = \exp{(4.4 - 2.4 \, w/c)}$
$f_c 28 = \exp{(4.7 - 2.1 \, w/c)}$
$f_c 91 = \exp{(4.8 - 2.0 \, w/c)}$

2. Rapid hardening Portland cement:
$f_c 3 = \exp{(4.5 - 2.4 \, w/c)}$
$f_c 7 = \exp{(4.6 - 2.2 \, w/c)}$
$f_c 28 = \exp{(4.7 - 2.0 \, w/c)}$
$f_c 91 = \exp{(4.8 - 1.9 \, w/c)}$

resulting from several years' testing of a large number of concrete cylinder specimens. We undertook this research because it was becoming customary at construction sites and in precast plants to prepare individual trial-testing as the basis for concrete mix proportioning, and for comparison with control test results for the production process. Our project showed that, with adequate entrance data supplied by the CtO, such individual pre-testing was superfluous.

Figure 27, from reference [85] shows the relationship, established by H. H. Bache, between the inherent strength of concrete aggregates and the strength of concrete containing such aggregates, ranging from the extreme lightweight (LECA insulation materials) over the heavier (LECA construction lightweight materials) to ordinary gravel and crushed granitic rock aggregates. Pragmatically, the figure is a guideline for effective mix design of concrete with lightweight aggregates, and it appeared in a report from a series on a project on that subject which ran for several years. However, as a realistic, dimensionless model it also shows that increasing density, i.e. strength, of aggregate particles contributes to the increase in the strength of concrete until one reaches the level of aggregate strength of the ordinarily used materials, which are stronger than the cement paste by orders of magnitude. The figure therefore was a precursory indication to us that we would need to find ways to increase the strength of hardened cement paste if we wanted to develop high strength concrete.

The figure was based on experimental research which had confirmed that the inherent compressive strength of lightweight aggregate (σ_a) could be accurately determined on the basis of the compressive strength of the concrete with the lightweight aggregates (σ), and of the mortar of the concrete (σ_m) (with ordinary sand aggregate). The relationship:

$$\sigma = f(\sigma_a, \sigma_m, n)$$

$$\text{where } n = \frac{\text{volume aggregate}}{\text{total volume}}$$

was made dimensionless:

$$\frac{\sigma}{\sigma_a} = f\left(\frac{\sigma_m}{\sigma_a} \times n\right)$$

The experimental testing showed that:

$$\frac{\sigma}{\sigma_a} = \left(\frac{\sigma_m}{\sigma_a}\right)^{1-n} \qquad \text{or}$$

$$\sigma = \sigma_a \times \sigma_m^{1-n}$$

Figure 28 shows an experimental determination of σ_a for a given lightweight aggregate by extrapolation to $n = 1.0$ of connected values of mortar and concrete strength, from reference [86]. The compressive strength σ (log scale) as a function of the relative volume of lightweight aggregate n (linear scale), the strength σ_a of the aggregate is found by extrapolation to $n = 1.0$ of connected values of mortar and concrete strength. Two determinations of σ_a are shown in the figure.

Figure 29, from reference [87], shows H. H. Bache's calculated perception of the potential for increase of the inherent strength of hardened cement paste in concrete by increase of its compactness, i.e. reduction of its porosity.

Figure 30, from reference [87] represents our perception, in about 1968, that effective compaction of cement paste in its fresh state was required for homogeneity and strength gains during hardening at elevated temperatures. Particles of unhydrated cement (black) are surrounded by a microstructure, which in cases (1) and (3) is uniformly distributed. In cases (2) and (4) the microstructure is heterogeneous as the cement grains are surrounded by a denser coating. With loose packings (1) and (2), the cement paste is strongest, when the microstructure is homogeneous, while the opposite is the case with dense packings (3) and (4). In the latter case the dense microstructure coatings (4) around the cement particles glue the particles together. The contemporary experience was, generally, that there were inevitable losses of final strength by accelerated heat curing of concrete. We explained that result as a consequence of heterogeneous hydration, as shown in the figure, but at that time we did not have sufficient insight into the situation to see hydration technology as an attainable accomplishment.

Figure 31, from reference [88], shows the VIPRES machine developed by Pedershåb Maskinfabrik A/S for the manufacture of precast concrete panel and wall elements by an integrated, monitored combination of simultaneous static

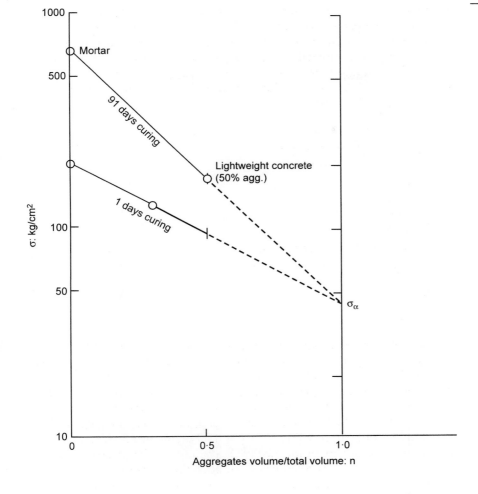

Fig. 28. Determination of the strength σ_a of lightweight aggregate in concrete, from H. H. Bache

pressure and high frequency vibration. The machine was based on a theoretical invention by H. H. Bache, and its exceptional compaction method densified the solids of the concrete to give a resultant strength twice that obtained for a given cement content with ordinary vibration, or equal strength for about half the cement content.

Figure 32, from reference [89], illustrates the effects of densification of the cement paste in prestressed concrete by the use of a high range water-reducing admixture. The admixture was manufactured by Westvaco Inc, USA after a patent by S. Brunauer for use with gypsum-free cement (the Low Porosity Cement approach, acronym LPC). As shown, prestressed concrete beams were produced (by the precast, prestressed concrete producing company Spæncom A/S) which had the same load-bearing capacity as I-profile steel beams of approximately the same weight and height.

We achieved the same strength levels through extensive research regarding impregnation of hardened concrete with epoxy,[90] and sulphur.[91]

Figure 33, from reference [90], illustrates fracture mechanics of concrete:

105

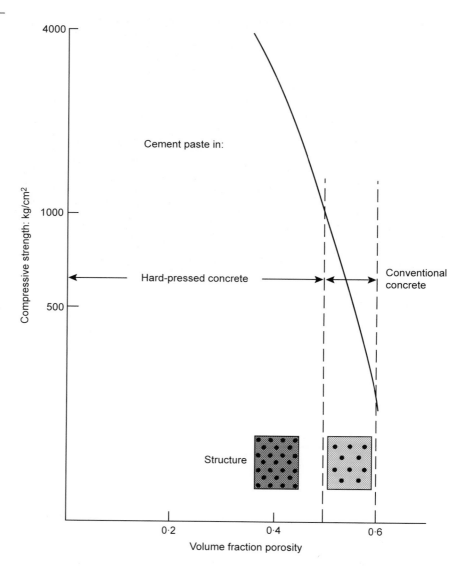

Fig. 29. *The effect of the initial
porosity of cement paste on its
compressive strength*

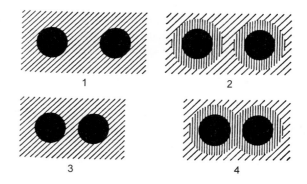

Fig. 30. *Effect of heterogeneity
of microstructure on the strength
of cement paste*

Fig. 31. The VIPRES machine for manufacture of precast elements by monitored, static pressure interacting with high frequency vibration for compaction

- ☐ with porous lightweight LECA aggregates of strength equal to the cement paste strength
- ☐ with ordinary, coarse gravel aggregates of strength which is orders of magnitude higher than the strength of cement paste, and
- ☐ of ordinary concrete with epoxy impregnation of the cement paste, which has increased its strength to equal to that of the coarse aggregates.

The figure illustrates distinctly that the rupture passes through the aggregates when the strength of the cement paste matrix equals the strength of the coarse aggregates (top and bottom), but runs along aggregate "surfaces" when the cement paste is the weakest component.

Figure 34, from reference [92], shows measurements of the rates of cement hydration plotted against the reaction temperature, as calculated in accordance with the simple temperature functions adopted by Nurse, Saul-Bergstrøm and Rastrup.[79, 80] Also shown is the rate calculated in accordance with the Arrhenius' equation. The latter invention was indispensable for the development of the maturity-based curing technology for concrete hardening at elevated temperatures. As can be seen, the cruder relationships had been satisfactory for

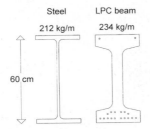

Steel
212 kg/m

LPC beam
234 kg/m

60 cm

Fig. 32. Prestressed, high-strength concrete beam produced by means of LPC to the load bearing capacity of a steel profile beam of the same height and approximate weight

107

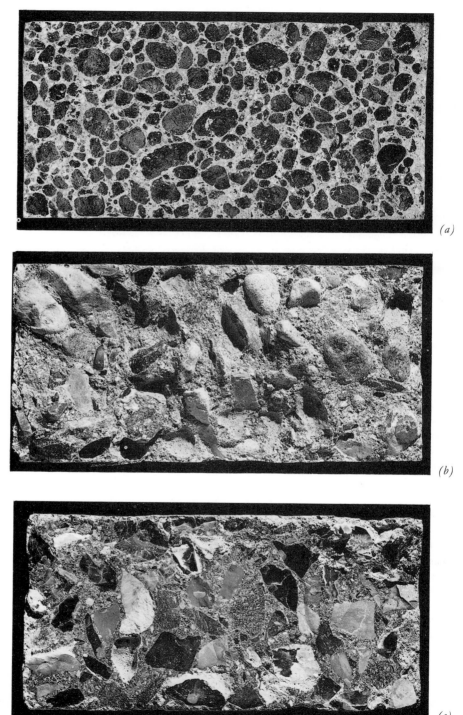

(a)

(b)

Fig. 33. Split tensile fracture
effects on concrete with (a)
weak, porous aggregate and (b)
ordinary, high strength aggregate
in ordinary cement paste, and
(c) ordinary aggregate in high
strength cement paste

(c)

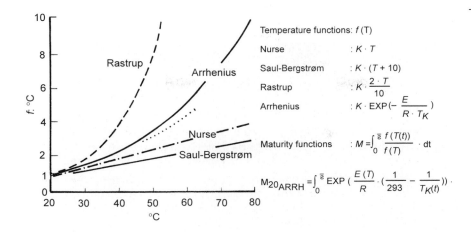

Temperature functions: $f(T)$

Nurse	$: K \cdot T$
Saul-Bergstrøm	$: K \cdot (T + 10)$
Rastrup	$: K \cdot \dfrac{2 \cdot T}{10}$
Arrhenius	$: K \cdot EXP(- \dfrac{E}{R \cdot T_K})$

Maturity functions $: M = \int_0^{\bar{z}} \dfrac{f(T(t))}{f(T)} \cdot dt$

$M_{20_{ARRH}} = \int_0^{\bar{z}} EXP\left(\dfrac{E(T)}{R} \cdot \left(\dfrac{1}{293} - \dfrac{1}{T_K(t)}\right)\right) \cdot$

Fig. 34. The original maturity functions by Nurse, Saul-Bergstrøm and Rastrup and the application of the Arrhenius' equation by P. Freiesleben-Hansen at the BFL

the winter concrete application in the 1950s, when we operated in the −5 to +40°C temperature range. As the figure confirms, we found the available maturity functions inapplicable above about +40°C.[87]

From the commencement of the BFL research, we were concerned about the rapid growth of the precast concrete industry. Its creation was a formidable engineering feat, with the new housing development as the market basis, and the accelerated plant manufacture of concrete as the new technology. To satisfy market needs demanded the introduction of three-shift plant operations. This necessitated application of steam curing of the concrete elements, and steam injection into the concrete mixers was also applied. There was no time to reflect about the rudimentary knowledge of the response of concrete to high temperature before and during its hydration. Impetuosity became an essential element of technology development in order to satisfy the Ministry of Housing's projected programmes for solutions to the housing problems.

We knew the rationale of the maturity technology concept for winter concreting, and travelling to eastern Europe and the USSR confirmed our belief that high acceleration of the hydration of cement paste in concrete should be seen as a positive progressive step, but were concerned that it might cause a deceptive appearance with hidden damage if not sustained by more than the available basic knowledge. A comprehensive search of the available literature revealed that theoretical exploration of the behaviour of concrete during steam curing was virtually non-existent.

In 1964 it became possible for us to arrange a fellowship with an engineer from Højgaard & Schultz A/S, a leading precast and construction company, for an introductory research project on accelerated hardening of concrete by steam curing.

Bache referred in reference [93] to Verbeck's original application of the Arrhenius model in reference [94]:

$$k = A \times \dfrac{-E}{RT}$$

where:

k = rate of hydration reaction;

A = a constant;

E = activation energy;

R = gas constant;

T = absolute temperature.

Verbeck's perception (which received very little response in the USA) became our indispensable guideline for the forthcoming years of intensive research in the chemistry of cement hydration at elevated temperatures.

In 1965, the precast concrete company Modulbeton A/S approached us with the problem that quality control concrete cylinders, produced and tested at the standard $+20°C$ conditions gave the requested 28-day compressive strength, whereas cylinders cored from precast wall panels cast with steam curing in vertical steel-battery forms gave far inferior strength. This experience directed our attention towards the other aspect of the steam curing technology, which the conventional specifications and test methods ignored, namely the stress situation in concrete resulting from abrupt temperature rise during the early phase of curing. The rupture deformations were studied by H. H. Bache with a fellowship student from Modulbeton A/S.[95] This was later supplemented by a fellowship study with J. Alexanderson from the Swedish Cement and Concrete Research Institute,[96] on the impact of heat curing on the contact phase between cement paste and aggregates, which became the basis for his doctoral dissertation at the Technical University at Lund, Sweden.[97]

Fig. 35. Maturity computer

Figure 35 shows the maturity computer which the BFL developed as the recording instrument for curing technology. Its introduction, with the implementation of the method, took place during a cooperative project with the two precast concrete companies Larsen & Nielsen A/S, and Højgaard & Schultz A/S.

That the new curing monitoring technology became a major innovation was due, in no small part, to P. Freiesleben Hansen's long-term persistent, theoretical and experimental studies and our implementation progress in the precast plants of the cooperative industrial companies in the early 1970s. In many ways, we were reverting to the leading principle of nineteenth century processing technology: that the vital aspect of quality control lay with the concrete itself. We eliminated the arbitrary sample testing as the primary measure of the quality of structural concrete, and replaced it by theoretical knowledge and advanced electronic recording of the dynamic course of the physico/chemical reactions which it underwent during processing.

The precast industry observed that the monitoring of the interdependent heat and strength developments made it possible to save expenses on external heating and to gain genuine assurance that the predicted strength development was attained. The construction companies and consultants learned, by implementations at major bridge projects in the 1970s, that the monitoring made it possible to manipulate heating or cooling of the fresh concrete, to determine and change insulation of formwork during the early curing phase, and to pre-calculate and check the proper times for form removals. Moreover, the risk of early thermal cracking could effectively be eliminated. The application of new, sophisticated isothermic calorimetry, X-ray diffractometry, scanning microscopy, and our

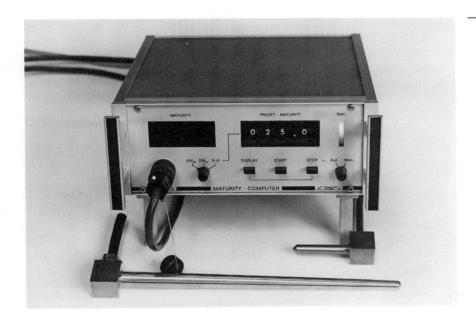

Fig. 35. Maturity computer

early investments in computerization also made it possible for Freiesleben Hansen, in a five-year programme, to investigate the influence of cement compositions and fineness on the course of heat curing, and to add systematic heat transmission calculation methods for up-scaling from the incremental features to actual concrete production circumstances. In the following years of successful implementation of the methodology, experience also revealed that site measurements of the heat of hydration development was an excellent means of controlling cement composition. Aalborg Portland responded with periodical measurements of their cements as a customer service.

The documentary basis for the curing technology was published by P. Freiesleben Hansen in 1978,[98,99] i.e. two years after the closure of the BFL. A comprehensive account of the use of the method at the construction of the Farø Bridges was presented by the Danish Road Directorate in reference [100], and supplementary presentations have appeared in references [101], [102] and elsewhere.

The resistance to acceptance of this new technology outside Denmark was a consequence of the prevailing hierarchy of concrete technology research abroad, which was institutional and more associated with gradual consensus evolution than with progressive innovation of production technology. This was compatible with the market conditions prevailing in the building and construction sectors, which did not provide any incentive for the introduction of new technology, unless specifically requested by governmental agencies for major projects. The changes therefore took place at a snail's pace, dictated by the confines of operating within the standard specification systems.

Other accomplishments

Visits to the BFL by outstanding cement and concrete research groups became, over the years, frequent and welcome breaks from the daily routine, with arranged seminars and workshops. Usually the Danish Concrete Association was invited to take advantage of the contacts we developed, arranging public lectures by our guests. Also, FLS and Aalborg Portland supported this international ingress of personal knowledge from abroad. Among the numerous guests, it is possible to mention only very few. T. C. Powers came in 1965, P. A. Rehbinder in 1967, St. Brunauer in 1975. K. and B. Mather, G. Verbeck, R. W. Nurse, W. Czernin, M. Regourd, and friends from VDZ in Düsseldorf were more frequent visitors and contacts for correspondence, and were visited by our staff members during frequent travel abroad. In addition, FLS and Aalborg Portland arranged visits to the laboratory for their contacts in order to illustrate the overall capability for technology innovation within the corporation.

Notwithstanding the emphasis of the BFL research on improvements in the technology of concrete production, concrete durability was also an important area of our research activity. I was granted periods of leave in 1961 and 1964 to complete the progress reports from the previous DNIBR/ATV research on deterioration of field concrete in Denmark, and also to prepare the doctoral dissertation: *Durability of concrete structures in Denmark*,[36] which was issued in 1967. The concurrent development of the methodology for petrography of concrete, installation of X-ray diffractometry and SEMEX with micro-probe, and the engagement and training of younger chemical engineers, encouraged us to renew the research on alkali-silica reaction. This led to a fellowship stay by Professor S. Diamond, USA, in 1972 and our arrangement of the first international conference on alkali-silica reaction in 1974.

The growing concern about the asbestos cement health issues resulted in comprehensive corporation-orientated investigations for the Dansk Eternit Fabrik, for rationalization of processing methods, especially the curing conditions, and in a search for alternative fibre materials. Alkali-resistant glass fibre was, for a while, a prominent objective of this research, and comprised cooperation projects with Pilkington Brothers Ltd, England. Our equipment, with sophisticated chemical analytical instrumentation, also caused us to be engaged, in cooperation with the FLS research group, on problem solving for the operation of new, large wet cement kilns at Aalborg Portland's Rørdal plant.

Research precursory to the later, spectacular development of concrete with silica fume and high range water reducers was commenced in 1975.

Research areas avoided at the BFL

From the outset, we decided not to pursue research which was in vogue elsewhere, but rather to become complementary to the international concrete research. This enabled us to be both receivers and suppliers of know-how in the international community. It also concurred with our need to be selective, and it motivated us to develop our own capabilities for imagination and competence.

Hence, there were several, widely popular topics in the international research community on which we did not spend many resources. The spectacular discoveries by T. C. Powers and colleagues on the physical structure of hardened cement paste had engendered complementary, modelling studies in many countries. We could not see improvements for technology in the different refinements of Powers' model, and the same applied to a wave of experimental and speculative modelling studies of the deformation characteristics, shrinkage and creep, of hardened cement paste and concrete. The development of purely vicarious empirical test methods for the properties of cement, other concrete materials, mortars and concrete, fresh and hardened, and concrete exposed to aggressive conditions, etc. was also a field of research which attracted enormous resources and interest, with powerful back-up from organizations such as RILEM, ASTM, Cembureau, the National Bureau of Standards, the US Army Corps of Engineers, etc. and the national standard specification communities. We found this kind of activity less challenging and interesting than studies of concrete as produced and used in "real life" situations, and we were not interested in tying up our limited capacity in round robin testing and committee administration. Popular undertakings, such as comparisons of cube and cylinder strength results, simply did not appeal to our intellectual ambitions.

During the early 1970s, the increasing applications of de-icing salts to concrete highway pavements and bridge decks began to take their toll on the commonly neglected areas of effective compaction and adequate curing of the concrete in the preceding decades. We hesitated to add the new field of steel corrosion chemistry to our competence, due to forthcoming constraints on the further extension of the BFL operations. And, before we could change this attitude, the closure of the laboratory took place.

The rise and fall of the BFL

With hindsight, it is useful to look at the accomplishments of the BFL vis-à-vis the expenses of establishing it and keeping it running, and the attitudes facing it in the two phases of its existence: the decade of creation, and the subsequent years as the industrial corporate R & D department of Aalborg Portland.

The decade of creation

The single-source financial basis of Aalborg Portland on behalf of its customers was the decisive factor in the freedom that the BFL enjoyed, enabling it to create its coherent architectural and pragmatic quality of concrete technology research for development in the Danish concrete producing industries. We were presented with the opportunity to learn, by trial and error and dedication, how to manage a combination of exploratory and mission-oriented creativity, or in other words, intelligent, visionary research and down to earth practicality. Consistent, extensive, financial support for the creation of such an environment of progressive technology had not previously existed for concrete development in Denmark.

The total balance sheet for this enterprise could not be made up in ordinary accounting (we tried in vain to do that a few times), but the expenses were tax exempt for the company; there was no charge to the customers for our services (or rather, there was an indirect charge incorporated in the cement price), and there was a consistent increase of cement sales with a corresponding increase of allowances for research. Consequently, everybody was happy with the arrangement. It had a flavour of the classical concept of research as an inherent element of culture, and the company gained public recognition for this policy.

113

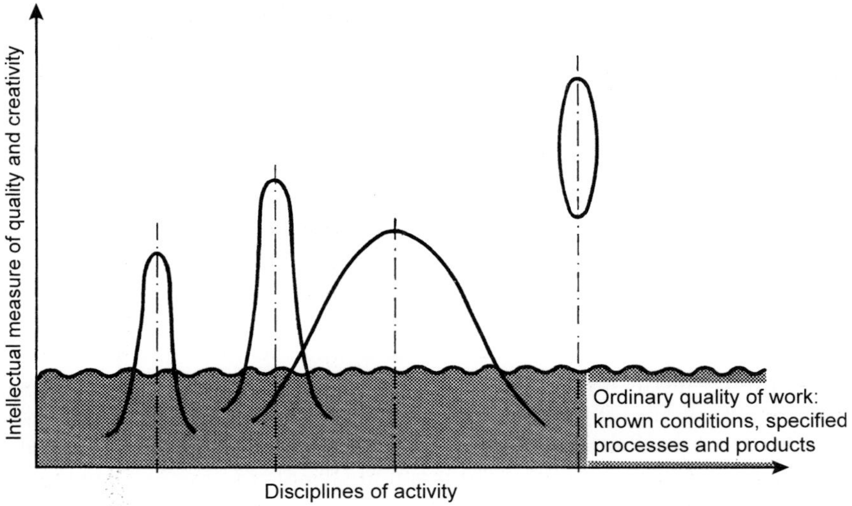

Fig. 36. Different mentalities of researchers in teamwork — beyond the solid workhorse base, innovative minds are required, and even a few of visionary brilliance

Intellectual measure of quality and creativity

Ordinary quality of work: known conditions, specified processes and products

Disciplines of activity

Adopting the industrial R & D attitude

I joined EIRMA in 1970 as the company representative, at a time when I began to feel an approaching insecurity because our responsibility ended with the communication of our laboratory accomplishments. In the typical EIRMA member companies, the products of the research departments were made for process or product development in order to maintain the competitiveness of the funding company. Contemporary literature from the USA suggested that innovations in industry relied on 80% basic research work, which was made available for the 20%, albeit much more expensive, development and construction work. I felt that we were beginning to do more and more "80% research" without seeing any "20% development" among the concrete users.

Figure 36, from reference [103] illustrates that we also had experience with a fruitful mix of research workers of different temperaments and attitudes to their work. I felt that more concise goals and interaction with industrial development were essential to ensure that the mix of employees functioned as a motivated, cross-fertilizing team. Creative research and innovative work form peaks above the ordinary quality of activity under secure conditions of work, which aim at maintaining specified processes to produce known products of predicted characteristics. The laissez-faire management style allows the creative mind to free itself from its basis of assistance and sponsorship. The analytical management approach is inclined to cut off the peaks of creativity and is likely to be satisfied with an ordinary, controllable quality of work, rather than the individualistic or team-spirited creation of new ideas for future technologies. The demand on R & D management is a "neither-nor" demand, and thus a continuous challenge to the leadership, who must steadily adjust the style of managerial operations to suit ever-changing conditions.

Personal analyses, the assistance of consultants and a general reconstruction of the rather conservative organization of the Aalborg Portland company resulted in the promotion of the BFL to the position of the company's research and development provider.

BFL as R & D department

The normal function of R & D provision in industrial companies was not effectively handed over to the BFL in the few years that it existed for that purpose. Both cement production technology and improvements of the cement types had, for more than 50 years, been in the hands of FLS and the plant managers, and the motivation for changing that practice was confined to the use of the BFL's superior analytical equipment and special knowledge on troubleshooting problems.

It was slightly easier to obtain service jobs from corporation-owned companies such as the Dansk Eternit Fabrik A/S when they admitted to having problems with elevated temperature curing. They were also in search of fibrous materials to replace asbestos, and we had contacts with producers of possible alternative fibre manufacturers in Europe and North America, and new competence in fibre reinforcement.

The most obvious segment of clients for our services were to be found among the construction and precast concrete companies who might be willing to pay for our "software" expertise along with the hardware – cement – which Aalborg Portland delivered. Despite the tradition that our service was free of charge, we did, in the years left to the BFL, carry out many pragmatic consultative service jobs besides the major R & D programmes on compaction and curing, albeit still with the company as part-investor. We also opened negotiations with industries abroad about fibre reinforcement and chemical admixtures.

Nevertheless, when the recession deepened in the course of 1975, it was clear that the BFL did not have a sustainable market for its services without substantial, basic financing from the sales of cement. It was, in other words, a torso – a beautiful one at that – but with a total, declining, annual turnover of 4 billion DKK in the Danish construction sector, and only a handful of companies exceeding 100 million DKK, the service market was practically reduced to a state of emergency. When Aalborg Portland decided to close five of its six cement plants, its board of directors, early in 1976, also decided to close the BFL, Karlstrup. The major part of the equipment and a selected half of the staff was moved to newly erected laboratory facilities in Aalborg, where the new company headquarters was built at the remaining Rørdal plant. The R & D function was confined to the service of the company's own process technology and product quality development, and to the development of new technology which could widen the field of application of cement, and thus create new markets for the company.

Closure of the BFL

A retrospective review of the reasons for the BFL closure in 1976 has merits even now, after two decades, because a similar obliteration of concrete technology research followed abroad, and an updated model for a powerful cement and concrete R & D concept to match the current challenges has not yet appeared.

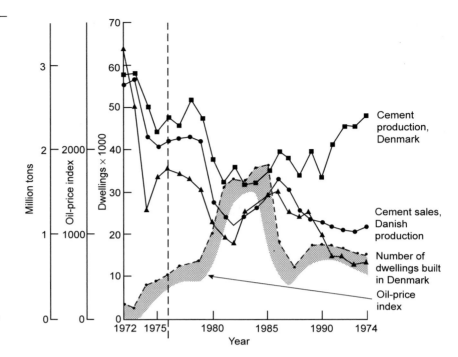

The basic reason for the closure was that the desire on the part of Aalborg Portland as a private company, and of society at large, to invest in concrete research and development, was more intimately dependent on the overall economy and its influence on building and construction than we were aware of or trained to consider at the BFL.

Figure 37, produced from various statistical sources, shows the concurrent development of Danish cement production throughout the years 1972–1994, Aalborg Portland's sales of cement in Denmark, the oil price index, and the production of housing by numbers of dwellings. (Housing production was used in Denmark as a good cement market indicator.) The dramatic collapse in 1973–74 illustrates the end of the post World War II golden decades of continuous progress, and it is evident that any conscientious corporate industrial leadership was forced to respond to such depressive prospects with drastic measures, among which the BFL, with its primary function to work for customers at no charge, was fair game. Incidentally, the subsequent longer term development of Danish cement production and consumption, which the figure illustrates, may seem to suggest that a farsighted, strategic wisdom on the part of the executive management and board of directors of the company was adopted in 1976. In reality, however, it illustrates the necessity of adapting to the inexorable realities of the general crisis in the industrialized countries.

The figure shows also that the oil price index development during the turbulent 1970s was an indirect indicator of plummeting cement production and the national sales of cement. However, during the following decade the oil price can be seen to have lost its power, and the trend of cement production versus sales suggests that national consumption has matured and the new markets are abroad.

At the BFL, all of us, including myself as the responsible director, fought intensely for the survival of the research with the assets of our accomplishments as weapons. But we could not perceive the fundamental, underlying issues, and we were not invited to assess and accept their indefeasible disregard of our dedication to the work, the personal engagements, and the exceptional team spirit which the staff had developed.

The BFL assets, as I have described them in the previous sections of this chapter, were, with our integrated, advanced knowledge of cement and concrete, well rooted both in updated theory and engineering practice. We had managed to come a long way with preparatory work on technology innovations such as:

- chemical admixtures for significant increases of the strength of cement paste and concrete
- use of GGBS, fly ash and silica fume for radical improvements of concrete
- packing and compaction of fresh concrete
- monitoring curing technology
- chemistry and mechanisms of deleterious reactions
- field concrete investigations with complementary petrography and micro-structure studies.

We had, in fact, moulded an exceptional R & D outfit with broadly acknowledged integrity and excellent interactive contacts in our homeland and abroad, and we had engendered a remarkable intellectual stimulation for concrete technology development in the national concrete industries.

The deficits, which came to outweigh the assets, encompassed aspects of our internal situation and insurmountable hurdles for our continuation in our outreach policies.

- We had consistently been trained to disseminate our knowledge free of charge, or, in the last few years for direct cost compensations, but never with the aim of existing and growing by annual profit making.
- Hence we had no marketing experience, no patents or licensing, and no in-built capacity to operate as a commercial R & D enterprise.
- The cement company ownership meant that the assets for the shareholders, customer service by free provision of supporting knowledge on the use of cement, could easily be seen as an expense which could be spared when the cement sales faltered.
- There were no Danish concrete engineering firms with strategy or capacity for substantial purchases at market price of research products for their own further development. In contrast, the threatening duration of the recession made them seek a form of commercial hibernation, for survival at minimum cost levels. The corporate FLS companies reacted in much the same way, and their residual, local development staffs became reluctant to purchase BFL services.
- The BFL had, by its nature, no standard as a public service institute, and no preconditions for operating in accordance with rules and regulations for that kind of service.

It was paradoxical that, while all concerned seemed to regret the termination of the BFL era, no one mobilized resources to prevent it; hence it happened.

The 1975–76 operating expenses of the laboratory were about 6 million DKK, or less than 0.2% of the cement and concrete contributions to the national economy. Consequently, the fall of the executioner's axe was not really providing an economy, but expressing the general attitude in the industry and society that drastic cost cuttings were the safest defence against the depressive trends in the national and global economies.

In my opinion, at the time it happened and until this day, the primary loss resulting from the closure of the BFL was the disappearance of a concentrated power centre for interactive cement and concrete R & D, which could support the international competitiveness of the national industries. This has, perhaps, been more visible in the long term, and especially in later years, when opportunities became associated with ever-tougher competition.

The productivity of the research

There were special reasons for the widely recognized, high productivity of the concrete research at the BFL, and for its remarkable ability to respond to the challenge of the changing situation in the wake of its transition in 1972 to become the company's R & D function.

One important advantage was the fact that we started from scratch in 1960. The buildings were new and designed for extension; there was no established staff with attitudes and programmes to renovate, and no outdated equipment. The economy made it possible, after the initial purchase of basic equipment, to continue with additions as needs and capabilities arose. And our sixteen years coincided with the tremendous, industrial commercialization of new, sophisticated analytical and testing instrumentation. Successively, that supplied us with flame-photometry, isotropic microcalorimetry, X-ray diffractometry, DTA, SEM with EDX, Instron testing machine, electrodynamic vibration machine, etc. Our staff of technicians qualified themselves to follow up these investments with in-house construction of all the required kinds of monitoring devices for project services; we were early pioneers of computer-aided data processing and documentation, minimizing administration and consistently updating the secretarial services.

Keeping the average age of the staff low by annually increasing staffing levels with the recruitment of two to three young persons, made the steady procurement of new equipment productive, because we unhesitatingly invested in relevant training, including extended stays abroad for researchers, and made fellowship grants for selected, foreign colleagues.

But there was also the mental factor to consider. The staff created a daily working atmosphere which stimulated cross-fertilization of ideas, and sufficient credit was given to productive performance to create satisfaction and dedication throughout the house. There were abundant opportunities for talented individuals to pursue personal ideas within the strategic framework of our policy, and that engendered, often serendipitous, coalitions (and some candid confrontations) which added value to cooperation and project outputs.

Thirty kilometres north-east of Karlstrup, at the company headquarters, there was a decisive leadership commitment in support of our research policy and work, until a new board of directors in 1975 terminated it. The late Mr. B. Nissen, the managing director over most of the years, always communicated his anxiety that we should accomplish results of true and visible value for the cement users and maintain unquestioned integrity. The late Mr. J. K. Rasmusen, CEng, who was technical vice president in 1960 and CEO for 1972–75, was a consistent and ardent fighter for the development of our research. He appreciated and made much use of the promotional effects of the research, both in the domestic market and among cement companies abroad, and he shared our belief in the short- and long-term benefits of our achievements for the Danish cement users. It was also his initiative to bring us into contact with EIRMA and use that contact for the application of professional R & D planning and management. His perception of an overall strategy for the cement industry helped, in many ways, the crew of young people, haphazardly compiled in 1960, to grow up to become the internationally acknowledged core of concrete technology research in Denmark by the time of the closure in 1976. Inevitably, the sudden loss of this powerful resource proved to have severe consequences for the subsequent, national concrete research and its position in international, interactive work for technology progress.

Denmark after 1976

Representatives of the construction and consultant engineers' professions had approached Aalborg Portland in the early spring of 1976 with appeals for the continuation of the BFL, but without offering means for alternative financing and, therefore, to no avail. Actually, the building and construction sector was labouring under the same depression as the cement industry in the wake of the oil crisis, with overcapacity within the building industries, and changes of the capital suppliers' investment priorities.

Twenty-two of the BFL staff of research workers and technicians were offered transfer to the Cement and Concrete Laboratory (CBL) at the remaining cement plant, Rørdal. A few others were transferred within the F. L. Smidth & Co. corporation. I was given a temporary position as manager of development projects which were transferred from the BFL programme.

The external, professional community in Denmark regretted the disbandment of the BFL, although there were voices from public concrete research who claimed that "the advantage of the closure is the transfer of research workers, individually, to different other institutes". Since no compensating funding appeared in the wake of these transfers, it was – and is – difficult to see the wisdom of such a research management judgement. But, worse than that, the serious consequences in the longer term of the disappearance from the scene of BFL's holistic architecture of cement and concrete R & D was generally unnoticed.

The concept we had developed, of the interaction of different disciplines of research and of the interdependence of R & D was unique in concrete research at the time, notwithstanding that it was the universal system for R & D management in manufacturing industries. We had won considerable recognition abroad for our adaptation of this management approach. But the subsequent events showed that this was regarded as an entertaining, intellectual achievement, not as an avenue to be followed in concrete research elsewhere.

H. H. Bache continued at CBL, with his rare combination of thorough knowledge of surface chemistry, compaction theory, fracture mechanics and mathematics, to develop high strength concrete by combined use of silica fume and high-range water reducers as the physico/chemical means of super-compaction of fresh concrete. The first of several publications on the Densit approach appeared in 1981.[104] By application of fibre reinforcement, H. H. Bache subsequently invented the new ultra-strong and extremely resistant type of reinforced concrete, CRC.[105] Concurrently, the CBL also embarked on programmes for improvements of concrete highway pavement construction methods.

P. Freiesleben Hansen completed, at the Beton Konstruktions Institut (BKI) in 1978, the publication of the two first books on monitoring curing technology based upon the maturity concept, which he had managed at the BFL.[98, 99] With subsequent public funding, the curing planning and quality control system was transferred to a computer program, which the institute made commercially available.

Aalborg Portland sponsored the preparation and publication of *Betonbogen* in 1979.[106] It was a 719 page textbook for concrete engineering education and design and construction practice, and represented a thorough updating of all aspects of the state-of-the-art knowledge about concrete technology. The research accomplishments from the former BFL and the holistic philosophy of its research and development activity were incorporated in the book, the first of its kind since Professor E. Suenson's famous *Jærnbeton* in 1933.

Aalborg Portland responded to the increasing awareness in engineering practice of the need to monitor the heat/strength development during concrete curing by providing information on request about the adiabatic heat of hydration of its different cement types. From 1983, the characteristic heat of hydration curves corresponding to the maturity (20°C) time were published annually in the CtO technical service publication series *Beton-Teknik*.

The Knud Højgaard Foundation financed, from 1978, a new Danish Concrete Institute (DABI) with the objective of establishing a system of postgraduate training courses in concrete structural design and technology for civil engineers.

The contemporary national (and international) recessions caused deferment of public and private building and construction projects. In Denmark, however, the Road Directorate became a conspicuous investor in a considerable development of the Danish highway infrastructure, with the major bridge projects:

- the Sallingsund Bridge: 1973–1978
- the Vejlefjord Bridge: 1975–1978
- the Alssund Bridge: 1979–1981[107]
- the Farø Bridges: 1980–1985[100]
- the Guldborgsund Tunnel: 1983–1987[108]

which, in many respects, were precursory to:

- the Great Belt Link: 1988–1998
- the Øresund Link: 1995–2000.

At the Sallingsund Bridge, P. Freiesleben Hansen had been engaged on behalf of the BFL to apply our curing technology as a remedial measure to prevent thermal cracking of the precast, prestressed box-girder elements during early curing.

At the Vejlefjord Bridge, the curing technology method was applied to assess the reason for cracking in large concrete foundation blocks during early curing, and as a control means when cement with blast-furnace slag was introduced to prevent the thermal cracking.

At the Alssund Bridge, the curing technology system was applied as specified means in the site quality control to eliminate the risk of thermal cracking during the early phase of the concrete curing.

At the Farø Bridges, the curing technology system was specified as obligatory for the contractor in the planning and execution of all concrete production. The tendering companies were requested to present calculated estimates of the maturity development during early curing of all concreting operations, with assurance that the temperature difference between the interior of any element and its surfaces would not exceed $+20°C$ and the peak curing temperature $+60°C$. During subsequent concrete production, compliance with these requirements was checked by the contractor's quality control officers and the resident engineer.

The Road Directorate, under the Danish Ministry of Transport, had actually sponsored several applied research projects into concrete technology, concurrent with the gradual implementation of curing technology and other adjustments of the specifications for the major bridge projects. Our classical rating system from the 1950s for the performance of field concrete was updated and incorporated in a "highway bridge inspection and management programme". Smaller bridge projects were selected for experimental field-scale utilization of concrete with fly ash and with silica fume, and studies of the structural implications of harmful alkali-silica reation in prestressed and ordinary reinforced concrete beams were carried out. The Directorate formed ad hoc project groups with consulting firms as project managers for this kind of sponsored research, and published the documentary reports.

In many ways, the research application efforts of the Road Directorate helped to draw a veil over the fact that a dense undergrowth of less conscientious concrete engineering and construction practice had prevailed throughout the decades of intensive development of concrete research, first at DNIBR and thereafter at the BFL. In the late 1970s, rapidly spreading recognition of severe damage to post World War II buildings and structures caught the attention of the public media. Extensive renovation works, especially for precast multi-storey apartment buildings, and advanced corrosion of concrete bridges, apparently enhanced by the abundant use of de-icing salts, brought Danish concrete into the broader picture of the "durability crisis". This contributed to the populist view of concrete as a "bad" medium, and fuelled the growing trend towards adversarial attitudes to the architectural style of the precast concrete standard element buildings.

The compromising aspects of the positive response by the engineering and architectural professions to the political demands for reconstruction and renovation of the building technology and techniques after the war now became apparent. Much design had actually been full-scale experimental solutions of the social problem with revolutionary improvements in housing installations and aesthetics.

It was evident that the demands had engendered overly ambitious production

Table 12. *Distribution of funding by the Danish Government 1982–1988 for research and publication aiming at improvement of the durability of concrete*

Operating category	DKK · 1000	%
Administration		
Public agencies	2170	11
ATV	2630	13
Consulting civil engineers (three selected firms)	1550	8
ATV R & D institutes	3640	19
Public research		
Building research	340	<2
Technological Institute	7940	40
Technical University	500	3
Educational courses	820	4
	19 590	100

schemes with competition focusing on capacity instead of quality. The absence of updated standard specifications (post-war editions were not available until 1974) and the neglect of testing as a means of quality control were among the reasons. But other contributory factors were the innovative development of higher yielding cement *per se*, and that the creation of precast technology with steam curing had been prematurely pushed ahead, while the BFL did not present its adaptable curing monitoring technology until shortly before its closure in 1976. In the highway sector, the abundant applications of de-icing salts had helped to advance corrosion. Similarly, the use of salt water in the many new public swimming pools played havoc with the saturation-exposed concrete in these constantly warm and humid structures.

The Academy of Technical Science (ATV) and several government departments were alerted to the gravity of the situation. ATV managed, in 1981, to coordinate the first major, public investment in concrete technology development since the 1950s, with a total allotment of 19.590 million DKK. The objective was to restore the traditional performance quality of field concrete with emphasis on the conspicuous, early degradation of the precast concrete in the housing sector.

Table 12 shows the distribution of funding for projects in the programme. 850 000 DKK from the Technical Scientific Research Council were additionally alloted for specific research projects on chloride-infected corrosion of reinforcement, and on alkali-silica reaction. A total of 24% of the budget was spent on administration. It is remarkable that the Technical University received only 3% of the total. (This was for one single project on chemical shrinkage in alkali-silica reaction.) The civil engineering departments of the university specializing in structural design and materials technology were not involved at all.

The programme administration issued 64 study reports in the period 1981–87. They comprised, predominantly, summation and updating of available knowledge from case studies of damage to concrete buildings and guidance for repair and maintenance work.

There was no new scientific information. Cooperation was established with a contemporary CEB-RILEM working group for concrete durability studies, with emphasis on chloride-infected corrosion of reinforcement. This was at the time the "hot topic" in concrete research all over the world and therefore the subject of considerable repetitive studies to which the Danish programme added but little original work.

The primary return on the 19.590 million DKK investment came when the *Basic concrete specification for building structures* (BSC),[109] was issued in 1988 by the governmental National Building Agency. This publication was imposed as the new standard concrete specification for all public building projects and was subsequently also accepted in many larger private building enterprises. It was, above all, an updating of many long neglected requirements for the making of quality concrete. It also contained much needed clarification for the proper use of the newer types of Portland cement, fly ash, silica fume and chemical admixtures. It aimed at decisive descriptions of "how the existing concrete technology is used in the best way". In other words, the 19.6 million DKK expenditure had not accomplished the creation of any innovative concrete progress. There was nothing left of the BFL philosophy and research strategy, and there was an unfortunate return to general reliance on empirical standard test methods, with the accompanying neglect of the incompatibility of laboratory models and field concrete performance. This regression to the neglect of concrete technology and research which prevailed abroad, buried the residual sharpness and progressiveness of the acknowledged Danish concrete philosophy. It also illustrated the serious effects of the disappearance of the BFL.

The BSC adopted the curing technology from the BFL epoch with requirements for peak curing temperature and maximum temperature differences between interior and surfaces of concrete elements in construction. It also introduced thin section microscopy for quantitative quality control testing of:

- the microstructure and air void systems in hardened concrete (on drilled cores)
- the mineralogical composition of sand.

These new elements of quality control in all public and many private concrete construction jobs launched a wave of investment in the corresponding laboratory techniques by consulting engineering firms. The special services became a market objective during pre-construction structural design, as site quality control, for investigations of damaged field concrete in relation to repair projects, and in litigation which followed in the wake of public concern over the many cases of premature depreciation of concrete buildings.

There was no concern about the limited scientific basis for the application of these undertakings. The need to ensure compliance of new technology with continuous updating of scientific background knowledge had apparently disappeared with the closure of the BFL.

This was also illustrated in the attitude toward alkali-silica reaction (ASR). The 6th International Conference on Alkali-Aggregate Reaction (ICAAR) was held at the Technical University in 1983 with considerable new explanatory information about the preventive effects on the reaction of additions of fly ash, GGBS and silica fume. Nevertheless, the BSC presented the preventive means in such terms that "triple prevention" of harmful ASR became a common feature in subsequent Danish concrete specifications by requesting simultaneous use of:

☐ low-alkali cement

☐ fly ash and/or silica fume

☐ non-reactive aggregates.

This was a radical change from the previous "low risk policy", and unfortunately relied on empirical sample testing control together with a crude characterization of the environmental exposure conditions. These were categorized as:

☐ passive

☐ moderate

☐ aggressive

failing to realize that even the most severe marine environment in Denmark (on the west coast of Jutland) is benign compared both with colder and warmer environments elsewhere. The new trend also caused low C_3A cement to be used in marine concrete everywhere, despite the moderate to low sulphate contents in the sea water in our interior seas, estuaries, etc., and disregarded the general international experience that quality concrete even with high C_3A is highly resistant to chemical attack in sea water. It also overlooked the fact that experience abroad classified low C_3A cements as engendering higher porosity of cement paste than ordinary Portland cement and lower capacity to bind ingressing chloride ions.

Maybe the most damaging, long-term effect of the programme management attitudes was the neglect of involvement of and requests for accompanying, new scientific research at the Technical University. The engineering professions were therefore forced to place ultimate confidence in the pragmatic and fragmentarily updated state of knowledge which the programme had achieved. No voice was raised for renewal of the university education programmes in cement and concrete technology, or for the supplementary student training programmes in industrial research which the BFL had introduced.

The final issuing of the BSC which terminated the research programme therefore left further concrete technology research more fragmented and more reliant on limited, piecemeal, troubleshooting funding than in any previous epoch. Concurrently, the public research institutes belonging to the different ministerial departments entered a period of considerable growth, but nowhere with effective, strategic concrete research programmes. The Building Research Institute (SBI) for instance, reported in 1988,[110] that with a staff of about 120 professional research workers, 24 technicians, and 60 secretaries it had no work on concrete in progress at all. The SBI 1994 annual report,[111] shows that with a staff of 103 professionals and technicians and 31 secretaries the institute had still no research in progress regarding concrete technology and construction.

The increasing ignorance of concrete at this and other public and semi-public research institutes for building and construction meant that public administration and legislators became isolated from any new trends of potential technical developments in concrete for the advance of employment capacity and international competitiveness of industry and consulting engineering.

ALKALI-SILICA REACTION

Alkali-silica reaction (ASR) has been the subject of substantial research investment in many countries all over the world for more than half a century. The long-term programmes in the USA, Australia, England and Denmark in the wake of its discovery in California in 1940, were scholarly examples of effective science—engineering interaction and international complementarity between a few research groups and independent institutes of high integrity. The cement and concrete professions in those days were accustomed to such high-level international cooperation which, for example within the fields of cement chemistry and cement hydration, had proved profitable to all parties involved since the nineteenth century.

The knowledge acquired via the research from 1940–1960 showed, incontrovertibly, that alkali-silica reaction might occur in many parts of the world in field concrete made with commonly occurring aggregates and ordinary Portland cement, and that suitable means for prevention of damaging reactivity were available.

During the general concrete construction and building boom in the 1950s and 1960s, the risk of wider occurrence of the reaction was inadvertently or deliberately neglected. But, from the early 1970s the situation changed, and gradually since then the reaction has been pinpointed as a threat to concrete durability in country after country, in all continents. Meanwhile, concrete technology research declined, with loss of authority and funding resources, due to changed social and commercial priorities. Hence, despite the fruitful growth of new international exchanges in the alkali-silica reaction research after about 1970, there has been no leadership to create a common strategy for the research and transfer of information to match the global uniformity of the issues. The results have been less conceptual research with disregard of reliable modelling of modern concrete materials, production and performance circumstances, and exaggerated emphasis on the development of empirical laboratory test methods in many of the countries concerned. Increasingly, duplication of programmes and reinvention of previously discovered knowledge has also been prevalent. Nevertheless, despite the lack of a single-entity management of the second phase of international research investments, substantial advances in the knowledge of ASR have been achieved. This is available in the total bulk of published information from the ten international conferences since 1974.

The present, and foreseeable, pressure on all the resources of concrete construction is now motivating a high-level scrutiny of how the accumulated knowledge from research and engineering experience can be pooled into internationally acknowledged guidelines for dealing not only with the harmful, but also the harmless and beneficial modifications of alkali-silica reaction.

Introduction and history

The story of alkali-silica reaction (ASR) in concrete commenced with the discovery in California in 1940 of this chemical reaction as the cause of cracking in a concrete highway pavement.[112] Now, after more than half a century, the original deleterious reaction in the opaline particles in the sand fraction of that pavement has "germinated", to such an extent that it now occurs in all the continents of the world except, as far as we know, in the Arctic and Antarctic. Many different siliceous rock types are now recognized as potentially reactive in coarse and fine aggregates. Denmark has figured in the story since the early 1950s, and I have been involved, in one way or another, since that time, at least sufficiently to review it now and propose a strategy for the eventual elimination of this cause of damage in concrete as a problem in engineering practice.

Scientific knowledge and methodology in chemistry, geology and mineralogy had an exceptional impact during the early days in this field of concrete research. In later years, the scientific achievements have been forced to submit to simplistic empiricism in the transfer to engineering design and construction. During the first twenty years, the occurrence of harmful ASR in field concrete was only recognized in two countries, the USA first and then Denmark, as a serious, national problem. Common use of alkali-reactive aggregates made major research institutes in two other countries, Australia and England, concerned enough to embark upon exploratory programmes for assessment of their risk situations and optional preventive means. Under the circumstances, the research in the four countries became very complementary. Free exchange and cooperation developed a high degree of mutuality, and the merits of this situation became obvious, when applicable solutions emerged in the course of the 1950s in each of the countries. With hindsight, I still consider the total investments of ASR research in the four countries to be an excellent yardstick for effective international concrete research. One may, therefore, also wonder why research, engineering and industry in all other countries, with free access to the research accomplishments, chose, from 1960, to consider the occurrence of alkali-silica reaction as being confined to two such different regions as the mighty USA in the new world and only tiny Denmark in Europe. But that is what they did. A dormant period followed until the early 1970s, after which harmful ASR gradually, and in some areas after considerable delay, was admitted to be a global affair. I describe this later development based primarily on the information in the proceedings of the ten International Conferences on Alkali-Aggregate

Reaction (ICAAR), in the arrangement and contents of which I have been closely involved. I consider a great deal of the 1940–60 accomplishments still to be indispensable for the basic understanding of the nature of ASR.

The course of research accomplishments has been far from a straightforward succession of accumulated scientific knowledge, in correspondence with a progression of knowledge transfer for concrete making. The common feature in the 1940–60 phase was outstanding research and international research cooperation, combined with fruitful interaction with industry and engineering. But in later years there have been equally remarkable periods of reluctance within the industry and the research hierarchies to accept the existence, or limitations, of the problems. Real or assumed conflicts between short-term and long-term economic or general interests have interfered, and fragmentary research policies have appeared in the wake of the broader recognition of the problem.

One may, therefore, roughly divide the almost 60-year story of ASR research into two major chapters, as mentioned above. The 1940–1960 period contained the long-term programmes in the USA, Australia, England and Denmark. In the USA and Denmark, the explanatory field and laboratory investigations worked towards establishing sufficient knowledge to adopt suitable preventive measures; and this was accomplished. In Australia, the research worked for the advance of scientific and empiric knowledge about the nature of the reaction, and this was accomplished outstandingly. In England, with flint gravel being a common concrete aggregate, the research confirmed the field experience that ASR did not represent a risk for damage to field concrete. This also represented a satisfactory output of the studies. It was an important asset for the research in this period that the international exchange was very open-minded and cooperative, and the programmes in the USA and Denmark enjoyed substantial public and cement industry efforts and sponsorships. In Australia, the public CSIRO and in England the BRS, i.e. public research institutes, were in charge, albeit with the National Cement Association as sponsor of the Australian programme.

The 1960–1970 decade was a period of tremendous development of concrete building and construction capacity and technology in the industrial parts of the world. The compositions and the fineness of cement properties were dramatically developed to give higher and earlier strength. This opened up the way for refinements of structural design, rationalization of concrete construction methods, and introduction of precast concrete with accelerated concrete processing. Concrete research followed suit, with high priority given to the mechanical properties of concrete such as strength, shrinkage and creep, and to concrete testing methods related to quality control. The development of laboratory facilities and equipment confined much more of the researchers' time to laboratory work than before. All over the world, research on concrete durability in general, and on ASR in particular, fell into a rather dormant situation. The bare mention of deterioration risks became unpopular, especially in marketing departments in the European cement industries.

The period after 1970 therefore represents a new, second phase of the research into ASR in concrete. The recognition of the reaction as a cause of cracking in both new and older concrete structures in one country after another, made the problem a global matter of expenses on research, structural repair, preventive

measures, and also, in some places, litigation. There are, therefore, still requirements for realistic solutions to the problems, especially in those regions of the
world where major building and construction investments are forthcoming.

The phase-two research originated dramatically with the reluctant German
admission, in 1969, that harmful ASR was the cause of severe cracking in the
prestressed Lachswehrbrücke in Lübeck, northern Germany, already taking
place within the period of construction. The case apparently took the authorities,
industries, and the German research community by surprise, since all concerned
in Europe – outside Denmark – had felt relieved until then, assuming that only
Denmark, using special, opaline modifications of flint, was subject to this
problem outside North America.

The Lachswehrbrücke broke the ice for commencement of the broader recognition of ASR as a matter to be taken seriously. The series of special international
conferences on ASR – later expanded to cover alkali-carbonate reaction (ACR) as
well and designated by the acronym ICAAR – were launched in Køge,
Denmark, in 1974.[113] This first meeting gathered 22 invited colleagues from
USA, Germany, Iceland, England and Denmark, comprising those known to
be engaged at that time in research into ASR and concerned about its consequences. The meeting appeared to be well timed. In the following years, ASR
was made "infamous" by tabloid newspapers and TV in some countries as the
cause of damage even to relatively young structures. ASR even came to be
described as a structural collapse risk, and in the UK the media invented the
condescending term "concrete cancer" for ASR.

Table 13 shows how the recognition of ASR as a serious international problem
spread, and caused the ICAAR meetings to continue and expand over the years
with the 9th held in London in 1992 and the 10th in Melbourne, Australia, in
1996. Remarkable absentees from the conferences, even in 1996, are Spain,
Greece, Finland, the CIS countries, Mexico, Central and much of South America
and the South-East Asia archipelago. The preventive means for eliminating
cracking due to ASR in field concrete, which resulted from the research in the

Table 13. Recognition of ASR in different countries as reported at the ten International Conferences on
Alkali-Aggregate Reaction, 1974–96

ICAAR			
No.	Year	Host country	Countries presenting research
1.	1974	Denmark	USA, England, Iceland, Germany, Denmark
2.	1975	Iceland	+ Canada, New Zealand, Turkey, Australia
3.	1976	England	+ S. Africa, Yugoslavia, Cyprus, Iraq
4.	1978	USA	No new countries
5.	1981	South Africa	+ Sweden
6.	1983	Denmark	+ Italy, Japan, China, Zambia
7.	1986	Canada	+ Brazil, India, Poland, Argentina
8.	1989	Japan	+ Norway, France, Belgium, Taiwan
9.	1992	England	+ Sudan, East Germany, Egypt, Ireland
10.	1996	Australia	+ Portugal, Romania, Israel, Hong Kong, South Korea

USA from 1940 to the mid-1950s and a decade later in Denmark, had been in reasonable accordance with the conditions in the two countries at the time. The ASR research and development since the mid-1970s in many more countries has yet to realize that many conditions which influence the performance of field concrete have changed profoundly since that earlier period.

The first international state-of-the-art review of ASR was presented at the 4th International Symposium on the Chemistry of Cement, Washington DC, 1960. [114] It reviewed experience with harmful and harmless ASR in field concrete, the acquired knowledge on the physico/chemical nature and mechanical effects of ASR in concrete, and the regulatory means and adopted testing methods. Its presentation was accompanied by vigorous discussions, in particular among American researchers with conflicting views regarding the chemistry of the reaction. It was a new field for application of chemistry in studies of field concrete, with communication problems arising between the research workers, because neither pure stoichiometry nor colloidal chemistry sufficed on their own to explain what one could see was happening. The preventive effects of pozzolans were explained by the new theory on the chemistry of the reaction, Powers and Steinour.[115, 116] A few cases were reported about ASR in dam concrete in Sweden, where phyllite was suggested to be the possible reactive aggregate, and American papers about the alkali-carbonate reaction (ACR) were presented.

The proceedings of the 2–10th ICAAR represent successive state-of-the-art reviews from 1975 to 1996 of the development of knowledge about ASR and ACR – now often jointly designated alkali-aggregate reaction (AAR). The independence of sponsoring organizations has meant that these conferences have not included updating consensus state-of-the-art reviews. Personal reviews have occasionally appeared as individual studies, and a few comprehensive books[36, 117, 118, 119] and special review articles in magazines and conference proceedings have also appeared.

The 1940–60 accumulated knowledge

The general report on "Chemical reactions involving aggregate"[114] at the 4th International Symposium on the Chemistry of Cement was presented by N. M. Plum, Director at the Danish National Building Research Institute, on behalf of the Danish team of researchers on ASR. We emphasized the experience with the occurrence and features of ASR in field concrete, with reference to published records from the USA and Denmark. Our review of theoretical research on the nature of ASR and of the development of laboratory testing methods referred to the Australian, American, English and Danish studies. In retrospect, this 1960 state-of-the-art knowledge still is the indispensable basis for a renewed updating. It is therefore summarized in the following section.

Harmful versus harmless ASR in field concrete

The records from the USA and Denmark suggested that structures with ASR as a cause of cracking, in other words with harmful reaction, were always found among others with no cracking, in other words a harmless mode of the reaction. There was even mention of a case of a "mild", beneficial modification of ASR in the USA.[120] The common occurrence of harmless reaction was substantiated by the research in England, where no cases of harmful reaction were found, despite the general use of reactive chert as aggregate and cement of medium to high alkali content. In Australia, there were reactive, sedimentary, siliceous and volcanic rock types in common use as aggregates,[121] also without any reported cases of harmful ASR. The Danish investigations had shown that cases of harmful reaction were in the minority in the populations of structures investigated, despite the overall use of typical Danish aggregates containing the reactive types of flint (generally designated chert in American terminology).[114]

Previous occurrences of undetected harmful ASR – and preventive means

The American literature mentioned that, since the 1920s, California had been plagued by unexplained deterioration of concrete structures about which T. E. Stanton said: *"In general, the number of opinions expressed equalled the number of reports made."*[112] His identification of ASR as a common cause was therefore a landmark achievement. In Denmark, ASR had actually occurred in coastal concrete structures on the west coast of Jutland since the late decades of the nineteenth century.[21] The typically observed map-cracking had, however, in accordance with the contemporary European conviction, been diagnosed as caused by chemical sea water attack, which was believed to cause the cracking by expansive ettringite crystallization. The Danish 1950s investigation, with access to the new American research and to thin section concrete petrography, clarified that the primary cause of deterioration in the older coastal concrete was actually harmful ASR, while the formation of ettringite was an accompanying consequence, not a cause of the deterioration. This implied, incidentally, that the pozzolanic material in the moler cement, not only was an effective preventive means against harmful ASR, but was actually the material which changed the reaction to a beneficial ASR modification. In accordance with the Powers and Steinour's work, this observation actually established that pozzolanic reactions are primarily alkali-silica reaction, in contrast to the classical theory of pozzolanic reaction as primarily being with calcium hydroxide. Time has since shown that this latter, classical perception has been so widely authorized that it is still difficult to change!

The observations in the USA and Denmark that ASR had occurred in concrete structures many years before they were diagnosed as suffering from this kind of distress, also implied that ASR might actually occur undetected in many other countries. But even such an obvious inference eluded wider recognition for a long span of years after the symposium in 1960.

Structural safety

The American and Danish investigations of harmful ASR in field concrete did not cause any concern about possible structural collapse risks as a consequence of the development of cracking in affected concrete. It was observed that visible cracks in the surfaces of concrete affected by ASR only reached "a short distance into the concrete".[122] American reports did, however, caution that cross-sections of ASR-affected concrete members would be weakened by the cracking

131

which originated in reacting aggregate particles, and that resistance to weathering of affected structures would diminish in the course of the development of surface cracking. Generally, the available information suggested that harmful ASR in field concrete should be considered to engender long-term, gradually developing surface cracking with distress incorporating weathering at severe exposure.

Geologists and mineralogists in concrete research

It was an important added value to the early ASR research that geologists and mineralogists gained due appreciation in the field of concrete research. For our colleagues with these backgrounds, a concrete structure in need of damage diagnosis was, in principle, comparable with a mountain or a plain in need of a geological investigation. Its visual features should therefore be carefully mapped, and should be interpreted as far as possible, by cross-reference to similar known and explained features elsewhere. Where insufficient information could be gathered by these means, the collection of hewn or drilled sample specimens (cores) was comparable with the geologists' samples from solid rocks, quarries or gravel/sand pits. The concrete samples were used for detailed assessments of properties, compositions and special features of the field concrete: first by visual assessment, next by microscopy, and possibly also by chemical analyses, etc. Petrographic methodology was therefore introduced as an aid to diagnosing investigations of concrete in distress. This new application of petrography gained its powerful position because the geological/mineralogical concept included the "return interpretation", back to the field behaviour, when the step by step examination, from the field concrete phenomena to the microscopic features, laboratory experimental research and creative speculative efforts, had been procured. Several American investigations, such as those by H. S. Meissner,[123] D. McConnell et al.,[124] B. Mather,[125, 126] K. Mather[127] and L. S. Brown[128] became tutorial textbooks for all new researchers working with ASR.

Climatic exposure

The American research had harmful ASR in field concrete on record in the different ranges of climatic exposure conditions in the 49 States. There were conditions which combined ASR with sea water attack and with freezing/thawing, and others, inland, combining very hot, humid summers and cold winters with heavy snowfall. There were also excessively dry, arid regions with hot days alternating with cold nights, meaning cyclic surface drying and water condensation, and there were all seasons, warm to hot environments, with and without marine exposure. Most affected structures were highway concrete pavements and bridges, dams, and marine structures; these were all of low-stress structural design, which is why corrosion of reinforcement had not caused sufficient concern to appear in the studies.

Table 14 from reference [114] shows that the Danish investigations, covering examinations of several hundred structures, had found distinctly more cases of cracking due to ASR in coastal environments than inland, even within our benign, northern-temperate environment. The Danish investigations also implied that "interior", dry concrete, such as slabs and walls in buildings, did not develop

Table 14. *Classification of condition of 431 concrete structures in Denmark, based on the survey inspections 1953–55, showing behaviour of structure against exposure conditions*

Extent of deterioration	Classification: %			
	Inland, no water	Inland, water	Coastal	Total
0	23	35	17	26
1	31	37	7	30
2	15	12	20	15
3	14	12	17	14
4	14	3	17	11
5	3	1	22	4
Total	100	100	100	100
Distribution according to classification	62	28	10	100

harmful ASR. The correlation of the intensity of ASR in field concrete and the climatic exposure conditions had been found by the introduction of a rating system with grades 0 to 5 as symbols of the extents of visual evidence of ASR at inspected structures.

The potential effects of different exposure conditions were not explicitly included in the basic studies of the nature of ASR in the USA. Maybe this was due to the predominance of the American school of theoretical research, which regarded freezing/thawing as the primary cause of problems in the USA. Implicitly, the effects of temperature, i.e. heat, on ASR were recognized by the application of elevated temperatures in experimental research with mortar bars in the USA and Australia. And heating was deliberately used in the ASTM C289 rapid chemical test to accelerate the test. It was not discussed in published studies that ASR, in principle a hydration reaction, must follow the Arrhenius law regarding the relationship between temperatures and rates of the reaction. With hindsight, this characterizes the absence of an overall scientific, holistic basis in the contemporary concrete research, because G. Verbeck had actually referred to the application of Arrhenius' law in studies of cement hydration at the symposium in 1960,[94] where the ASR review paper was also presented.

Cracking and expansion

Map- or pattern cracking in concrete surfaces, such as shown in Figure 38, was recognized as the conspicuous, primary indicator of harmful ASR in field concrete, whereas few of the case studies mentioned gross structural expansions. Explanatory studies of the overall cracking mechanisms were not presented. Linear expansion was, on the other hand, applied by mortar bar testing as the quantified measure of alkali reactivity of aggregates. Alignment of ASR surface cracking longitudinally, following the direction of reinforcement bars, was recorded in an Australian experimental test with concrete bars,[129] but had not been observed as a diagnosing feature in field concrete, probably due to the contemporary low-stress structural design practice. The apparent discrepancy between the predominance of absent expansion with ASR in field concrete versus

Fig. 38. Main pier of the Vildsund Bridge, Jutland, Denmark, with severe map-cracking due to ASR. The pier was cast in 1938 and the photograph taken in 1954 during the Danish long-term ASR research programme

reliance on expansion in aggregate testing and research was an obvious "black hole" in the achieved stage of knowledge.

Reactivity of aggregates

The initial discovery of ASR in California had identified the opaline component of an opaline-magnesian limestone (an opaline dolomite) as the susceptible silica reactant. The further observations of harmful ASR in concrete structures along or close to big rivers in the American north-west and south-west States identified volcanic rocks, such as andesites and rhyolites, as reactive, with silica-rich, glassy components as the reactants. The investigation of structures in the north- and south-eastern States of the USA identified mylonitic granite and gneiss, phyllites and (later) types of quartzite as reactive, with distorted micro-crystalline quartz as the susceptible reactant. Our contacts with the research abroad, including thin section examinations of Swedish concrete with phyllite as the reacting rock type, led us to suggest that its reactive constituent was micro-crystalline quartz, "as well as hydromica", which had been assumed by American researchers.[114] In 1958, the Highway Research Board summarized the state of the art about alkali-reactive rock types.[130] Observations of ASR in concrete in the central prairie States (uncertain at the time of the report) implied that components of the glacio-fluvial sand size aggregates contained reactive silicious components. Reports from mid-prairie States, notably Iowa,[131] and from Canada, had also identified dolomitic rock types as the cause of ACR.[132]

The Danish investigations had been confined to examination of the different modifications of cretaceous flint types as the susceptible components of reactive aggregates in Danish structures. These investigations represented the first thorough geographical characterization of the national aggregate resources, comprising gravel and sandpits of fluvio-glacial and marine, Quarternary origin. The special investigations of the types of flint added significant new knowledge to the mineral composition of the variety of flint types. Chalcedony (as in flint) was found to consist of alfa-quartz particles of about 400 Å particle size. Opal was found by X-ray diffractometry to consist of subsidiary crypto-crystalline silica with 2-d-cristobalite.[133]

The British investigations had also concerned types of flint, although from formations older than the Danish cretaceous limestones. The "non-expansive" reactivity of these materials was suggested to be due to more elaborate crystal-linity of the chalcedonic silica than of the more amorphous opaline in the younger Danish types of flint.

The Australian research had concentrated on exploring essential facets of the nature of ASR by comprehensive series of laboratory experiments with pure opal as the aggregate reactant. This systematic research presented funda-mental knowledge for the 1960 state of the art on ASR, complementary to, and much relied on, the formidable accumulation of knowledge by the American investigators.

The entirety of the research confirmed that different types of reactive aggre-gates gave different rates of ASR under laboratory testing. There were therefore good reasons to adopt the designation slowly versus rapidly reactive aggregates (rather than the more imprecise: "more or less reactive aggregates" without qualifications). This grading of alkali reactivity was, however, in 1960 not yet sufficiently clarified to be related to the apparently different rates of ASR in field concrete.

The first cases of harmful ASR in California had been with the reactive, opaline material in the fine (sand size) fraction. This, and practical considerations, pro-moted the use of mortar bars rather than concrete bars in testing and experi-mental research and therefore required crushing of coarse aggregates when examined for reactivity. Australian experiments with coarse aggregates in concrete bars showed delayed reaction compared with the rate of expansion of the same aggregates crushed down for mortar bars. The Danish studies revealed further observations of expansions in mortar bars as related to particle size frac-tions of graded sand. The rapid chemical test implied that even finer fractioning gave excessive reaction rates, but did not directly relate this to particle size grading and expansion in mortar and concrete.

In the cases of harmful reaction with polymineralic rock types, such as phyllites, it was implicitly realized that the reactive component, micro-crystalline quartz, was heterogeneously occurring among the non-reactive rock consti-tuents. The implications of this in field concrete, and by the crushing of these rock types down to finer gradings for mortar bar or chemical testing, were not observed.

Release of alkalis from certain components of rock types, for instance zeolites and montmorillonite, was referred to in American literature as a source of alkalis supplementary to the supply from cement in concrete. No actual reference to the uses of such rock types as aggregate in field concrete was made.

Cement

T. Stanton's initial discovery of ASR was apparently triggered by observations of map-cracking in a highway concrete pavement made with a Portland cement of alkali contents, calculated as eqv. Na_2O, higher than 0.6%. An adjacent pave-ment section made with a cement lower than 0.6% eqv. Na_2O showed no cracking. Subsequent series of laboratory testing with mortar bars and repeated substantiating cases of ASR in field concrete in the USA, resulted in the general perception that Portland cement with less than 0.6% eqv. Na_2O was an effective safeguard against harmful ASR if there were susceptible rock types in the aggregates. There were, however, contradictory results and opinions, including advice, for instance implied by Stanton himself in 1943 and other workers, that expansive reaction may take place with low-alkali cement.[134]

In a personal letter of 23 June 1956 to F. N. Hveem, Director of the California Highway Research Department, Sacramento, Cal., I had mentioned that: *"in our opinion . . . the actual amounts of alkalis in the concrete are among the important factors which are controlling the alkali-aggregate reactions"*.[135]

Two years later, in a preliminary survey of ASR in concrete, which was prepared on behalf of the Danish research in progress,[136] we identified as decisive parameters for the course of the reaction in concrete:

- the alkali content of the cement
- the supply of alkalis from the surroundings
- the cement content of the concrete
- the water content of the concrete.

Possibly, the generally rather low cement content in ordinary concrete at the time, and the availability of low-alkali cement, made the American engineering practice insensitive to the third of these parameters.

Pozzolans

The theoretical studies in the USA, with reference to preceding studies by H. E. Vivian,[137] offered reasonable explanations on the observations that fine grinding of opaline aggregates impeded expansive, i.e. harmful ASR, and actually suggested addition of pozzolanic materials to cement in concrete as a precautionary measure. This was confirmed by Danish experiments with pozzolanic materials.[138] There was also substantiation from the historical Danish experience with use of the pozzolanic moler cement in coastal concrete works. Notwithstanding this early experience, the effects of pozzolanic materials and blast-furnace slag later became a hot topic in ASR research for many years.

Water

Table 15, after reference [114], was shown as a record of the supply of alkalis beyond those that came from the cement in case of use of sea water or alkaline

Table 15. Supply to concrete of alkalis from mixing water when different water types and different w/c ratios are used (data correspond to Danish circumstances)

Type of water	Sodium: mg/l	Supply to alkalis in cement Na_2O: % by weight		
		w/c = 0.5	w/c = 0.7	w/c = 1.0
Sea	12 000	0.8	1.1	1.6
Brackish	4000	0.3	0.4	0.5
Ground	250–1500	max. 0.15	max. 0.15	max. 0.20

groundwater. Also, several of the authors referred to in the 1960 review paper called attention to the possibility of addition of alkalis from mixing water.

Chemistry and mechanism of ASR

The 1960 review paper acknowledged the American concept of the nature of ASR as presented in references [115] and [116]. These relied on previous American studies in silica chemistry and on the contemporary Australian research. In brief, their theory suggested that alkali and calcium hydroxide in solution in the pore liquid penetrated by diffusion into siliceous aggregate particles, and there transformed the interior mineral structure into an alkali-silica gel compound. In case of a high alkali to calcium ion ratio, the gel would become an alkali-rich "unlimitedly swelling gel", and thus cause expansive pressure in the reacting aggregate particle. With a low alkali to calcium ion ratio, the gel would become calcium enriched and non-swelling. The theory offered plausible explanations for the distinction between harmful and harmless ASR and also for the "pessimism proportion perception". This stipulated that a certain ratio of reactive to non-reactive materials in mortar bars would give peak expansion, and had actually been found extensively in previous mortar bar experimental testing in American and Australian research, although primarily with opaline material.

Figure 39, from the Danish research[114] (in final publication, 1966[139]) shows expansion ranges, including pessimum, in mortar bar tests with Danish opaline limestone. Each curve shows the combination of reactive material in

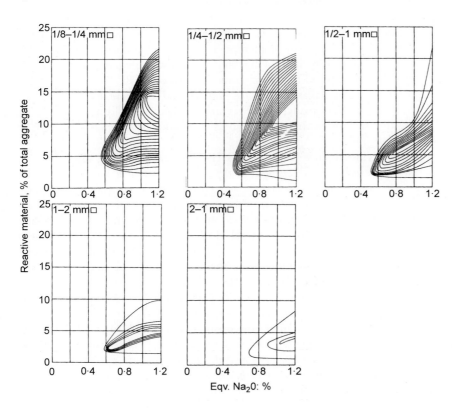

Fig. 39. Iso-expansion maps for different particle sizes of Danish, porous flint

the aggregate and alkali content in the cement giving equal expansions. The size of expansion corresponding to each curve is indicated in percentages to the right of each map. The ranges of expansion depend on:

- ratio of reactive to non-reactive material
- particle size of reactive material (screened fractions)
- alkali concentration (as a measure of alkali to calcium ion concentration).

A few American,[124, 140] and one Australian,[141] studies substantiated these findings which, regarding preventive measures, admonished that if the contents of cement with a given alkali content is increased in concrete, the ranges of expansive reaction, i.e. the risk of harmful reaction will also increase. This inference from the research was, as mentioned above, not subsequently adopted in North American regulatory practice.

Powers' and Steinour's work did not include analyses of, or reference to, cases of harmful or harmless ASR in field concrete. Nevertheless, their theory seemed realistically to establish the importance of the alkali to calcium ion ratio in the pore liquid of concrete. This was corroborated by the inevitable coexistence of the two species in any concrete, and explained the merit of the American distinction between the use of low-alkali (harmless ASR) and high-alkali cement (harmful ASR). The theory also described that the seat of the chemical reaction which created the unlimitedly swelling gel was in the siliceous interior of the reactive aggregate particles. This implied, although it was not explicitly stated, that the gel caused enlargement and subsequent cracking in the reacting particles, after which the released, swelling gel escaped into the radiating cracks which were created in the cement paste by particle expansion and rupture. There were many observations in the contemporary American studies, see for example references [124] and [126–128], of cracking of reacted aggregate particles, which supported this perception of the basic mechanism of ASR. There was further evidence in the Australian studies of mortar and concrete bars with opal, [142–145] and we had many, albeit yet unpublished, supporting observations from the thin-section examination of cores from affected concrete structures in Denmark.[40, 146]

Vivian had, in reference [142] at pages 71–72, as early as 1947, suggested that *"the reaction product of alkalis and opal on expanding (by absorbing water) is eventually forced into the cracks in the mortar, and may assist in lengthening and widening them"* [my emphasis]. The first part of this statement is in accordance with his numerous, elegantly interpreted observations about the mechanism of cracking and expansion of mortar bars in several of his papers. The second, emphasized part, appears as an assumption related to his perception of the swelling capability of alkali-silica gel, but there are no further observations or references in the Australian studies which corroborate that Vivian and colleagues should have considered swelling of gel in cracks after expulsion from reacting particles as contributing to expansion and cracking of ASR-affected concrete.

Powers and Steinour stated in the discussion in reference [114] in 1955 (in reply to W. C. Hansen's preceding discussion) at page 789 that *"in mass concrete, however, isolated cracks may fill with alkali-silica solutions, and therefore the soft gel or solution in such cracks may develop osmotic pressure, the concrete itself functioning as a semi-permeable membrane"*. This was, incidentally, in an argument against Vivian's perception (that the reacting particles were the exclusive seats of expansion and cracking), holding that his observations were not with mass concrete, but with mortar bars, which made it plausible that *"When cracks occur in such specimens, soft or fluid gel may exude to the surface without producing further swelling"*.

Much later, in 1967, I wrote in reference [36], at page 130, (referring to the examinations made in the 1950s) that: *"There is thus also the possibility of crack formations in alkali-aggregate reaction arising due to swelling of gel that has flowed out from the point of formation, i.e. not confined in the structures of the particle"*. We had, in fact, often encountered development of swelling gel on the cut surfaces of reactive flint particles during storage of drilled cores in their brass containers in the laboratory. We had also, like our preceding American colleagues, Stanton, Mielenz, Mather and the British researchers at the BRS, seen viscous gel growing as exuding drops on surfaces of concrete with reacting flint aggregate.[147] Nevertheless, in our numerous thin section examinations, we never observed radiating cracks in concrete full of exuded gel, and since we only saw the cracks in the section-plane, there were sound arguments for agreeing with Vivian's preferential perception: *expansion and cracking in concrete due to alkali-silica reaction is due to the formation of swelling gel within reacting aggregate particles, resulting in fracturing of the particle and hence of adjacent cement paste.* Powers' and Steinour's theory did not oppose this perception of the mechanism of the crack formation, although they did not relate it to the applied measurements of mortar bar expansion, which McGowan and Vivian had done so elegantly.[145] Hence, both Vivian and Powers and Steinour relied on experience with mortar bar behaviour. Neither had, as we had in Denmark, access to an arsenal of thin section examinations of concrete in cores from affected structures. They therefore lacked the comparison of their models, mortar bars, with the real concrete.

One reason why Vivian and Powers and Steinour, and myself (for a while) kept the possibility open that gel might further swell and widen cracks after its exudation with the cracking of the reacting particle, presumably lay in the fact that we all dealt with highly reactive, siliceous rock types – pure opal, opaline limestone, volcanic rhyolites – which produced abundant amounts of gel and large mortar bar expansions under favourable circumstances. Delayed expansions and much less gel development with polymineralic rocks, such as greywacke and phyllites, had not yet been the subject of systematic and phenomenological investigations.

Another issue of the research was also not yet sufficiently clarified. It was clear that uptake of calcium ions in alkali-silica gel made it a non-swelling solid which could not exert swelling pressure. (This was indeed a prominent element of Powers' and Steinour's theory.)[115] But it was not yet perceived that this is what happens when the swelling alkali-silica gel issues out into the freshly opened cracks in cement paste from the reacting particles, and becomes a non-swelling, solidifying lime-alkali-silica gel. There were apparently contradictory observations, as referred to above, of viscous, swelling gel appearing as jelly-like exudations on concrete surfaces. The British gel pat test also illustrated this behaviour.[147] But such gel had not passed through cement paste for uptake of calcium ions; where we in Denmark had seen gel exudations on concrete and core surfaces they were associated with reacting particles in concrete surfaces, or just below, and therefore creating "pop-outs".[39]

There were vigorous discussions within the American research community, see discussions in reference [114], as to whether the expansive pressure associated with gel development should be considered osmotic and thus require the existence of a semi-permeable membrane to confine the expanding gel. Chemists perceived that the presence of a concentration of calcium ion was necessary for the membrane to be formed around the particles. Other authors tended to consider the cement paste itself around reacting aggregates as functioning as semi-permeable membranes. It had not been possible by experimental observations to disprove or confirm any of these hypotheses.

In retrospect, it is noteworthy that the research in the four countries, with its limited resources compared with later days, achieved so much for a holistic concept of ASR, integrating the chemistry and the mechanical effects of the reaction. A theory with its basis in recognized silica-chemistry, corroboration by intelligent application of mortar bar expansion measurements, and visual observations which explained how cracking and expansions developed – it all was there, although it was not yet conceived to be a holistic concept. This situation left challenges to future research, but also contained inherent elements of insufficient "bridging" of field investigation observations with the theoretical work. The philosophy that laboratory test specimens sufficiently covered the desires and working capacity in much research without correlation with engineering practice and field behaviour of concrete had, perhaps even in 1960, commenced to take effect.

Test methods

The only system approach to examination and testing of the reactivity of concrete aggregates had been developed in the USA and given authority as the ASTM C33 standard in 1952. It comprised:

- ☐ C295. Petrographic examination of aggregates with identification of potentially reactive rock types and mineral components in the aggregates
- ☐ C227. Mortar bar testing, measuring the linear expansion as evidence of potential reactivity of aggregates with suspicious rock types, thus reflecting the engineering defects to be feared if the aggregates did not pass the test
- ☐ C289. Chemical testing of the solubility of suspicious aggregates, crushed to powder, in an alkaline solution, thus imitating the chemical reactivity in an accelerated modification.

The logic of this system is evident, and an illustration of the high level of collegial consensus in concrete research in the USA at the time, despite disagreements regarding basic scientific issues. It included the factual establishment of whether susceptible siliceous rock types were present in aggregates. Next, it tested whether the dreaded expansivity of aggregate particles in hardened cement paste was present, and it also provided a simulation of the chemical nature and intensity of the reaction as a supplementary means of characterizing the aggregates. The ASTM C33 cautioned that the laboratory testing did not reveal whether siliceous aggregates, which failed in the tests, would cause harmful ASR in field concrete. Accompanying compilation of experience with uses of such aggregates in existing structures was therefore recommended.

The contemporary civil engineering community had associated harmful reaction with map- or pattern cracking in surfaces of concrete structures, in some cases already appearing within the first years of structural performance. Mortar bars which showed cracking quantitatively characterized by the equivalent linear expansion, were therefore readily acceptable for civil engineers as a reasonable, visual and measurable simulation of the actual reactivity of concrete. The test had, however, some disadvantages:

☐ it took a long time, which often meant delays of acceptance of aggregates for use in construction

☐ it failed to identify why susceptible siliceous aggregates in many field concrete structures did not cause harmful ASR, whether passing the test or not

☐ it did not identify "pessimum proportions" of reactive aggregates of different rock types, particle size distributions, and alkali contents in mortar bars

☐ it made linear expansion a characteristic and decisive feature of harmful reaction. This was in contrast to the experience that in most cases of harmful ASR in field concrete there was no structural expansion

☐ it made uniformity of mortar bars with regard to composition, preparation, and storage a crucial matter. This was reasonable for the use of the method as a screening test in the ASTM system, but it was preventive for any model transfer and misleading in experimental testing for research purposes.

The advantage for engineering practice of reducing the length of time which the mortar bar test required, had promoted the use of the C289, Rapid Chemical Method, by means of which the potential reactivity is measured in the course of only two days. In principle, this method was a "purified" simulation of the chemistry of ASR. The rate of the reaction is accelerated in accordance with the general law of the kinetics of hydration reaction, namely that the rate of reaction doubles per 10°C increase of the reaction temperature. (At the test temperature +80°C, the rate of ASR is therefore ten times the rate at +20°C.) The advantage of the test was obvious – it saved time. The trade-off was that its kind of modelling of the reaction was even further from reality than was the mortar bar test.

Transfer of laboratory modelling

The exposure conditions for field concrete in Denmark required serious attention to the possible interaction of freezing/thawing and ASR, in some cases with chemical sea water attack as a third interactive cause of distress.

Figure 40 from reference [114] suggests that the increasing reliance on laboratory test methods required even further attention to the different mechanical effects of the deleterious chemical reactions. Linear expansion was, and is, commonly used both for sulphate reaction and ASR by laboratory testing, while in field concrete the first mentioned chemical reaction results in surface crumbling and wear, in contrast to the map-cracking and possible, but rare, structural expansion by ASR. In concurrence with the cautionary comments in ASTM C33 the review paper concluded about this issue that: *"the possibilities for erroneous interpretation of the results of experimental work are considerable if due regard is not paid to both the mechanism of the investigated reactions and the practical conditions that are believed to be imitated by the experiments"*. These words of caution were inadvertently

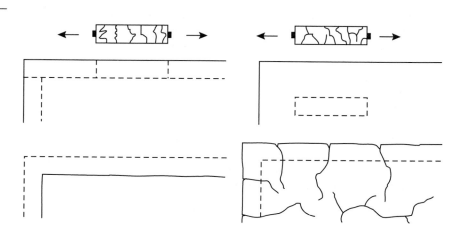

Fig. 40. Test methods use linear expansion of mortar bars as a measure of chemical reactions in concrete, such as sulphate attack and alkali-silica reaction. In field concrete the former affects the cement paste, causing crumbling and volume reduction (left), while the latter affects the aggregate and causes map-cracking and sometimes volume expansion (right)

predictive of major obstacles for realistic transition of much concrete research during the subsequent decades. Our Danish emphasis on the behaviour of concrete during exposed structural performance did not possess sufficient international authority to balance the influence of the, in many ways, more convenient and easier reliance on laboratory specimens.

The response to the 1940–60 ASR state of the art

Tables 16 and 17 summarize the state-of-the-art knowledge about ASR, which is extractable from the 1960 review paper. Table 16 summarizes the achieved knowledge related to ASR in field concrete and about the concrete materials. Table 17 covers the explanatory theory, and the developed test methods, concentrating on the ASTM system approach – the only one introduced for standard specifications at the time of the review. The tables comprise both the definitely stated findings referred to in the review paper, and reasonable deductions which, with hindsight, could be made on the basis of the accomplished knowledge. It may be a surprise to many readers to see in this rear-view mirror how much of the 1960 ASR knowledge base seems to have passed into oblivion, when the ASR research came into its worldwide renaissance after 1970.

Tables 18 and 19 are, together, a scrutiny of the established stage of knowledge for follow-up research after 1960, which could have led to the "final kill" of harmful ASR in field concrete if the established international research exchange had been strengthened and supported by cooperative funding. Some readers might indeed think that Tables 18 and 19 are reproduced now from original recommendations for an international consensus master plan for continued ASR research. Such a reader would, however, be entirely unfamiliar with the ways in which concrete technology research develops and operates, both at national levels and in multinational cooperation and exchange arrangements.

As mentioned previously, the research in the UK had practically dismissed harmful ASR as a national problem, and in Australia a similar attitude seems to have prevailed. The Australian research had consistently focused on studies with opal as reactive aggregate, which was not, as such, occurring in commonly used concrete aggregate materials. Support for pursuance of the public ASR research programme disappeared when other priorities appeared.

In other countries, the intellectual flavour of research on ASR was neither in 1960 nor in subsequent years sufficient to attract sponsor interests to new research efforts. In the United States and in Denmark the ASR research had, each under the different national circumstances, attained "mission accomplished" stages. As results of the high-priority, long-term investments, viable measures for the mitigation of harmful ASR had been found in the two countries. In the USA this had firmly authorized a "no-risk ASR policy" with the ASTM test method system and regulations. In Denmark the research had substantiated that a "low-risk ASR policy" with free choice between none or available preventive measures would be most cost-effective.

USA – land of the no-risk ASR policy

The early adoption of the no-risk ASR policy in the USA, in the wake of the research and testing development during the 1950s, was in accordance with the market conditions and was easy for engineering practice to work with. And, like everything authorized by ASTM and ACI, its impact on the further research and practice became profound and lasting. The ASTM C33 examination and testing system was introduced at the commencement of a formidable breakthrough era for laboratory concrete testing with the use of laboratory manufactured specimens, be it of cement paste, mortars or concrete, for modelling of the materials behaviour in field concrete. This concept of research to rely on measurements of data for the behaviour of laboratory specimens as directly representative of the properties of field concrete became predominant from the 1950s. For the ASR policy this helped greatly to establish a quality "testing culture" with high demands on laboratory workmanship, equipment development, "round robin testing", statistical data analyses and evaluations as a means to improve the data processing validity for empirical correlations and interpretations. This was of unquestionable benefit for quality assurance in construction works, in university education and research, and in broader cooperation for concrete technology progress.

In the longer term, however, this hegemony of laboratory specimen testing also became a factor of conservation and resistance to changes of views on ASR, and of precautionary policy. A serious effect of this policy was that the ASTM, C33 caution – to take the experience with field concrete into consideration and not rely on quantified transfer of the testing results – apparently passed into oblivion in general practice and research. Another unsolved problem was the reactivity of the polymineralic rock types with micro-crystalline quartz or incipiently crystalline silica as the reactive constituents. Aggregates with these kinds of rock type had in several cases caused harmful ASR in the eastern States of the USA, despite having passed the ASTM tests.

A third consequence of the "indoor empiricism" was that research workers lost the incentive to be curious in terms of what the behaviour of test specimens might disclose besides the specified data accumulations. Hence, the entrance into reaction kinetics studies of ASR from parallel mortar bar test series at room and elevated temperatures, and to fracture mechanics studies in the appearance of severely cracked mortar bars, was ignored. The examination and testing

143

Table 16. *Summary of accomplishments of the ASR research 1940–60 and deduced implications*

Issue	Statements	Deductions
Harmful versus harmless ASR in field concrete	Harmless ASR is more common than harmful ASR in field concrete in Denmark.	Harmless ASR is more common than harmful in ASR in field concrete in the USA and presumably in Sweden.
	Beneficial ASR modification occurs in field concrete.	"Mild" ASR in reactive particle surfaces may improve aggregate–cement paste bond quality.
Cracking and expansion	Map- or pattern cracking is conspicuous field evidence of harmful ASR and conclusive evidence when occurring along with gel exudations.	Surface cracking in field concrete is usually not accompanied by gross expansion.
	Structural expansion is rare.	Cracking and expansion in reacting particles is the basic mechanism.
	Experiments show alignment of cracking parallel with reinforcement bars.	Features of surface cracking in field concrete are related to reinforcement amounts and positions.
Climatic exposure	Harmful ASR is found in all types of severe climatic exposure conditions in the USA.	Heating accelerates ASR (Arrhenius law is applicable).
	Humid, coastal environment is found to be an aggravating factor in Danish field investigations.	Complex climatic exposure is likely to aggravate deterioration commenced by harmful ASR.

Table 16. (continued) Summary of accomplishments of the ASR research 1940–60 and deduced implications

Issue	Statements	Deductions
Aggregates	Silicious, amorphous, low-order crystalline, and glassy mineral phases in sedimentary and volcanic rocks are the primary alkali-reactive aggregates.	Observed different rates of ASR with different types of reactive rocks are related to rock composition and particle sizes, etc.
	Distorted, micro-crystalline quartz in metamorphic rocks is found to be reactive in field concrete in eastern USA and Sweden.	Broader characterization of potential reactivity of polymineralic rock types is needed.
Cement	Low-alkali cement, i.e. with 0.6% eqv. Na_2O is found to be an effective preventive measure in the USA under the given historic conditions.	Alkali contents in concrete, i.e. alkali contents of cement multiplied by the cement content in concrete, is the decisive parameter regarding ASR.
		Release of alkalis in aggregate minerals is a possible source of alkalis in addition to the alkali contents in cement.
Pozzolans	Preventive effects of pozzolans are explained by Australian empirical and American theoretical research.	Fly ash as pozzolan and ground, granulated blast-furnace slag in blends with Portland cement may be used effectively to prevent harmful ASR.
		Pozzolanic reaction is basically alkali-silica reaction – not, as previously considered, primarily a reaction with calcium hydroxide.
Water	Supply of alkalis by use of sea water as mixing water for concrete is possible.	Alkaline groundwater and sea water might, if used, change harmless to harmful ASR

Table 17. *Summary of accomplishments of the ASR research 1940–60 and deduced implications*

Issue	Statements	Deductions
Chemistry and mechanism	Powers' and Steinour's theory is widely accepted. Alkali : calcium ion ratio is decisive for harmful or harmless course of ASR. Presence of calcium ion is necessary for ASR to occur.	Qualified interpretation of ASR as cause of damage in field concrete is not established by theory – except that low-alkali cement under given conditions in the USA is an effective precaution.
	Swelling gel develops in interior of reacting aggregate particles, and causes enlargement and subsequent cracking of particle. Low alkali : calcium ion ratio produces non-swelling gel.	Cracking originating by swelling pressure within reacting aggregate particles creates radiating cracks in ambient cement paste. Expansion by swelling of gel does not happen after gel has been exuded from interior of reacting particle into radiating cracks.
	"Pessimum proportion" of reactive particles versus non-reactive, producing maximum expansion in mortar bars is explained by theory.	Harmless ASR is logically the most frequent modification of reaction in field concrete because: low alkali : calcium ion ratios give non-swelling gel
	Relationships between size fractions and amounts of reactive particles and alkali concentration are found to be critical parameters decisive of harmful versus harmless ASR in mortar bars (Australian and Danish experimental research. Powers and Steinour explanation.)	"pessimum" is not commonly occurring and therefore does not cause cracking and expansion.

Table 17. (continued) Summary of accomplishments of the ASR research 1940–60 and deduced implications

| Test methods | ASTM C33 test and acceptance criteria for alkali reactivity of aggregates and preventive measures is the only conceptual approach consisting of:

□ C295 – petrographic examination
□ C227 – mechanical effects
□ C289 – chemical reaction
□ Supplementary establishment of field experience with relevant concrete materials and performance.

Particle size and applied external saturation (C227), and external heating (C289) is utilized for rapidity of test. | Test methods C227 and C289 are not modelling or simulating the course of ASR in field concrete, but useful as comparable substitution tests for prior-to-work selection of materials, and in quality control.

Applicability of tests for polymineralic rocks such as phyllites and mylonitic gneiss, etc., is questionable and not tried.

Danish research is proposing a fruitful simplification of C289. |

Table 18. Topical issues of ASR research meriting further efforts in continuation of the 1940–60 programmes

Field of further research	Topical issues meriting research
Field investigation	Field investigations with protocols comprising records and examinations of: 1. extents, types and ratings of visible evidence of deterioration 2. exposure conditions 3. concrete materials, cement quality control and properties – specifications. 4. structural safety issues 5. coring and core examinations including thin section petrography for studies of the mechanism of ASR in field concrete.
Aggregates	Characterization, geological and mineralogical, of potentially reactive, polymineralic rock types, and their special influence on the ASR development. Quantification of occurrence per region, country and continent of reactive rock types which qualify for use as concrete aggregates.
Cement	Exploration of beneficial "trade-off" effects of high-alkali cement □ for workability of fresh concrete □ for high early strength development vis-à-vis risk of harmful ASR.

Table 18. (continued) Topical issues of ASR research meriting further efforts in continuation of the 1940–60 programmes

Pozzolans	Characterization of pozzolans and blast-furnace slag by:
	□ granulometry
	□ chemistry
	□ mineralogy.
	Exploration of beneficial effects of "pozzolanic alkali reaction" in concrete by:
	□ improving workability of fresh concrete
	□ decreasing curing temperatures
	□ decreasing permeability of hardened concrete.
Water	Exploration of the effects on the course of ASR of the use of salt water as mixing water, or by exposure of field concrete to saline water along with cyclic wetting and drying, and heating and cooling.

Table 19. Topical issues of ASR research meriting further efforts in continuation of the 1940–60 programmes

Field of further research	Topical issues meriting further research
Chemistry and mechanism	Exploration of the reaction kinetics and the thermodynamics of the reaction.
	Exploration of reasons for preferential occurrence of harmless ASR in field concrete as related to:
	☐ threshold values of alkali : calcium ion ratio causing development of non-swelling, rigid gel, or colloidal, dissipating alkali-silica solution
	☐ aggregates unlikely to occur in "pessimum" ☐ insufficient amount of pore liquid ☐ low permeability of hardened concrete.
	Substantiation that the interior of reacting aggregates are the seats of reaction, and cause cracking by enlargement in the course of the transition of the solid siliceous components.
	Substantiation that swelling alkali-silica gel takes up calcium ions and loses expansivity when exuding from the reacting interior of aggregate particles into radiating cracks in ambient cement paste.
	Exploration of mechanisms and features which make cracking by reacting particles able to accumulate into crack pattern and visible map-cracking on concrete surfaces, leaving the interior uncracked – dependent on the intensity of the reaction, the geometry volume, and shape of concrete bodies, and of exposure conditions.

Table 19. (continued) Topical issues of ASR research meriting further efforts in continuation of the 1940–60 programmes

Test methods	Analyses of the defective modelling relationship between laboratory experimental test methods and the development of ASR in field concrete.
	Development of protocol for investigating existing field concrete structures for prediction of the course of ASR in new concrete consisting of similar materials.
	Development of special test methods for estimation of alkali reactivity of polymineralic rocks with distorted micro-crystalline quartz.
	Investigation of the practicability of proposed simplifications of the chemical method, ASTM C289.
	Development of protocol for thin section petrography of concrete aggregate materials, coarse and fine, and of mortar bars used for testing and experimental research.

system also did not account for the impact of climatic exposure conditions or the influence of special new concrete manufacture techniques, such as steam curing.

The inflated reliance on laboratory specimen testing was in remarkable contrast to the concurrent development in the R & D of the leading cement industries. They undertook high-level explanatory research about the nature of cement as related to the manufacturing technique, and they applied concurrent modelling studies of the influence of kiln operations. They checked this theoretical research by critical accumulation of the blue-collar cement kiln operators' practical knowledge.

The Danish way – there were maybe no rules, but good reasons

In Denmark, which covers a total of about $43\,000$ km^2 with 5 million inhabitants, the adopted low-risk ASR policy was advantageous for the development of housing, commercial building and infrastructure during the 1960s and the early 1970s. During this period, our country experienced its greatest ever boom in building and construction, illustrated for instance by the increase of the national production of cement from 1.2 million tonnes in 1960 to 2.9 million tonnes in the peak year, 1973. The almost exclusive utilization of concrete using indigenous, potentially alkali-reactive sand and gravel resources along with ordinary and rapid hardening Danish Portland cement of about 0.6–0.8% eqv. Na_2O was without premium costs. That made imported non-reactive aggregates and special low-alkali cement non-competitive. With hindsight, it is plausible to say that the policy chosen by the authorities and the concrete professions was indispensable for the social and economic progress of the national welfare development in the considered period. I estimated, in 1975,[148] a total, national saving of about 500 million DKK in the period 1956–1975 by not having compulsory, regulatory ASR precautions with enforced, relevant testing. This was substantiated by the small number of new cases of harmful ASR which occurred in the period. There was also the benefit that investments in testing laboratories with implementation and normalization of test methods were saved. This made the modest concrete research capacity available for innovative service for the industrialization of concrete production. It also helped to keep engineering practice alerted to technology innovations, such as the use of new admixtures, cement types, and production technology development in the concrete industry companies, and it facilitated the acceptance of the ready mix industry development, bulk cement transportation, etc. It helped, in other words, to stimulate a developmental mentality within the Danish concrete engineering establishment, and it also created fruitful contacts with the contemporary developments and research abroad and with the progress of the national concrete research.

The reverse side of the coin of these progressive attitudes to concrete research and development appeared in the mid-1970s with the recession and the deep, lasting plunge of the production and profits in the building and construction sectors. The destructive effects for concrete research, including the closure of the Concrete Research Laboratory, Karlstrup, in 1976, coincided with the appearance of a Danish "brand" of the international "concrete durability crisis". The preceding decades' neglect in failing to update the concrete standard specification with its system of new test methods now demanded its price. A turnaround period in attitudes then also commenced, which tied much of the residual concrete research capability up in rigorous, regulatory systems with empirical laboratory testing, just as it was happening in the world around us.

Concurrently, the cement industries had, in all the industrialized countries in the 1960s, faced increasing pressure on their production capacity, along with improvement of the properties of cement, especially by increase of the strength and rates of strength development. In this context, high alkali contents of cement were advantageous in increasing the high early strength. Deliberate reduction of the alkali contents by dumping alkali-high dust was also undesirable as a waste of source materials and fuel. In western Europe, the cement companies and concrete engineering professions had therefore egged each other on to claim that ASR was simply "something rotten in the state of Denmark" with the special Danish flint in sand and gravel, and not likely to spread throughout Europe. It became unpopular to make any public fuss about concrete deterioration under these circumstances. Actually, also the function of air entrainment and the corresponding theoretical studies were widely contested in several European countries; the introduction of this new technology was deferred, sometimes with reference to the more benign climatic exposure during winter seasons in Europe than in the USA and Canada.

In contrast to these predominating European attitudes, the general response to the accomplishments of the ASR research after 1960 was, both in North America and Denmark, that it was the long-term integration of explanatory and applied, empirical research efforts which had satisfactorily resolved the problems with harmful ASR. Concurrently, the American basic studies of the physical structure of hardened cement paste had helped to explain the mitigating effect of air entrainment in the cement paste on freezing/thawing. Outstanding research in the USA and Canada had also resulted in solutions to problems with sulphate attack on concrete in alkaline soils and in sea water.[149] These three contemporary landmark achievements in research on concrete durability were formidable illustrations of the value of application of chemical and physical sciences in concrete technology research for engineering practice.

ASR research management by dedication

The first twenty years of ASR research have, even today, a valuable story to tell about the ways in which the research was run in the four countries involved. Its complementarity was not the result of any preconceived masterpiece of an international research management school. Indeed, the traditions and capabilities of concrete technology research differed in the four countries to an extent which must be inconceivable for research workers anywhere today. Besides, the means of international exchange of information were poor, and practically confined to slow surface mail correspondence, very slow indeed overseas. Mutual visits were impeded by currency regulations, visa restrictions, and more than enough work on the home-fronts for those engaged in the research.

There were three major reasons for the surmounting of these obstacles to mutually supportive research. First of all, World War II had created a unique basis for Anglo-American leadership of research internationalization. Secondly, the American supremacy was unquestionable and unquestioned, both in availability of means and resources, and in concepts of the needs. And thirdly, there was excellence and outlook in the leaderships, and this was undisputed in the civil engineering and the cement industry professions, where, in those days, technical competence prevailed at top management level; as it also did among leaders of public agencies and administrations.

The Australian ASR research programme from 1942 to 1958 is still, as regards strategy and ways and means of execution, accessible for an updated evaluation, because we have the series of published articles which describe the work, and references to the accomplishments in this book and in contemporaneous American research. Apparently, the public Australian technical research organization Commonwealth Scientific and Industrial Research Organization, CSIRO, became alerted to the ASR problems through contacts with the research in California before the war commenced in the Pacific, and because opaline and volcanic rock types were commonly occurring in concrete aggregates with Australian cements of alkali contents up to above 1.0% eqv. Na_2O.[150] A small task force of researchers was created, along with a strategy which complied with the conditions. The magnitude and nature of the continent must have made a start with field investigations virtually impossible, while the chosen emphasis on mortar bar behaviour was adaptable to the resources at hand – and certainly, opal as reactive model aggregate was in plentiful supply. It is immediately apparent from the pages of the concise articles on the research, that the outstanding achievements from the tedious making, storing, measuring and observing of the behaviour of many series of mortar bars were attained because the researchers displayed:

- a high level of quality in the experimental laboratory test operations
- an exceptional ability for phenomenological observations and logical interpretations of what they saw and measured.

Their expansion measurements on mortar bars were not merely taken as figures, but superbly related to the amounts of cracking and the mechanism of cracking by the gel swelling in the interior of reacting particles. The cracking was correlated with the measured linear prolongation of the bars by meticulous measurements of crack widths and numbers. Migration of the alkali hydroxide pore liquid solution to reaction sites in individual reactive aggregate particles was experimentally established and logically interpreted. Model relationships between the rates of expansion in mortar bars and comparable concrete prisms were found, and the function of the OH^- as the reacting ion on the solid silica structures in aggregates was elegantly demonstrated by parallel mortar bar experiments with alkali and tetramethyl ammonium hydroxide alternately used in pore liquids. The phenomenological incisiveness of the work gives it high scholarly marks even today, not least because the difference between phenomena in the experimental laboratory specimens and in field concrete was consistently recognized. Hence, a retrospective view discloses an admirable course of development throughout the programme in what now appears to have been a well conceived, predestined order.

Early in the Australian research it was noted by Alderman *et al.* that weathered rock types with secondary silicification should be considered potentially reactive. This observation implied that the very hot climate in the larger parts of the continent engenders gradual dissolution of siliceous minerals in exposed rock formations, and might thereby convert otherwise durable rock types to reactive silica and residual, innocuous constituents.

The British ASR research by the Building Research Station at Garston (BRS) was, like the Australian research, alerted by the American studies to the possible occurrence of harmful ASR, particularly in the south-east of England where alluvial, flint-rich gravel and sand was a predominating aggregate resource. Moreover, British Portland cement brands with eqv. Na_2O up to 1.0% were commonly used in the area. The British programme commenced about 1950, with a thorough summary of the foreign state-of-the-art knowledge. A special qualitative "gel pat test" confirmed that the reaction might occur with British aggregates and cement. Thorough experimental mortar bar testing of relevant combinations of suspicious aggregates and cement eventually showed convincingly that harmful ASR was difficult to provoke with the materials in general use and unlikely to occur in practice. Concurrently, not a single field case of harmful ASR had appeared in the course of the programme, which terminated in 1958 with the final dismissal of ASR as a British engineering problem. The relatively high degree of chalcedonic crystallinity and the absence of opal in the common British flint type was considered to be the cause of the apparent "non-expansive reactivity" of the British flint aggregates.

As would be expected, the BRS programme was competently managed and executed, and the basic knowledge of concrete chemistry at the research station was sufficient to accept the contemporary theoretical perceptions in the USA on the nature of ASR as satisfactory for the purpose. In the final concluding statements the critical, scientific minds at BRS cautiously mentioned that: "*There remains the possibility therefore that some flints . . . may be encountered which, under adverse conditions of dilution, alkali content, water content and temperature, may cause trouble. So far as present evidence goes, however, this is considered to be highly unlikely*".[151] This reservation was conveniently overlooked by those with top responsibilities in engineering practice and associated industries, with severe adverse consequences when the "unlikely" conditions turned up in the 1970s.

The American ASR research had the whole gamut of needs and capabilities for their magnificent exploration of the problems from the time of discovery in 1940. So it appeared when we became acquainted with the publications in about 1950 and, with hindsight, our opinions are unchanged. There was serious ownership concern in western, eastern and southern States about hydropower plants with large concrete dams which appeared to develop map-cracking, gross structural expansions, and even distortions and warping. There were sluices, docks and highway pavements and bridges in several States which were also found in disarray. Concurrently, there was a rich society eager to get access to more and bigger power plants, to a new interstate highway system, airports, seaports, and all kinds of industrial and social buildings and construction in concrete. The national cement industry therefore mobilized to conquer new market sectors and to compete with the classical preference for steel in construction. As in all industries in the USA at that time, the leaderships decided to embark upon long-term, exploratory research as the basis for new technology.

Cement and concrete research in the USA was very different from that in Australia and the UK. It had no single, decision-making funding source, but many independent and strong-minded ones. The US Army and the US Navy had each their own large concrete research institutes, with cement and concrete research both for defence and for service to the civil construction works, *inter alia* for the control of federal waterways regulation. The Bureau of Reclamation had similar, large research resources for concrete technology for dam constructions. Many state highway departments established comparable research institutes and private and state universities were able to follow suit. Portland Cement Association had, in the late 1930s, created its influential basic and applied cement and concrete research team of brilliant scientists, and the federal Bureau of Standards had built up a worldwide reputation in basic cement chemistry research along with its applied work for the development of standards for materials. Hence, there were many independent centres of excellent scientific research with unprecedented competence in basic chemistry, physics, mineralogy and geology, yet closely associated with cement and concrete technology and with the urgent national needs for effective engineering development. There were ample opportunities for recruitment of brilliant candidates and the management teams were of adequate, high technical knowledge standard.

The ASR research was abundantly sponsored and created the need for interactive communication between engineers on the one side and science-trained chemists, physicists, and geology/mineralogists on the other. This led to rapid progress towards basic concepts of the nature of ASR among many, often apparently controversial confrontations. The progress was nurtured by frequent conferences in the ASTM, ACI and the Highway Research Board, with substantial discussions and published proceedings. The interaction thus created, driven by common dedication to the cause, was then moulded into consensus implementation by ASTM and further communicated through ACI. No other country had, at that time – or has had since – such a powerful, omnipotent creed of integrating basic cement and concrete research and application to serve engineering practice. In many ways, it was a unique demonstration of an R & D management system with absolute deregulation for the research planning and execution as the basis for voluntary, yet effective, regulatory implementation. And the new holistic intrusion of chemistry, physics and geology/mineralogy elevated concrete research from its former, crude empiricism to the level of applied science. It worked due to the quality of leadership and brilliant and dedicated performance of the operating researchers.

The Danish ASR research, 1952–61, (with last progress report issued 1968) was organized and managed very differently from operations in the above countries. It commenced because P. Nerenst on behalf of the Danish National Building Research Institute (SBI), having seen harmful ASR in the USA during a study tour in 1951 and meeting with most of the researchers involved, observed map-cracking, delineation and gel-exudations in the main pier of the Vilsund Bridge in North Jutland, with plenty of white flint in the aggregate.[152] Hence, the Danish starting point for the research was field concrete affected by harmful ASR. Next, a small group of civil engineers, including myself, was engaged at the SBI to absorb the available knowledge, especially from the USA, inspect more field concrete, reshape our education in chemistry, mineralogy and geology, learn to use optical microscopy, and find ways of putting experimental laboratory work into practice. Our initial efforts confirmed the seriousness of the problem, and the Academy of Technical Science (ATV) moved in. A broad, national management committee, to which we referred

Table 20. Sequence of publishing of the series of progress reports from the Danish SBI/ATV committee on alkali reaction, 1956–1967

Subjects of published progress reports	Series no.	Year published
Survey of initial field inspections	N1	1956
State of the art, ASR discovered	A1	1957
Field concrete, general – marine structures and railway bridges	B1, 2, 3	1958
Field, core and thin section investigations	I1, N2, 3, 4, 5, 6	1958, 1961, 1964
Aggregates in Denmark	D1, D2, E1	1957, 1958, 1959
Pozzolans and cement	L1, F1, 2, 3	1957, 1958
Quick chemical method	H1	1958
Mortar bar experiments	I1, 2, 3	1958, 1966, 1967
Concrete bar experiments	K1, 2	1958, 1960
Core drilling equipment and thin section manufacture	M1	1958

through three subcommittees, was established for:

- field investigations
- experimental laboratory testing
- aggregate studies: geology, mineralogy, resource mapping.

Two civil engineers, E. Poulsen and myself, were engaged full time for the two first committees, while the Danish Geological Survey operated for the third. We depended entirely on cooperative support from external, trained chemists and mineralogists, and on access to the F. L. Smidth & Co. and the Technical University laboratories, where one fellowship chemical engineer was engaged. We obtained secretarial and trained technical assistance for core drilling and development of thin section manufacturing, and later added one chemical engineer and several temporary petrographers to the staff. Besides this, the deluge of new American publications, preprints, reprints, and personal correspondence, opened the doors to the new cement and concrete technology which, in our minds, was absolutely vital for building and construction development in our country.

Table 20 shows how the management committee for the programme published the accomplishments of the different phases of the research in a series of progress reports issued by the SBI. Most of the topical reports were issued in the years 1956–1960 (the programme was launched in the late autumn of 1953). The bulk of the information from the detailed field investigations with core and thin section examinations was not in print before 1961 and 1964, and the comprehensive reports on the mortar bar experiments with Danish flint and chert were the latest to come out, in 1966 and 1967. These delays were, among other things, due to changes of positions by myself and

E. Poulsen, who had been the chief operating researchers. It is interesting that E. Poulsen's original development of a portable concrete core drilling machine and of the manufacture of epoxy impregnated thin sections was published in 1958.[73] The new techniques were indispensable for my use of concrete petrography at the field concrete investigations, and we told that to the world in the frequent publications. (The methodology was introduced abroad only after substantial delays.)

Our entire research set up was consistently improvising, often at the brink of bankruptcy, because funding came piecemeal when we exerted pressure accompanied by frequent internal progress reports. Actually, at the end of about ten years of hard work to create a brand new concrete research capability in Denmark, it appeared that we had spent about 1 million Danish kroner, of which the Danish cement industry and F. L. Smidth & Co. had supplied about 80%, because no one else had such means available for concrete technology research. We could not have done the job without generous collegial support from the scientifically trained colleagues abroad, especially in the USA and England. Likewise, the cooperative assistance from the chemical and mineralogical/geological departments of the few Danish universities was important. The management attitude in the steering committee was to delegate responsibility and decision-making power to us, the operators, and we repaid this trust by consistent communication, by ignoring work-hour rules, and by creating irresistible fellowship dedication in the new, challenging world we had entered. I would say, looking back to those days, that as a "microcosmos" of the American ASR research, we commenced and accomplished our missions under a completely deregulated management system. This did not result, as in the USA, with consensus regulations. The managing leaders adopted the special Danish "low-risk policy" solution as the most cost-effective return on the ten years' research investments.

As we shall see in the following chapters, the four-country "non-managed" complementary ASR research cooperation system described above could not continue when the international research took off again after its dormant decade from 1974.

6

The dormant decade of ASR research

As explained in the preceding chapter, the research on ASR was given low priority in North America and Denmark after 1960, and did not commence in other countries until almost 1970. In the USA and Canada, the highest priority of theoretical research remained the physical properties of hardened cement paste during the 1960s. The strong and prestigious "constituency" of academic and institutional research had won wide recognition for the American leadership in this field. It was excellent for education and academic research and suitable for the application of new analytical equipment such as the transmission and scanning electron microscope. Besides this, the application of the scientific research by air entrainment to mitigate damage by freezing and thawing of concrete was an essential factor in the ongoing, massive interstate highway programme where concrete was in tough competition with bituminous pavements and steel bridges.

In the building sector, reinforced concrete took up the challenge against conventional steel-frame construction by advanced, new structural design, use of lightweight aggregate, and chemical admixtures. The introduction of the pre-war Danish ready mix concrete methodology, vertical concrete pumping, and general mechanization of construction operations also made the cost of concrete in construction competitive. The research had to follow up with radical progress of structural design development, studies of the mechanical properties of concrete, such as strength, shrinkage and creep, and with emphasis on updating standard specifications and empirical quality control testing methods.

The concurrent development of laboratory testing and analytical equipment also fell within this field, and absorbed much of the available capacity and money. At the same time, the strong boom in infrastructure and other construction sectors and commercial high-rise buildings began to confine consulting and construction practice to short-term technology thinking, and to leave the basic physico/chemical refinements of the nature of concrete to the esoteric indulgence of academia. In the broader societal picture, the building/construction sector lost ground to the entertainment, consumption, and high-technology industries. Highways and railways lost their former preferential attraction for investments to airports. The most outstanding students turned to applications of basic physics in the new boom of electronic R & D and computer development. And the major university business schools began to feed all industries with financial and marketing wizards. All these factors combined to relegate technology knowledge to a secondary position.

Western Europe still differed in many respects from North America, with a construction history less dominated by steel and spectacular traditions for advanced structural design with reinforced concrete, now progressing further with the introduction of prestressed and prefabricated concrete. In many countries, the governments supported massive, more or less socialized, habitation developments with standard, module-designed concrete element units, produced and sold as commodity products for erection and assembly on site. Moreover, the cement industry was largely structured to operate within the national markets with protected profitability and was more inclined to cross-border cooperation than to fierce competition like in the USA. The European cement industries therefore remained strong supporters of concrete research, both under public auspices and in its own institutes until the plunge in cement sales during the oil crisis from 1974. This background orientated the research towards improvement of structurally related concrete properties, strength and acceleration of strength development, shrinkage and creep, correlated with the increase of the capability to provide strength by change of the cement chemistry and finer grinding. Also, the aesthetics and homogeneity of concrete came into focus due to the close association with modern architecture in the social housing development. The concurrent development of standard specifications and test methods was also attractive for funding of applied research. Characteristically, RILEM/ Cembureau was a strong factor in public and industry cooperation during this progressive period of concrete technology development. In retrospect, it should really not surprise anybody that issues of deterioration, such as ASR, prompted an almost antagonistic reaction in most countries, and no support for research.

In the eastern European countries and the USSR, the powerful development of industrialized housing production with precast concrete continued. Also, outstanding engineers, such as Michailow in prestressed concrete and Rehbinder with the basic packing and rheology science for fresh concrete and cement paste, had a significant impact in the west. Exchange on concrete durability in general[153] and special problems with sulphate attack[154] made also inroads. RILEM, CEB, FIP and JABSE created exchanges and contacts. Nevertheless, ASR was not acknowledged to occur in the eastern hemisphere.

In 1961, two guidelines,[155, 156] were published in Denmark, one for the use of available preventive measures against harmful ASR, and one for repair of affected structures. This completed the national research programme, except for the subsequent publication of the delayed progress reports. I completed my petrographic ASR examinations "between times" in my new job as chief of the new Concrete Research Laboratory, Karlstrup, BFL. E. Poulsen, responsible for the reports on roughly 4000 mortar bar experiments, became a full-time professor at the new academy for civil engineers in 1957 and completed his ASR work in 1966 and 1967.

BFL, Karlstrup during the ASR interregnum

In between the intense occupation with new research programmes to support the development of new concrete technology, we did find it necessary to work with selected studies related to ASR and also with concrete durability in its broader aspects. Two of my progress reports were issued in 1961,[40, 146] and three in 1964,[41–43] as forerunners of the dissertation, which was issued in 1967.[36] This book presented a diagnostic system for investigation of distress in field concrete, based on my involvement in the 1953–60 research programme and supplementary, personal research. It was the first systematic description of integrated field-core thin-section investigations and dealt with the effects of ASR, sulphate attack and freezing/thawing.

Alkali-silica reaction

Table 21, after reference [40] represents the number of 1.25 × 1.0 × 0.40 m slabs of three grades of condition, seriously and slightly deteriorated, and undamaged, covering the ramp slopes at both ends of the Oddesund Bridge, North Jutland, as observed in 1955. The concrete was, at that time, 17 years old. The bridge had been a prominent object of thorough investigation in the national research programme on concrete durability, and was seriously, although to varying extents, affected by harmful ASR. The table, along with Figures 7–10 and Plate V in reference [40], illustrate that harmful and harmless ASR do occur side by side in concrete structural members of the same composition and under the same exposure. In the case concerned, the exposure conditions included occasional splashing of sea water and freezing/thawing. This exposure was severe, due to the position of the slabs, and the concrete had no air entrainment. The aggregates were local beach materials, comprising dense and porous flint and non-reactive rock types. The number of slabs with harmless reaction is noteworthy. The significant difference between east and west ramps could not be explained.

The detailed field investigations of selected structures throughout the period 1954–1960 revealed the same typical evidences of harmful ASR which were

Table 21. Conditions of slabs on bridge ramps to the Oddesund Bridge, north-west Jutland. Characterization according to field inspection 1955, with legends of extent of deterioration (0–5) added to original description

| | Extent of deterioration | | | | | | Total | |
| | Serious (4–5) | | Slight (2–3) | | Negligible (0.1) | | | |
Position of slab	No.	%	No.	%	No.	%	No.	%
West ramp, north slope	158	29	126	23	269	48	553*	100
West ramp, south slope	39	11	57	16	268	73	364	100
East ramp, north slope	0	0	0	0	271	100	271	100
East ramp, south slope	6	1	7	2	397	97	410	100

* Five slabs were not recorded and are not included.

known from the American case studies and review papers: map-cracking, pop-outs and occasional exudations of alkali-silica gel. Gross expansion and distortions were a problem in the hollow piers of two bascule bridges. They were submerged caissons and subject to percolation of sea water. Macro-examination of drilled cores showed repeatedly that the surface cracks only advanced a few centimetres into the concrete mass and then were replaced by delaminating cracks sub-parallel to the surface. Altogether, the compilation of observations with comprehensive core and thin section examinations from all major concrete structures in Denmark which were visibly affected by harmful ASR, substantiated the observations in Tables 16–19. They also still support the deductions in these tables.

Figure 41, reproduced from Plate III in reference [40], shows a compilation of chemical analyses of alkali-silica gel from the contemporary literature and from our investigation. There were three "grades" of gel compositions:

☐   true alkali-silica gel with eqv. Na_2O from 5–25%, and CaO ⩽1.4%
☐   low lime alkali-silica gel with eqv. Na_2O from 5–30%, and CaO from 2–5%
☐   high lime alkali-silica gel with eqv. Na_2O from 11–12% and CaO from 17–23%.

This distinction was later confirmed by other studies.

Figure 42 from the same progress report are sketched reproductions of illustrations from previous American studies.[112, 124, 126, 157] These suggested that chemical degradation with swelling of the interior mineral structure of reactive rock types is the basic expansive mechanism of harmful ASR.

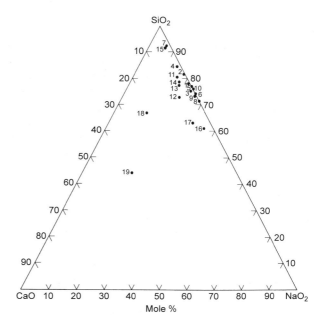

Fig. 41. Chemical analyses of gel, recorded in the Danish ASR research investigations 1954–60, showing the percentage molar proportion CaO : Na$_2$O : SiO$_2$

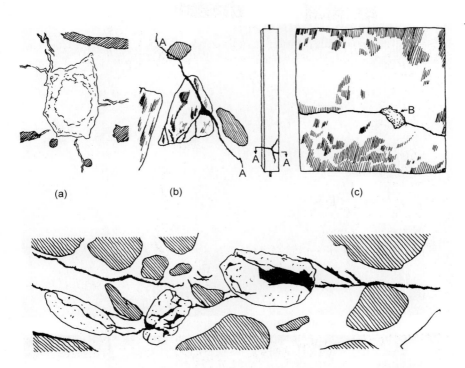

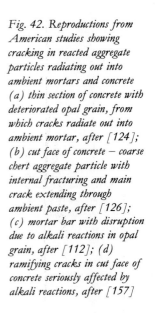

Fig. 42. Reproductions from American studies showing cracking in reacted aggregate particles radiating out into ambient mortars and concrete (a) thin section of concrete with deteriorated opal grain, from which cracks radiate out into ambient mortar, after [124]; (b) cut face of concrete — coarse chert aggregate particle with internal fracturing and main crack extending through ambient paste, after [126]; (c) mortar bar with disruption due to alkali reactions in opal grain, after [112]; (d) ramifying cracks in cut face of concrete seriously affected by alkali reactions, after [157]

Figures 43 and 44 from reference [36] show two typical modes of the effects of harmful ASR in reacting aggregate particles in thin sections of cores from ASR-affected Danish concrete structures. Figure 43 is a sand particle of primarily dense flint. The particle has been able to withstand internal pressure during the initial gel formation until a sudden tensile rupture caused the creation of the radiating cracks out into the adjacent cement paste, and the excessive gel was expelled to deposit and solidify in these cracks. The widths of the cracks in the particle represent the extent of the increment expansion. The primarily porous flint, Figure 44, has been almost entirely "consumed" by transformation into a residual, gel-like substance which has shrunk considerably afterwards. The radiating cracks in the cement paste are less distinct than in the case of the dense flint, whereas a consolidated "reaction rim" is conspicuous. Tangential cracking is visible in the adjacent cement paste, presumably due to the tensile stresses accompanying the drying shrinkage of the weakened particle substance. Supplementary photomicrographs of thin sections of concrete with polymineralic, volcanic and metamorphic aggregates with glassy silica or micro-crystalline quartz as the reactive component, illustrated that the features of enlargement and cracking in reacting aggregates related in an explainable way to the modes of occurrence of the susceptible silica and the texture and shape of the particles.

Figure 45, from reference [158], originally prepared for a lecture on ASR in Sao Paulo, Brazil in 1986, is a later review of the mode of cracking of harmful ASR in different types of reacting aggregates as revealed in thin sections. This display illustrates many observations referred to in reference [36]. It corresponds

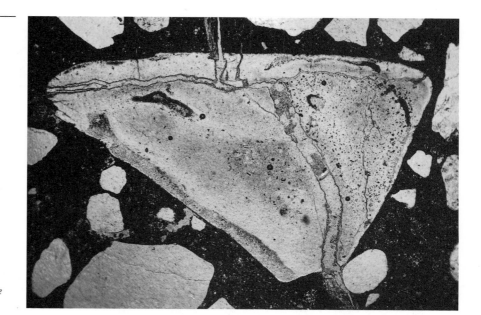

Fig. 43. Reacted particle of dense flint in thin section of concrete core, Oddesund Bridge (31×)

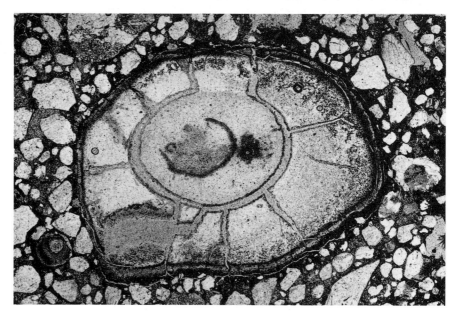

Fig. 44. Reacted particle of porous flint almost completely altered into a viscous gel which has dried and shrunk during the laboratory treatment of the concrete (10×)

also to later published studies by researchers from many countries of reacted aggregate particles of greywacke, phyllites mylonitic granites, etc.

Figure 46, from reference [36], illustrates the same expansive mechanism, but with freezing as the cause of the cracking in a stone found in an abandoned gravel and sandpit in North Jutland. Prior to the winter season, the porous interior of the stone had been water-saturated. The subsequent ice formation in the confined space had then caused the interior swelling, and exerted pressure on the outer

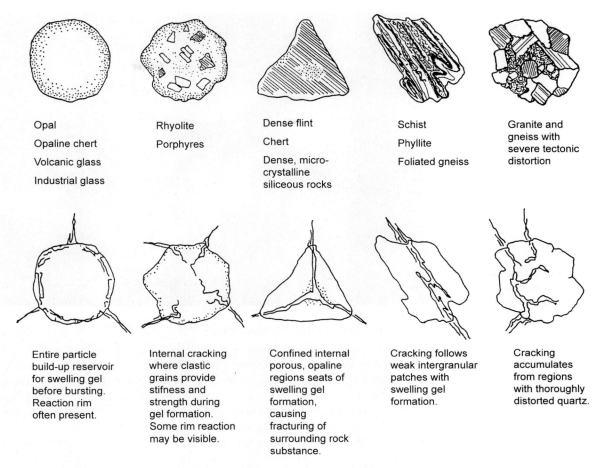

Opal	Rhyolite	Dense flint	Schist	Granite and
Opaline chert	Porphyres	Chert	Phyllite	gneiss with
Volcanic glass		Dense, micro-	Foliated gneiss	severe tectonic
Industrial glass		crystalline		distortion
		siliceous rocks		

| Entire particle build-up reservoir for swelling gel before bursting. Reaction rim often present. | Internal cracking where clastic grains provide stifness and strength during gel formation. Some rim reaction may be visible. | Confined internal porous, opaline regions seats of swelling gel formation, causing fracturing of surrounding rock substance. | Cracking follows weak intergranular patches with swelling gel formation. | Cracking accumulates from regions with thoroughly distorted quartz. |

Fig. 45. Sketches displaying texture, morphology and compositions of the primary alkali-susceptible rock types, and characteristic features of micro-cracking within and radiating from siliceous aggregate particles of different mineralogy and morphology, when affected by expansive alkali-silica reactions, from reference [158]

"shell" of dark, dense flint in excess of the tensile strength of the material. The photograph was taken at the end of the winter as being typical of numerous examples of explosive cracking due to swelling pressure resulting from freezing of the porewater in flint. All cracked pebbles which were opened had a porous interior, often with a hollow space or with rust stains, indicating that the penetrating water had contained iron. The mechanism of the disruption must be considered to be very much the same as when alkali-silica gel accumulates in the pores of reacting dense flint in concrete and then imbibes water.

Figure 47, reproduced from Figure 59 in reference [146], shows a quartz grain in a thin section of a mortar bar which had been exposed to severe sulphate attack. We observed that this kind of chemical reaction happened in the cement paste and created the peripheral separation of cement paste and the non-expanded quartz grain.

Fig. 46. Fist-sized pebble of dense flint from the foot of slope in gravel pit at Outrup, Jutland

Calcium hydroxide in concrete

The study of the "Morphology of calcium hydroxide in cement paste",[159] presented at the Highway Research Board Symposium in 1965 in honour of T. C. Powers, was an explanatory study based on observations in thin sections of Danish field concrete structures. Our thin section methodology and petrography was still, at that time, unique and our study was a landmark elaboration of the "Powers model" of the microstructure of hardened cement paste. His pioneering theoretical model of the interactive cement "gel" of calcium silicate hydrates in a porous morphology with a saturated calcium hydroxide solution as the pore liquid[76] did not contain crystalline calcium hydroxide as a significant constituent.

Figure 48 illustrates our observations and confirms that crystalline compounds precipitate from the pore solution and grow in the course of time in cavities and cracks in hardened concrete, without causing expansive pressures resulting in cracks in the brittle matrix. I had previously found similar micro-crystalline growth of ettringite, calcite, aragonite, brucite and gypsum in concrete with chemical deterioration.[43, 44] In ancient concrete I had seen massive precipitations of calcite in Roman concrete as a durability-promoting long-term conversion of calcium hydroxide.[7] We referred to the relationship between saturation concentration and crystal size in pure water:

$$\log C_{DT} = \log C_{\infty T} + \frac{k}{d}$$

where C_{DT} = concentration at temperature T of a solution in equilibrium with crystals of diameter D and $C_{\infty T}$ = equilibrium concentration at temperature T with crystals of infinite size.

As the saturation concentration increases with decreasing size of crystals, there will be a tendency towards growth of large crystals at the expense of smaller ones,

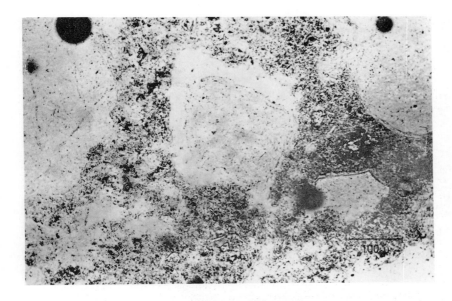

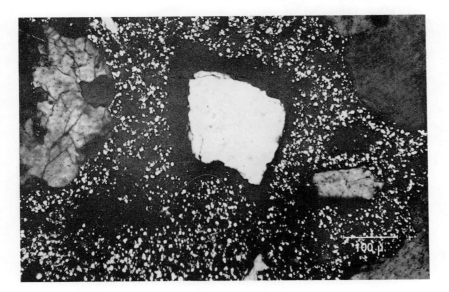

Fig. 47. *Quartz grain in thin section surrounded by periphery crack. Nicols parallel and crossed. 140× magnification, from reference [146]*

depending on the rate of diffusion of calcium hydroxide in the liquid filled system. We did mention that the situation would change if other ions were present in the solution. Alkali-ions for instance, which are present in concentrations depending on the water/cement ratio and the alkali content of the cement, would significantly suppress the concentration of calcium hydroxide. We also discussed the long-term filling of air bubbles by crystallization of calcium hydroxide, and implied that our study merited further work regarding the impact of aggressive, external water (as e.g. with sulphates) and of de-icing salts.

167

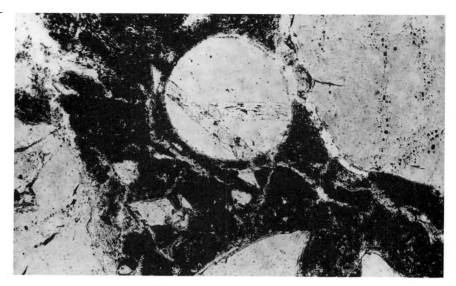

Fig. 48. Subhedral calcium hydroxide filling an originally air-filled bubble in Portland cement mortar. Nicols parallel and crossed. (150×)

Pop-out formation

Another BFL study[160] concerned modelling of "pop-outs" in concrete surfaces. These had frequently, during my previous field investigations, been found on concrete surfaces created over coarse limestone and chert particles. Undoubtedly, interior expansion in particles had caused the expulsion of the overlying mortar "cone". In the case of chert pop-outs there were often remnants of alkali-silica gel on the broken surfaces of the mortar. The study modelled the features of cracking of a brittle matrix over an expanding aggregate particle. A hollow rubber ball was placed in a block of cement mortar, with a tube connected to the ball to pump oil into it as an expansion medium. The oil pressure was increased until rupture of the brittle matrix occurred.

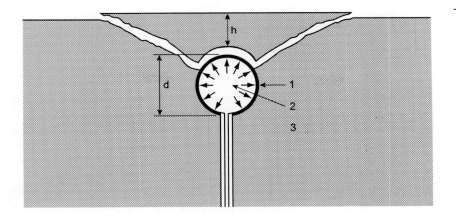

Fig. 49. Hydraulic device for producing pop-outs; (1) rubber ball (external diameter d); (2) oil (pressure p); (3) cement mortar (tensile strength σ_t) from reference [160]

Figure 49 illustrates the applied experimental set up, and Figure 50 displays the results of the test corresponding to the dimensionless relationship:

$$\frac{p}{\sigma_t} = f\left(\frac{h}{d}\right)$$

where p = hydraulic pressure, σ_t = tentile strength of mortar, h = depth below surface and d = diameter of ball.

Freezing and thawing had, since bygone days, been considered the cause of such pop-outs in field concrete in Denmark. The model is, however, equally applicable for alkali-silica reaction in chert particles in concrete, and might in many cases be a simulation of the two causes combined. The study also implied that if the pressure did not suffice to "lift the pop-out" away, the surface cracking would appear as map-cracking, although it would be more convincing as such if the experiment were undertaken with more than one particle. We published the study in the hope that, somewhere, other researchers

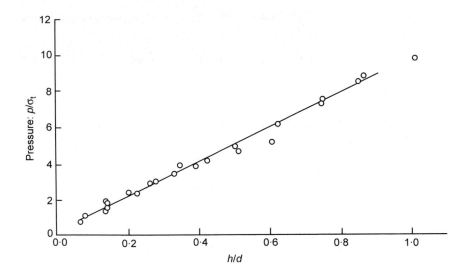

Fig. 50. Ratio of pop-out pressure p to tensile strength of the mortar σ_t versus ratio of distance from surface h to diameter of rubber ball d; test results and regression line are shown, from reference [160]

might advance the study, *inter alia* by making more particles interact. (Recently, mathematical development of the subject has appeared from E. Svensson,[161] J. Holm and P. Golterman,[162] and P. Golterman.[163])

Cement–aggregate bond

The effect of bond between coarse aggregates and mortar in concrete was studied in a research project by comparing the compressive strength of concrete with glass marbles as the coarse aggregate with the "natural" bond to the mortar, and in which the bond had been prevented by coating the marbles with a thin layer of plastic.[164] The study showed that prevention of the bond creation caused a considerable loss of the compressive strength of the concrete. There was increase of bond strength with age of the "uncoated" specimens up to 28 days, but then a decrease at 91 days. This was suggested to be due to surface degradation of the glass marbles caused by ASR. The bond strength of "uncoated" specimens related to the test results is expressed by the equation:

$$\sigma_G/\sigma_p = 1 + nb$$

where σ_G = strength with uncoated marbles, σ_p = strength with coated marbles, n = volume fraction of aggregates, and b is a parameter which is proportional to the dimensionless bond strength. The fundamental nature of the bond was not examined in this study and some "crumbling" of the plastic coatings, which was visible after the failure at the compressive strength test, suggests that interfacial friction may play a part in the effect of bond on strength.

The situation at the BFL was that we were able to undertake brief studies like those referred to, in addition to the longer term programmes for improvements of concrete technology in correspondence with the needs of the concrete industry, and also as student fellowships projects. We published the results as increments of knowledge about ASR and concrete durability, assuming that larger research institutes elsewhere might "take the bait" and initiate more comprehensive studies of the issues, or make use of the information to interpret related observations in their own work. We were too busy to appreciate that fragmentary publication of novelties has very limited impact on the overall development of knowledge.

The second phase of ASR research

The reopening of the research on ASR in the 1970s originated in countries which were newcomers to the ASR problems. In Iceland, investments in new hydro-power plants with large concrete dams had commenced. The available aggregates were potentially reactive volcanic rocks, the national cement brand was high-alkali, and security against harmful ASR was an ultimate goal. ASR cracking in the Lachswehrbrücke in Lübeck, Germany, was quite unexpected by all authorities, and an immediate response was required, *inter alia* because the bridge was ordered to be removed and replaced. In England, some researchers were uncomfortable with the unbounded confidence in the general belief of non-expansivity of British aggregates. Contacts and staff exchanges between the USA and Denmark had been strengthened by the BFL during the 1960s. This had created a heightened awareness of the possible effects of changed conditions on the ASR situations. Moreover, at the BFL we had invested in equipment for X-ray diffractometry and in electron scanning microscopy with chemical analyses, and were prepared for the quest for deeper knowledge about the chemistry of concrete and its field behaviour. Professor Sidney Diamond had been a visiting researcher in 1972 and worked with us on ASR issues. The US Army Corps of Engineers' European representative, Mr. H. Lemons in London, recognized the interest of his organization in the new initiatives in Europe and contributed funding to the first three ICAARs.

Figure 51, from reference [165], is a conceptual display of the "history of ASR research and transition". The first phase (1940–1960) had accomplished the creation of the scientific knowledge base for transition of the research to cost-effective preventive measures (low-alkali cement, non-reactive aggregates, pozzolans) which could effectively eliminate harmful ASR as an engineering problem. However, during the 1960s and onwards, the composition and use of concrete changed radically. Therefore also the conditions which made ASR harmful changed, whereas the preventive measures, test methods with acceptance criteria for materials, and the knowledge base were left unchanged. The changing conditions comprised the increase of alkali contents in cement and increase of cement contents in concrete due to higher requirements for the strength and the rates of strength development in structural concrete uses. Besides, there had been unexpected cases of harmful ASR with aggregates other than opaline

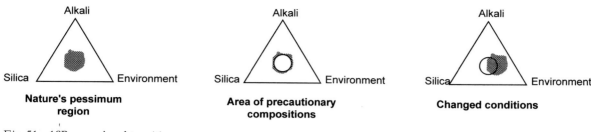

Fig. 51. ASR research and transition

and volcanic rock types. These other rock types passed the standard tests despite reactivity. There were also changes of concrete construction technology and new investments in construction in regions with severe exposure conditions.

The new conditions undermined the reliability of the preventive measures and the relevant control systems. In Denmark, the failure to introduce the test methods into engineering practice and the correspondingly outdated standard specifications gave rise to problems. In other words, there was no perception that the low-risk situation had changed to cause higher risk levels. Incidentally, this coincided with a general disregard of concrete durability in the rush to satisfy the demands for concrete. Under the circumstances, it would therefore be an appropriate strategic goal for new ASR research to identify the changed area of "pessimum conditions for harmful ASR" by explanatory research, and then to develop revised test methods and cost-effective preventive measures. But, at the time there was no broad engineering or research institute awareness of the need to do this. That was why it was only a small number of individual researchers who felt the need to renew the international exchange.

That this informal gathering in 1974 of 22 invited people from five countries at the "Hvide Hus" in Køge should become the first in a series of international conferences on alkali-aggregate reaction (ICAAR) was beyond my imagination, when I issued the invitations. And I am also fairly sure that it was not in the minds of any of the other participants. Nevertheless, the 10th ICAAR in Melbourne, 1996, assembled 189 delegates from countries all over the world and the proceedings counted 133 papers, amounting to 1063 pages which brought the total of published information from the ten conferences up to 6533 pages. The conferences have been unique in concentrating on alkali-aggregate reaction over 22 years, concurrent with the recognition of the reaction in more and more countries. They have therefore, over the years, offered consistent updating of knowledge by and for new research both in the "old" and newcomer countries.

Each conference has had its particular emphasis on issues of special concern in the host country, and in accordance with the advance of the knowledge by the continuous accession of research from an ever-growing number of countries. The conferences have also differed from the general "conference growth syndrome" in having all been organized by ad hoc groups of dedicated research colleagues with support from sponsoring sources in their homelands.

The first ICAAR was an initiating exploratory exchange about the ASR situation as seen by the participants. But at the 2nd ICAAR it was possible to categorize the contributions largely in accordance with the disposition:

- field investigations
- aggregates
- cement, pozzolans and slag
- mechanisms and chemistry
- test methods.

At some of the conferences contributions were invited about underlying reasons, or needs and means of the ASR research, and about strategy of explanatory and applied research policies.

At the 2nd ICAAR in 1975, the alkali-carbonate reaction (ACR) was introduced, and was actually the reason why the conference acronym did not become ICASR. In the present review, ACR has only been mentioned sporadically, mainly because "there are so few of them" and clarification of their basic nature has begun to dawn only at the later conferences.

1st ICAAR, 1974, Køge[113]

The Danish Concrete Research Laboratory, Karlstrup (BFL), made the invitations to the first meeting for several reasons. We had contacts in Germany about the new cases of harmful ASR, and cracking had appeared in younger Danish structures. There was serious concern in Iceland where we also had good contacts. And theoretical research was under renewal in the USA, encouraged by K. and B. Mather, and with S. Diamond in cooperation with the BFL. In the UK, a case of harmful ASR in a dam on the Channel Island Jersey aroused the interest of the Cement and Concrete Association.

I introduced the Køge conference, or perhaps more accurately "workshop", by a reminder that the 1973 consumption of concrete in the world, estimated to be about 7000 million tonnes, would increase towards 10 000 million tonnes in the foreseeable future due to the growth of the world population and its demands on social and industrial development. I mentioned that this would create resource problems of great orders of magnitude regarding cement production and capital investment capacity, water availability, aggregates availability and environmental protection restrictions, knowledge about cement and concrete technology, and time for any innovation and its implementation.

Therefore, I said:

"*It will become considered unacceptable irresponsibility on the part of R & D, if the unavoidable growth in the use of concrete results in increased quantities of early and severely deteriorating concrete*".

Referring to recently identified cases of harmful ASR even in quite new concrete structures in Germany and Denmark I mentioned that increasing:

- sizes of cement kilns
- preference for the dry process
- use of high quality concrete, rich in cement
- reduction of structural coefficients of safety

173

☐ numbers of uneducated people making large volumes of concrete in developing countries

would be accompanied by:

☐ increasing contents of alkalis in cement with eqv. Na_2O 1.0% being a likely future average.

I stipulated therefore that: *"when our meeting is over, there will be little doubt left among us that the classic identification criteria for alkali-silica reactive aggregates now need thorough reconsideration"*.

The different categories of ASR problem which were on the agenda for the small group of people who represented the amount of concern about ASR in the world at the given time are shown in the following list of discussion titles:

☐ Underlying reasons for new ASR research
☐ Scientific state-of-the-art revision
☐ Alkali contents in concrete decisive
☐ Preventive effects of slag and pozzolans
☐ Impact of cement manufacture technology.

The presentations and discussions during the two days covered the fundamental issues of the chemistry and mechanism of ASR as well as new test methods and the use of slag and pozzolans as preventive measures. S. Diamond reviewed the state-of-the-art knowledge, and explained why ASR need not result in expansion. Several delegates brought up related issues requiring new research. S. Sprung from VDZ (Forschungsinstitut der Deutsche Zementindustrie, Düsseldorf) referred to the conclusions of the recent German research: *"tests with opal as aggregate have indicated that even under pessimum conditions no expansion occurs if the alkali content of the concrete does not exceed 3 kg Na_2O-equivalent per m^3"*. This was the first time that the American limit of the alkali contents – 0.6% eqv. Na_2O in cement – was logically linked to the cement content in concrete with a threshold value of 3.0 kg eqv. Na_2O per m^3 concrete. The German research had also found GGBS to be an effective inhibitor of harmful reaction. G. Gudmundsson mentioned that natural pozzolanic materials were used successfully in Iceland in blends with the local, high-alkali cement (1.5% eqv. Na_2O), and N. Thaulow discussed ongoing experiments at the BFL with fly ash as preventive means. H. Alsted Nielsen from F. L. Smidth & Co. discussed the penalty of extra initial costs to the cement industry for reducing the alkali contents. He mentioned the loss of energy and source materials by this technology, and the environmental issue arising with increase of deposited alkaline dust as waste in old quarries.

During our meeting, the Icelandic delegates suggested a continuation in Reykjavik in 1975, so the series of the ICAAR was actually inaugurated by H. Asgeirsson and G. Gudmundsson on behalf of the Building Research Institute and the State Cement works.

2nd ICAAR, 1975, Reykjavik[166]

The proceedings of the conference comprised contributions by 22 of the 26 delegates. The underlying reasons for the renewal of the research and exchanges and of the guidelines for engineering practice were emphasized by American and

Danish delegates, and confirmed by reports of cases of harmful ASR in two new countries, Cyprus and New Zealand. Canadian delegates stipulated the occurrence of a special "alkali-silicate" type of reaction which, along with a paper about alkali-carbonate reaction, caused the organizers to accept the common denomination: alkali-aggregate reaction (AAR). Icelandic delegates informed the conference about the indigenous, volcanic pozzolans and their suitability as preventive measures. Also, the inhibitory effect of GGBS was discussed. The application of the new French pore-squeezing method was described, and the chemistry and physical nature of alkali-silica gel was discussed. Two new test methods were presented for assessment of the possible alkali reactivity of aggregate materials.

Underlying reasons

B. Mather presented "three reasons why there is new concern over alkali-aggregate reaction":

"1. The simple cheap precaution of specifying low-alkali cement, and obtaining it at no increase in price over cement not required to be low-alkali, will no longer be widely available.

2. Aggregates not previously regarded as reactive are being found to have reacted in concrete in old structures and to be associated with significant cracking and damage.

3. Serious early damage to concrete structures has occurred in places where it was previously unknown, especially in North Germany".

In my introduction to the conference, I reviewed the consequences of the "low-risk policy" which, from 1961, had been the actual implementation in Denmark of the 1952–61 research as the most cost-effective approach to the ASR situation under the given circumstances:

"The premium to be paid by the cement consumption for applying safeguards would have been about 40% addition to the cement price over the years.

In 1956 this premium would probably have comprised about 40% of the Danish cement consumption; in 1975 about 20% of the Danish cement consumption. For 1975 this would amount to about 50 million DKK, to which must be added the costs of extra design work, materials testing, approbation, committee work on standards, etc., say all together 60 million DKK.

Summarized back over 20 years, one attains a total of 300 to 500 million DKK (1975 DKK) as the order of magnitude of expenses saved by not introducing compulsory alkali-silica safeguards in 1956.

This must be balanced against:

1. *The expenses to research and technical service work. Over the years this amounts to about 5–8 million DKK, including the costs involved in cooperation with research in other countries (which, accumulated, amounts to many times the costs of Danish research).*

2. *The expenses on maintenance or replacement of deteriorated concrete or structures. So far, the records show that the quantity of concrete annually being repaired or removed in Denmark because of proven alkali-silica reactions is negligible in the total picture of concrete being repaired or removed, and this is negligible compared with the quantity of concrete annually made.*

3. *The expenses on precautionary measures, when and where applied. We know that also these expenses have been negligible over the years.*

Obviously, neither research nor practice or authorities have made records year for year to establish the above economic picture. But broadly speaking: for Danish engineering and for the society as such, it is clear that the liberal policy regarding precautions against alkali-.silica reactions has paid off very well until now. Nobody will question that".

The contributions of B. Mather's and myself in fact suggested a new framework for a possible international strategy to match the same problem, ASR, under different technological and economical conditions. The forthcoming conferences would show that no corresponding international "research commonwealth" was available to implement such joint, overall goal-setting for the research and its transfer; except for minor issues, such as reproducibility of laboratory test methods.

Field investigations

A few reports were presented about field occurrence of ASR. A. Poole described a case from a jetty on Cyprus, and R. A. Kennerley, D. A. St. John and L. M. Smith reviewed the nature of aggregates of natural rock origin in New Zealand, and the tests made for characterization of their reactivity, if any. The occurrence of harmful ASR in New Zealand was limited to cases where a high-alkali cement had been used with a glassy aggregate.

Aggregates

J. E. Gillott introduced the designation alkali-silicate reaction, after identification of a slowly developing, harmful reaction in polymineralic, metamorphic and igneous Canadian rock types in which neither opal nor chalcedony had been identified as reactive constituents. As a tentative hypothesis it was suggested that exfoliation of clay minerals in the rock types had caused the expansive reaction. The presence of potentially reactive, micro-crystalline quartz in the rocks was disregarded as the cause. The purely speculative designation of a new kind of alkali reactivity of aggregates was an omen of much time-consuming discussion to come at subsequent conferences about this theoretical reaction, which was consistently characterized as being "not fully understood", and yet persistently referred to as existing in Canada, until the 9th ICAAR in 1992. Petrographic characterization of reactive aggregates and alkali-carbonate reaction (ACR) was also discussed by Dr. Gillott. Also in this reaction, the presence of clay minerals in the matrix, in which minute dolomite crystals were embedded, was proposed to play a part in observed expansive reaction, and pozzolans had been found to have no mitigating effects.

Cement and pozzolans

H. C. Alsted Nielsen reviewed the conditions for reduction of the alkali contents in cement related to the different types of operating cement kilns and to environmental concern and costs. G. Gudmundsson and K. Sæmundsson reported on the preventive effects of Icelandic pozzolans and on geological prospecting for discovery of the national resources of such materials.

Mechanisms

H. Vivian mentioned in his scientific review that alkalis consumed by ASR could be "rejected" along with ageing and uptake of calcium ions in alkali-silica gel. He further mentioned that the alkalinity reduction in the ASTM C289 test "*is much less significant than the dissolved silica determination*", thus substantiating earlier work by K. E. Haulund Christensen.[167] He also mentioned the acceleration of ASR with elevation of temperatures as a matter of caution by evaluation of room temperature testing. S. Diamond referred to pore solution studies, with reference to the new French pore-squeezing technique. He discussed the role of the calcium ion in the formation and subsequent transition of alkali-silica gel with reference to previous Danish research by myself and updating studies by N. Thaulow and T. Knudsen. They had, by SEM and microprobe analyses, shown that when alkali-silica gel exuded through cracks from reacting particles, it exchanged alkali with calcium ions and solidified. These studies of the interrelated chemistry and mechanism of ASR substantiated the essence of the American and Australian research in the 1940–60 period.

H. Krogh presented a study of the swelling capability of synthetic alkali-silica and alkali-calcium-silica gel of different compositions, and calculated stress development in cement paste when the swelling gel types exude out into cracks in cement paste from their origin in reacting particles.[168] The study did not include supporting experiments with ASR in mortar or concrete, but was, nonetheless, referred to in later research studies as an argument that the swelling power of alkali-silica gel in the cement paste is the mechanism of expansive ASR, see e.g. discussion to reference [114]. The opposing observations by Thaulow and Knudsen received less attention in the years to come, despite their logical compatibility with the chemical theory and observations on affected field concrete and mortar bars. With hindsight, the escalated acknowledgement of the chemical study by Krogh over the chemical/mechanistic perception by Thaulow and Knudsen, was a presage of forthcoming fragmentation in the research, when new colleagues from more countries came in with less overall experience.

H. G. Smolczyk had found that GGBS had a strong bonding effect on Na^+ ions in the pore solution of cement paste. This was an advance accomplishment for the later general perception of pozzolanic and slag reactivity with alkalis in concrete.

Test methods

D. Hirche suggested IR spectroscopy as a new test method for the alkali reactivity of siliceous aggregates, the philosophy being that aggregates with a high level of infrared transmittance would cause expansion by ASR in concrete. Including preparation, etc., such tests would probably last only a few hours per aggregate sample.

L. Dolar-Mantuani suggested undulatory extinction in quartz (UEA) as a suitable criterion for evaluating the alkali reactivity of the igneous and metamorphic, polymineralic rock types, which had caused harmful ASR in Canadian concrete structures. This was the second Canadian hypothetical idea regarding the alkali reactivity of rock types without visible contents of silica in amorphous or glassy, volcanic modifications. Considerable Canadian investment, critical reproducibility testing and much discussion time was spent during the next six conferences before UEA was eventually dismissed as a reactivity criterion, also by Canadian petrographers.[169]

Hence, the 2nd ICAAR was, in many ways a yardstick for what was to come during the forthcoming years, concurrent with the gradual acknowledgements of the "spread" of harmful ASR. Surely, the delegates in Reykjavik did not anticipate this future development, but were satisfied that there were sufficient unanswered questions to warrant acceptance of the invitation from the Cement and Concrete Association and the Queen Mary College of London University to the third conference in England the following year.

3rd ICAAR, 1976, Wexham Springs and London[170]

When this conference convened, the cement industry and building and construction in western Europe were choked by the oil embargo and the soaring energy prices with the enormous capital flow to the Middle East. I referred, in introductory remarks, to this underlying situation as a serious challenge to cement and concrete research, also about ASR, with the further complications of apparent conflicting interests in *"that the authorities as the overall political controllers do not themselves invest in the manufacturing crafts and industries, that the cement manufacturers are predominantly locked for long periods to given manufacturing technologies, and that the cement consumers, who possess most of the technology flexibility, generally speaking have the least capability available for exploitation of their development potentials"*. It was also apparent that, under the given circumstances, several cement companies in our part of the world were still reluctant to see ASR broadly publicized as another threat to the declining business. I therefore said that the creation of new explanatory and applicable knowledge, including information about the beneficial aspects of ASR, was an essential obligation for our research and for the exchange of progress in the represented countries. Increasing concern about harmful ASR in several parts of the world was reflected in the attendance of delegates from five "new" countries since the previous year: Sweden, Holland, Yugoslavia, Iraq and South Africa. The interest aroused in England since the two previous meetings was demonstrated by the attendance of 14 British delegates.

Field investigations

Studies of field cases revealed that harmful ASR were being reported in "new" countries such as Iceland, the Middle East, South Africa, and the Channel Island, Jersey. In Sydney, Australia, a field case was referred to as having shown excessive amounts of a sodium-rich, crystalline exudation on concrete slab surfaces shortly after placing. The basaltic aggregate was found to contain easily soluble alkaline phases. Cracking was not reported.

Aggregates

The characterization of alkali-reactive aggregates was extended in a British study with petrographic identification of opal and chalcedony as secondary minerals in igneous rocks and devitrified rhyolites. Strained quartz in Canadian igneous rocks was suggested to be reactive. The Canadian perception of alkali-silicate reaction was again presented as a designation for reaction in rocks such as quartzites, greywacke and phyllites without opal or chalcedony as the susceptible constituents, and of slower reactivity than ASR. The particular mechanism was again said to be unknown.

Cement

Three presentations – from USA, South Africa and Denmark – dealt with the technical/economic issues of alkalis in cement production and stated that increased costs were the trade-off for lower alkali contents. Information was also given about the higher early versus lower late strength with high alkali contents, and the mitigating effects of pozzolans, including fly ash and slag.

Chemistry

Figure 52 from H. Vivian's updated review paper on the mechanisms of ASR, described the change of the pore solution composition in cement paste in the course of the hydration process, with reference to a 1966 paper by C. Lawrence.[171] It was essential new knowledge, frequently referred to and confirmed by later research, that the OH^- ion concentration of the pore liquid increases sharply after the initial dormant period, while the CA^{++} ion, the SO_4^- ion concentrations decrease, and the K^+ and Na^+ ion concentrations increase moderately. In other words, the pore liquid is practically a strong

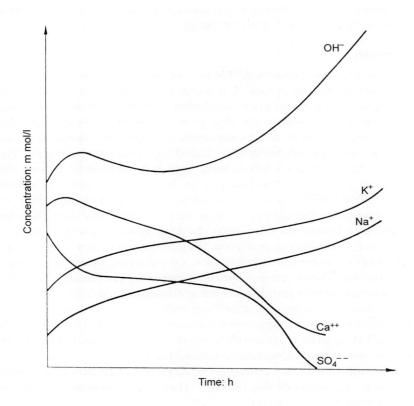

Fig. 52. Changes which occur in the composition of the solution phase in contact with hydrating cement, from reference [171]

179

alkali hydroxide solution. (Other previous investigations had shown that the decrease of the Ca^{++} and the SO_4^- ion concentrations are balanced by the interstitial crystallization in available pore spaces of calcium hydroxide and ettringite.) S. Diamond presented a study of the consumption of K^+ and Na^+ ions in the pore solution of hardened cement paste in mortar prepared with a high-alkali cement and Beltane opal as reactive aggregate. In the long term, close to 30% of the alkalis and about 40% of the opal (calculated) had been converted to alkali-silica gel, albeit with the reservation that possible "recycling" of alkalis after the reaction with silica could not be determined. A. Poole introduced the use of the electron microscope in a study of the variation of the concentrations of the K^+ and Na^+ ions from the interior and over the rim to the cement paste in reacting Beltane opal particles. There were obvious concentrations of the ions in the "reaction rim" zone, whereas Ca^{++} ions predominated in the cement paste. The introduction of pore-squeezing for pore solution analyses and the electron microprobe analyses for the ion composition of the solids engaged in ASR would, during the subsequent years, prove to be spectacular innovations in concrete research. S. Sprung and W. Rechenberg had studied the influence of the alkali content of cement on the properties of the cement paste during the initial phase of hydration. They found that the alkali sulphates in solution increased the initial hydration of C_3A, and suppressed the Ca^{++} ion concentration, thereby increasing the OH^- ion concentration. With a balanced alkali/sulphate content, high-alkali cements could improve the workability of fresh concrete. It was suggested that elevated temperature of the fresh concrete would also depress the Ca^{++} ion concentration and thus increase the OH^- ion concentration.

Test methods

Canadian research had found the ASTM test method C227 too slow and C289 not reliable for Canadian conditions. A new concrete prism test, a modified rock cylinder expansion test, and a new, accelerated rock prism test were presented. I cautioned that the reactive constituents in polymineralic rocks, silica and, perhaps, silicates, are only minor components that will influence the behaviour of ASR if such rocks are the subject of crushing for mortar bar testing. The three new Canadian test methods were apparently introduced because the alkali-silicate reaction was considered to be different from ASR and because the rock cylinder and rock prism test had been introduced already, albeit for alkali-carbonate reactive aggregates. There were, however, now some Canadian reservations concerning the relevance of the designation alkali-silicate reaction.

The highlight of this conference was the introduction to new insight in the chemistry of ASR in concrete by application of the new pore-squeezing technique and the scanning electron microscope and microprobe. The Canadian contributions demonstrated their particular interest in development of different modifications of laboratory expansion test methods with mortar bars, concrete prisms, and even cut rock prisms. Apparently, this priority was created by the inability of the ASTM methods to cope with the reactive, polymineralic Canadian rock types with low rates of expansions in mortar bars.

It was easily agreed that a fourth conference would be beneficial, and an invitation to convene at Purdue University, Ind., in the homeland of ASR, in 1978 was unanimously welcomed.

4th ICAAR, 1978, Purdue University, Indiana[172]

The highlight of this conference was the presentation by Professor F. Locher of the German regulations for preventive measures against harmful ASR. These were issued in 1973 as the result of a concentrated research programme, necessitated by the unexpected first case of harmful ASR in northern Germany in 1968.

Tables 22–25 from reference [173] summarize the regulatory requirements which categorize the relevant environments, reactive aggregates, cements and concrete. Like earlier in Denmark, the environmental exposure was taken into consideration, and the reactivity of the aggregates was related to:

- particle size of reactive material
- amount of reactive material in the aggregates
- mineralogical composition of the reactive aggregate component.

The German research and implementation programme, executed in the course of less than five years, was a thoroughly planned and executed feat of research in ASR, involving the minimum of repetitive work, i.e. it relied on previous research elsewhere. It was an improvement, compared with the ASTM mortar bar test, in that it applied measurable distinctions of the alkali reactivity of the relevant types, amounts, and particle sizes of aggregates, and related these characteristics to the relevant types of cement, including the German types of blast-furnace slag cement. It was an important clarification that corresponding requirements to the acceptable alkali contents in concrete were introduced. The programme also encompassed a new chemical test method consisting of treatment of the aggregate (minus the < 1 mm size fraction) with 10% NaOH at 90° in four hours. The dissolution of silica is then determined by weight loss as a measure of non-reactive versus (a) conditional acceptability, and (b) reactive with precaution request. With imported Danish gravel containing flint and opaline sandstone dredged from Baltic sea formations as the only known reactive aggregate in West Germany, the clear objective of the new regulations was to eliminate the role of cement as the possible contributor to harmful reaction in concrete in Germany. No efforts were made to supplement the scientific knowledge about ASR. The classification of the environmental impact and the gradings of aggregate reactivity were considered sufficient, along with the empirical laboratory testing of mortar bars and concrete specimens.

Underlying reasons

I introduced the conference with a paper entitled "Fear of flying", which was meant to alert the research on ASR to the actual challenges, under the constraints of the general recession situation for concrete research in the USA and western Europe. In relation to the much debated energy crisis, I reminded delegates of the enormous release of chemical energy in the expansive movements of large dams with ASR, which the research ought to find ways to harness and utilize for making durable concrete. I discussed why the profitability model of research transfer in the manufacturing industries did not apply in the concrete construction sector, and urged the audience to find new ways to make progress by mobilizing audacious creativity, with reference to a much lauded, contemporary book by a young American writer, Erica Jong. In a subsequent contribution, "Alkalisilica reactions – simplicity and complicity", I discussed why the cost-effective

Table 22. Evaluation of environments

Dry	Concrete which remains dry during performance, such as in the interior of buildings, or outside if protected against moisture.
Moist	Concrete which often or in the long term is under moist conditions; generally external structural elements such as bridges, marine structures and foundations.
Moist with external alkali supply	Concrete under moist conditions with possible external supply of additional alkalis, for instance from sea water or de-icing salt solutions.

Table 23. Evaluation of aggregates with alkali-reactive components

Alkali-reactive component	Limit of content in weight: %		
	Unconditionally acceptable	Conditionally acceptable	Not acceptable
Opaline sandstone: >1 mm	<0.5	0.5–2.0	>2.0
Reactive flint: >4 mm	<3.0	3.0–10.0	>10.0
5 × opaline sandstone plus reactive flint	<4.0	4.0–15.0	>15.0

Table 24. Cement with low active alkali content (LA cement)

Type of cement	Total alkali content in weight: % eqv. Na_2O	Blast-furnace slag content weight: %
Portland cement	≤0.60	
Blast-furnace slag cement	≤0.90	≥50
	[≤2.00]	≥65

Table 25. Preventive measures against alkali reaction in concrete

Aggregates	Environments		
	Dry	Moist	Moist plus alkalis
Unconditional acceptance		No measures	
Conditional acceptance	No measures	LA cement recommended*	LA cement required
Not acceptable	No measures	LA cement required	Non-reactive aggregate required†

* For structures with high performance requirements.
† For structures with high performance requirements, or use of LA cement.

precautions against ASR, which the 1940–1960 international research had managed to get widely used, were not suitable any more. I mentioned some still unsolved basic ASR problems, such as how the minute chemical reaction in individual aggregate particles could accumulate into gross expansive power, for instance in dams, while more often merely causing surface cracking or no harm at all. I cautioned that the popular "pessimum proportion" concept is without model transfer validity. I suggested work for clearer classification of the reactivity of different rock types, and more basic exploration of the nature of pozzolanic reactions, and mentioned that they ought to be recognized as primarily being ASR in a beneficial mode.

Field investigations

D. Stark discussed the recognition of many cases of harmful ASR in concrete structures in the Rocky Mountain States from Wyoming to New Mexico, despite the use of low-alkali cement (<0.5–0.6% eqv. Na_2O). The aggregates were reported to have passed ASTM C227 testing with the low-alkali cements used, while the cracking in the field concrete had developed in less than ten years, meaning that the ASR had developed during the early years of concrete performance. It was suggested that the environmental, climatic exposure was of influence with heating/cooling, wetting/drying, and evaporation of porewater leaving high concentrations of alkali hydroxide available for the reaction in drying concrete. The author suggested, based on the C227 test series with 20% fly ash in the cement, that application of fly ash as a pozzolan would eliminate harmful ASR under the given circumstances.

D. Palmer reported that harmful ASR had been identified in a limited number of concrete structures in England. The general British Portland cements were of medium and high alkali content, and the reactive aggregates were sea-dredged chert, sandstone and – in Scotland – greywacke. The case in Jersey,[174] recognized in 1971, had been considered to be "away from the mainland". The first case in south-west England recognized to be an occurrence of ASR was in late 1976.

D. A. St. John and L. S. Smith reported that the ASR policy of the New Zealand authorities had incurred requests to the cement industry to reduce alkali contents to below 0.6% eqv. Na_2O. This policy had eliminated the occurrence of harmful ASR. For a new cement plant, an increase to 0.9% eqv. Na_2O was considered with the provision that a Portland-pozzolan cement should be used, where non-reactive aggregates were inaccessible.

R. E. Oberholster, M. P. Brandt, and A. C. Weston referred to problems that had recently been discovered with harmful ASR in concrete structures in the Cape Peninsula, South Africa. Field investigations had disclosed that more than 40% of the highway bridges showed the type of cracking associated with ASR. Similar distress was observed in other kinds of structures, usually 4–5 years after construction, and the frequency of cracking seemed highest in structures built during the last 10 years. Examination of cores showed evidence of ASR.

Aggregates

R. E. Oberholster, M. P. Brandt, and A. C. Weston reported South African investigation of polymineralic rock types such as greywacke, hornfels and granite used as aggregate in the Cape Peninsula area. The rock types are similar to those investigated in Canada, and had caused harmful ASR in South African concrete structures. The testing included the use of concrete prisms, and the ASTM C227 mortar bar test. The petrographic examination suggested strained quartz with undulatory extinction as the potential alkali reactive rock constituent.

J. E. Gillott and L. Dolar-Mantuani presented brief surveys of ongoing examinations for identification of alkali-reactive Canadian aggregates, with a wider range of compositions and "grades" of reactivity than the classical opaline and chalcedony rock types. Carbonate rocks were included. The latter author referred again to the undulatory extinction in quartz in polymineralic rock types as a possible evidence of alkali-silica reactivity, and had recognized that "the aggregates may be reactive without expansion".

S. Diamond had, from a western American rock outcrop, obtained access to substantial quantities of a homogeneous, opaline material, Beltane opal, which was introduced as an available standard reference aggregate material for comparable international research and testing purposes.

D. Lenzner and U. Ludwig presented a study of ASR with the northern German opaline sandstone, which sustained the validity of the new German regulations. In several respects, the contents of the study substantiated previous experimental research with mortar bars, in particular work by H. Vivian during the 1950s.

British and Canadian researchers had examined aggregate materials from Middle Eastern countries petrographically and tested their alkali reactivity, presumably as consultants in the wake of the regional construction boom and affluence. The predominating limestone aggregate resources in the area were found to encompass both siliceous and magnesium carbonates and cherts, and potential alkali-silica and alkali-carbonate reactivity was demonstrated.

Cement

M. S. Y. Bhatty and N. R. Greening referred to the trend of increasing alkali contents and concurrent increase of the calcium-silica ratio (C/S ratio) in Portland cement. They had found that ordinary cement with lower C/S ratio during the course of hydration could accommodate more alkalis in the hydration products than those with higher C/S ratios, thus making the alkalis unavailable for ASR. This was suggested to be the reason why cements with $< 0.60\%$ eqv. Na_2O had earlier been found to be an effective precautionary measure. They also demonstrated that the amount of retained alkalis may not increase with increasing hydration time due to "competition" with lime, which may recirculate alkalis out into the pore solution. In the presence of sodium chloride in solution, the alkalis from the cement and the chloride were found to be retained relatively independent of each other.

Mechanisms

W. J. French presented a thorough study of the mechanism of deterioration of concrete and porous natural rocks by crystallization of salts present in solution in the capillary porosity of the concrete and rocks. The basis for the study was widespread and rapid deterioration of concrete structures in the coastal regions of the Middle East, with focus on the Arabian Gulf coast countries. Field investigations supplemented by experimental laboratory modelling resulted in the evaluation that, under the given circumstances, crystallization of salts in the pores of concrete in conjunction with alternations of environmental conditions caused the disruptions. Heating/cooling was found to be the predominant causative factor.

A. D. Buck and K. Mather had identified the reaction products of ASR from several affected structures, with opal, quartzite and quartz, chert, and granite-gneiss believed to be the reactive aggregates. Alkali-silica reaction products (gel) were found to contain minor amounts of calcium in the early stages of formation, and calcium subsequently "*moves into the product from the large supply available in the cement paste and calcium hydroxide, but moves at varying rates over unknown distances. Supplementary thin sections had shown crystalline $Ca(OH)_2$ depleted in parts of the mortar where reaction has proceeded*".

A. E. Moore discussed laboratory experiments made to examine whether electric stray currents in concrete might contribute to making ASR harmful. The hypothesis was due to the occurrence of the first identified ASR cases on the British mainland at electric substations near Plymouth, south-west England. The hypothesis was not sustained by the experiments.

The viscosity of different compositions of pure alkali-silica gels at 20°C and of the vapour pressure of the systems at 25°C was discussed with reference to H. Krogh's presentation at the 2nd ICAAR 1975.[168]

Test methods

P. Grattan-Bellew reported Canadian investigations of the alkali reactivity of the polymineralic, metamorphic quartzwackes, argillites and quartz arenites by the accelerated Canadian concrete prism test, ASTM C227 mortar bar test, and the Canadian miniature rock prism test. The testing was correlated with petrographic classification of the textures and compositions of the rock types. The tests demonstrated that the slopes of the expansion curves in the concrete prism test were reliable expressions of alkali reactivity. "*The slope of expansion curves in the rock prism test suggested that it was the expansion of the aggregates in the concrete prisms which controlled the expansions of the concrete.*" The mortar bar test did not reveal expansivity of the aggregates. It was suggested that micro-crystalline quartz was the reactive component in the aggregate.

5th ICAAR, 1981, Cape Town[175]

The fifth conference lifted the scope and contents of the meetings to a level of importance which warranted the involvement of the entire globe for the forthcoming ASR research. Until that point, it had at first been only the USA and Denmark which recognized ASR as serious national problems, with silicious limestones as the predominating reactive material. The Rocky Mountain region and, after some delay, also Iceland and New Zealand, brought the glassy volcanics into the family of "potential", reactive rock types ("potential" in this context meaning capable of producing harmful ASR, but only under certain conditions). Now South Africa disclosed the third "overseas connection", like Canada, experiencing harmful ASR with metamorphic and igneous rocks containing micro-crystalline quartz. With these three groups of rock types acknowledged to be susceptible it was ineluctable that harmful ASR would continue to be found in an ever-increasing number of countries.

Another novelty was the remarkable contributions by South African civil engineers. Their concern was the effect of harmful ASR on the performance of structural concrete, especially in highway bridges and pavements, and therefore they also added repair methods and costs to the contents of the conference. This meant that ASR as merely an issue of materials research was a thing of the past.

A third new reality was the considerable interest in the capability of fly ash and GGBS as preventive measures, and with the Icelandic research and cement industry the first to realize that the recycling product silica fume is also an effective inhibitor.

It was remarkable that the different parties in South Africa concerned with ASR, the industries, the National Building Research Institute, the civil engineering profession and the universities, had since 1977 operated an effective conglomerate for the research, testing, structural preservation and protective measures. This was an obviously fruitful cooperative model, similar to those previously created for the ASR research in Iceland and Denmark.

There was, perhaps, one more thing lurking in the minds of the delegates – the forthcoming "concrete durability crises". The National Materials Advisory Board of the National Research Council in the USA had published its comprehensive report on the dilapidation of the American infrastructure and the related decline of concrete research.[65] In the UK and Denmark, the media consistently made concrete the scapegoat for the dilapidation of precast concrete from the 1960s housing boom. The 1970s construction boom in the Middle East was known to have created a vast assembly of modern concrete ruins. Most of this was not related to ASR, but in the general opinion ASR was made part of the problem. Hence, all things considered, the fifth conference steered the ICAARs back towards the field of concrete behaviour and conditions as the first and final objective of the ASR research. The South African contributions deserve to be acknowledged for their part in this research and practice integration.

The South African ASR research programme

D. E. Davies referred, in the opening keynote address, to the absence of widespread concern about ASR until about 1980 in South Africa, which had found reassurance in the fact that opaline and volcanic siliceous rock types did not occur in the country. In about 1977 it was found that the Malmsbury group of aggregates in the south-west provinces, comprising greywacke and other rock types with micro-crystalline quartz, were used in structures which appeared to show undeniable evidence of ASR. The four years of research since then had highlighted the need for more knowledge regarding:

☐ mechanisms of the reaction
☐ testing methods for aggregates
☐ preventive effects of fly ash and slag
☐ practical approaches to the problem solutions.

It was emphasized that unexpected cases of harmless ASR occurred as well as cases of surprisingly violent reaction. The limitations of laboratory model testing were recognized, as was, on the other hand, the need for a reliable, better petrographic characterization of aggregates and a rapid test for alkali reactivity. The benefits of fly ash and GGBS as preventive measures were recognized, but in

South Africa the production of these materials took place far from the sites where the reactive aggregates were used. Since the required investment capital for new cement plants was also soaring, the economics of potential ASR damage in concrete structures should be judged against the cost/benefit by using cement with fly ash or GGBS. Above all "double checking precautions", such as low-alkali cement together with non-reactive aggregates should be avoided.

J. E. Damp suggested, in conjunction with the overview in the keynote address, the following preventive measures against ASR as suitable for South Africa:

- use of sulphate resisting cement
- production and use of low-alkali cement
- use of fly ash or GGBS.

The issue for engineering practice among these optional measures would be to select the best solution by evaluating the economic consequences.

In the course of the conference, it was repeatedly illustrated that the effectiveness of the less than five years of South African research was due to scrutinized utilization of the available knowledge from the previous, foreign research, and to professional management, and interaction among the different involved parties. Close cooperation with civil engineering in public service and private enterprise had made thorough field surveys and investigations possible, and structural rehabilitation programmes had commenced, along with studies of the possible effects of harmful ASR on structural safety.

R. E. Oberholster presented a review of the cooperative South African research programme. In the field investigations were included monitoring of expansive ASR over four years in a bridge element in the Cape Province. Detailed analyses of the cement and aggregate resources had been made. The aggregates had been found to include alkali-reactive, metamorphic rock types which the classical test methods did not classify as expansive reactive. A scrutiny of the available test methods and criteria had resulted in requirements for improvements of the ASTM C227 mortar bar method. It was substantiated that the alkali content of cement as a parameter for ASR risk should be replaced by the alkali content of concrete.

G. E. Blight, I. R. McIver, W. K. Schutte and R. Rimmer presented a thorough investigation of concrete bridges in the Witwatersrand area, made with a quartzite aggregate and cracked due to ASR. Ultrasonic velocity measurements were found to be insensitive to internal strength, and the cracking in concrete surfaces did not significantly reduce the sustainable structural stress. C. J. Semmelink reported a field investigation of damage to 131 concrete structures in the Cape Province. A systematic programme showed that about 50% of the structures suffered harmful ASR in slight to severe degrees. The aggravating impact of humidity and heat was indicated; dry, protected structural elements were unharmed. Structures made with mixtures of ordinary Portland cement and GGBS clearly showed the mitigating effects of the slag. A 50% "slagment" (South African brand name) had appeared effective in reducing expansion of mortar bars.

C. R. Freeme and B. Schackel examined a 27 km long concrete pavement in the Cape Town region. There was spalling at joints between pavement sections, indicating expansions or effects of vibratory traffic load. N. van der Walt, P. J. Strauss and O. Schnitter described rehabilitation of a concrete pavement with cracking due to harmful ASR, with emphasis on an economic model. W. A. Coull presented a geological and mineralogical characterization of the rock types in South Africa which, due to their content of siliceous minerals, were considered to be potentially alkali-reactive. The characterizations comprised detailed information about the physical and mechanical properties of the rock types and of their occurrence and importance as aggregate resources.

M. P. Brandt, R. E. Oberholster, and W. B. Westra had conducted an investigation of the aggregates in South Africa which caused harmful ASR in many concrete structures, using the different foreign test methods. The C289 quick chemical test did not give reproducible results. The acceptance criteria for the C227 mortar bar test could not be applied. It was necessary to use a cement in the test with specified alkali content, and the necessary test period was apparently longer than with the classical, siliceous aggregate types. The Canadian rock cylinder test showed expansive reactivity in veins in the rock samples, corresponding to the petrographic observations of the complex mineral composition of the reactive South African rock types. The examinations suggested that the reactive components were modifications of strained, micro-crystalline quartz.

R. E. Oberholster and W. B. Westra presented a study of the mitigating effects on ASR in concrete of different pozzolans, comprising fly ash, silica fume and GGBS. The reductions in expansion obtained by the cement replacements were greater than could be explained as a diluting effect. In other words, it was implied that the added materials created a beneficial ASR moderation. The blend of slagment and high-alkali Portland cement, not only effectively reduced expansion, but did so without reducing the compressive strength – in contrast to what happened with fly ash and calcined shale. B. D. G. Johnson presented a characterization of the available fly ash in South Africa and its influence on the properties of concrete. J. C. Flanagan presented a general guideline for the making of durable concrete with special attention to ASR.

Canadian research progress

The Canadian contributions to the 5th ICAAR were in several respects closely related to those from South Africa. High-alkali cements predominated in the eastern regions of Canada where alkali-reactive aggregates of various compositions were most common as concrete aggregates. Low-alkali cement was available in western Canada, but at prohibitive distances from the market needs. The reactive Canadian aggregates comprised metamorphic, quartzose rock types such as greywacke, hornfels, etc., and also igneous granites and gneissic rock types. In Quebec, large deposits of limestone were used, some were siliceous, others dolomitic, and apparently some dolomites had siliceous or illitic matrix components. As in South Africa, the classical test methods for alkali reactivity of aggregates were inadequate for evaluation of the alkali reactivity of these aggregates. P. E. Grattan-Bellew reviewed the state of knowledge as attained by the national research. A survey of cases of harmful ASR in the Appalachian region, Quebec and Ontario was presented, and locations of alkali-reactive aggregates across the country were displayed. In Nova Scotia, premium prices for low-alkali cement resulted in frequent use of high-alkali cement together with reactive aggregates. Recorded good results of this practice confirm that harmless ASR may occur in many concrete structures.

The presented map of occurrence of alkali-reactive aggregates in Canada shows so few identified localities that tremendous quantities of non-reactive rock types must be assumed to be available. If one combines this observation with the apparently satisfactory use of reactive aggregates and high-alkali cement, it would seem relevant to study the overall issue of ASR and ACR research in terms of cost-effectiveness. It might have been a possible barrier to such an approach that the AAR research in Canada was apparently concentrated at public research institutes and universities, with little or no cooperative activity within the cement and construction industry.

Field investigations elsewhere

J. W. Figg presented an investigation of a field case of ASR in England in concrete made with an artificial glass aggregate in a non-structural, precast concrete cladding. The claddings were produced in 1967–68, and failure occurred in 1978. The concrete was thoroughly cracked and showed extensive exudation of alkali-silica gel. It was extraordinary to find harmful ASR with white Portland cement, which is of low alkali content. The investigation revealed that the glass aggregate contributed a supplementary supply of alkalis to the concrete. R. T. I. Allen briefly reviewed a number of identified and presumed field cases of harmful ASR in the UK, with chert, quartzite and greywacke as reactive aggregates.

Cement

J. Skalny and W. Klemm reviewed the chemistry of alkali formation in cement during the cement manufacturing processing and mentioned the influence of the burning characteristics. They also discussed the effects in concrete dependent on the composition and solubility of the alkaline compounds. J. Svendsen presented a model for prediction of the state and amounts of volatile matter in cement kilns and described kiln design with a view to the reduction of alkalis.

GGBS and fly ash

P. J. Nixon investigated the preventive effects on ASR of substituting Portland cement with fly ash and GGBS in concrete. Mortar bar testing in accordance with the ASTM C441 method was applied with chert, Beltane opal, and Pyrex glass as reactive aggregates. It was concluded that 30% fly ash or 50% GGBS are sufficient to reduce the expansion in mortar bars to a level equivalent to that produced by using low-alkali cement as the sole precaution. The results were consistent with published German DIN limits on the alkali contents in slag. F. G. Buttler, S. R. Morgan, and E. J. Walker examined the rate and extent of reaction between calcium hydroxide and pulverized ash at 38°C. The ASTM C311 method for determination of the available alkalis in fly ashes and natural pozzolans was used. The inhibition of ASR by the use of fly ash was related to the fly ash–$Ca(OH)_2$ reaction. D. W. Hobbs had examined the preventive effects on ASR of the addition of fly ash to concrete. The examination was made by expansion tests on mortar bars with Beltane opal as reactive aggregate. The results substantiated that the basic perception was correct.

R. F. M. Bakker had found that the diffusion coefficients of Na^+ and K^+ ions were substantially less in mortar with slag cement than with ordinary Portland cement. The reduction was remarkably greater after 14 days than after 3 days. Likewise, it was found that slag cement mortars were 10–100% less permeable than Portland cement mortar. The results were found to confirm the known high resistance of concrete with slag cement (of 65–70% blast-furnace slag content) to sulphate attack (ascertained through many years' experience with marine concrete along the North Sea coast), and to ASR as shown by the newer German research.

The presentation of the use of testing in accordance with ASTM or alternative procedures for laboratory modelling research illustrated the trend in newer concrete technology research to rely on test results of laboratory specimens for unwarranted conclusions about the behaviour of exposed field concrete.

Mechanisms

S. Diamond reviewed recent research at Purdue University on the chemistry and mechanism of ASR. He categorized the reaction analytically in two steps: (*a*) purely chemical transition, and (*b*) swelling at the reaction site. The new pore-squeezing technique was used to show that only 40% silica were consumed when the alkalis were used up in given compositions of mortar with Beltane opal. He also confirmed Powers' and Steinour's theory about diffusion rate determined ingress of Ca^{++} and alkali ions into the reactive particles as the basic reaction mechanism. L. S. Dent Glasser and N. Kataoka reviewed the chemistry of the reaction of alkalis with silica, dependent on the modification of the silica structure, whether as amorphous or crystalline quartz, and on the concentration and basicity of the reacting alkali solution. In three display figures they illustrated their perception of swelling of alkali-silica gel in spaces between aggregate particles in mortars or concrete, *inter alia* referring, surprisingly, to the fact that "*cracks filled with gel are a common feature of concretes disrupted through reactive aggregates*". It was stipulated that gel, which has dissipated from reaction sites (in reacting aggregates), may further swell and "*contribute to disintegration of the concrete*", for instance if wetting/drying may enable dried gel to pick up water during wetting cycles. There were no substantiating examinations of field concrete.

M. Regourd, H. Hornain and P. Poitevin had studied the microstructural features of the development of ASR under controlled conditions with a glass aggregate, and with South African reactive greywacke and hornfels aggregates. They used SEM, energy dispersive X-ray analyses, electron probe analyses, X-ray diffractometry and X-ray photoelectron spectometry. They found that ASR with glass aggregate at 20°C/100% RH produced alkali-silica gel incorporating the CaO, MgO and Al_2O_3 of the glass. Under heat and pressure (autoclaving) the gel crystallized to become a substance close to tobermorite, as in autoclaved concrete. With the natural aggregates, crystallization of gel was promoted by heating. The presence of ettringite and $Ca(OH)_2$ was proposed to reinforce ASR. The authors referred to and agreed with my characterization of ASR as a hydration reaction.

H. E. Vivian reviewed the effect of drying on reactive aggregates and mortar expansions and stated that:

"*At late ages the expansion increments of all mortars and concretes may be diminished for reasons other than exhaustion of the supply of one of the major reactants. The swelling aggregate particles by producing cracks in mortar or concrete create space which can accommodate large volumes of deformable gel or sol without undergoing further change. In addition the deforming gel or sol comes into contact with an increasingly large amount of hydrated cement paste and can react with calcium hydroxide to form a non-water absorbing, non-swelling calcium hydroxide-silica complex*".

And further:

"*(c) In the presence of large amounts of alkali and free water, aggregate particles not only react rapidly but the reaction product also transforms very rapidly from a rigid gel which expands and disintegrates mortar and concrete to a deformable gel or to a sol which cannot cause expansion.*
(d) Mortar and concrete expansions are caused by the lengthening and widening of cracks. Displacements induced within the mass, and the presence of the reaction product in cracks, ensure that expansion is permanent and that damage is irreparable".

These perceptions were based on his many years of observation during experimental ASR research. In discussion, S. Diamond suggested that uptake of calcium in alkali-silica gel flowing out in cracks in concrete from reacting aggregate particles, presumably by dissolving calcium hydroxide crystals, simply "*added to the existing alkali-silicate burden so as to give a mixed alkali-silicate without necessarily liberating much of the sodium and/or potassium*".

Test methods

P. E. Grattan-Bellew reviewed the established test methods for AAR, the ASTM C227-71, mortar bar test, C289-71 quick chemical test, C586-66T rock cylinder test, the Canadian concrete prism test, CAN3-A23.2-14A, and the newer miniature rock prism methods. The need for methods other than the first two had appeared especially in Canada, where the harmful reaction was usually so slow to develop that the aggregates often would pass, when tested in accordance with the ASTM criteria for acceptance. This had led to the development of the Canadian concrete prism test in which the ASR is deliberately accelerated by means of addition of NaOH to 1.0% eqv. Na_2O, or higher if higher alkali cement is to be used. In addition, coarse aggregates are not crushed down to mortar sand particle sizes. The rock cylinder test was originally designed to identify alkali-carbonate reactive (dolomitic) aggregates. The cylindrical specimens are of 35 mm length × 35 mm diameter. The miniature rock prisms are 3 × 6 × 30 mm, and therefore more quickly saturated in the applied 1 N NaOH solution. The latter two methods were presented as unsuitable for classical ASR-reactive aggregates, due to disintegrating dissolution of the specimens by the NaOH. Reported comparable tests sustained that ASR and ACR examined by laboratory expansion tests showed an initial indecisive, or dormant, period, followed by the expansive phase, and subsequently a "fading" phase towards termination.

L. Dolar-Mantuani presented a detailed procedure for the method for determination of the undulatory extinction angle in quartz in concrete aggregates as "*the generally accepted method for identifying alkali-reactive quartz*". It was concluded that the method was applicable for slowly reacting rock types which contained crystalline quartz. The underlying assumption was that quartz under deformation stress shows undulatory extinction, and that quartz in such stress situations will be susceptible to ASR.

During the discussion session, R. E. Oberholster questioned the Canadian introduction of the special designation alkali-silicate reaction as distinct from alkali-silica reaction and being a special mode of reaction with phyllosilicates in greywacke and similar rock types. J. E. Gillott conceded an uncertainty, and that it might be *"the fine grained quartz, or other forms of silica in the rock that were the major factors in the mechanism of expansion"*. P. E. Grattan-Bellew shared the doubt that there was *"any fundamental difference in the mechanism of the classical alkali-silica reaction, and the mechanism of the slowly expanding siliceous rock"*. He preferred the terminology *"slowly expanding silica reaction"*. He further suggested that in classical ASR *"the gel-impregnated pores in the concrete absorbed water and swelled creating internal pressure which resulted in the expansion of the concrete"*, whereas in the slowly expanding silica aggregates, the grain boundaries between the quartz grains were attacked by alkali and dissolved, which resulted in expansion of the aggregate. Expansion of concrete might be due to either of these mechanisms.

J. Sims reviewed UK experience with the available test methods. He considered petrographic examination indispensable, admonished that in the ASTM C289 the presence of sulphates or carbonates may cause erroneous evaluations, and that in the ASTM C227-71 expansions which suggest non-reactivity should be scrutinized due to slow reactivity of some aggregates. He had found the ASTM C586-89 rock cylinder test dubious for evaluation of the alkali-carbonate reactivity of Middle Eastern aggregates. He considered that the use of low-alkali cement might not always be a safe precaution.

Underlying problems

I dwelled on the technical/economic implications of ASR, as the problem appeared to be relevant in an ever-increasing number of countries, and its effects in structural engineering therefore became more visible and required practical solutions. I suggested an ASR guideline for structural concrete design practice in which the preferential materials precautions – low-alkali cement, non-reactive aggregates, pozzolans or GGBS – were considered vis-à-vis the available engineering options. I reminded the audience that ASR is a hydration reaction, that the kinetic modelling in laboratory testing is inadequate, although the proper hydration kinetics knowledge, based on the Arrhenius equation, was available for application in ASR research. The neglect by most current research of reckoning with temperature dependence was suggested to be one element of ignorance within general concrete development which made the existing use of precautionary measures and test methods unreliable. I also mentioned the insufficient knowledge of the ways by which ASR in individually reacting aggregate particles may or may not accumulate to become harmful ASR in structural masses of concrete. I proposed that the most fruitful perspective was not massive expenditure on new research, but rather the channelling of some of the ongoing work into more rewarding goal-setting. I also urged construction engineers to incorporate risk analyses on a probability basis in the design of concrete structures and for evaluation of the need to apply precautionary measures.

Silica fume

In a special discussion session I reviewed recent Icelandic research, for which delegates could not be present. The national ASR research committee had made remarkable progress with the introduction of 5% silica fume in the Icelandic, very high-alkali cement. The addition of silica fume not only seemed totally to eliminate harmful ASR, but gave also the cement increasing strength capability. In addition, monosilanes were being tested for prevention of moisture ingress in exposed concrete, while allowing evaporation of superfluous pore water. This was tried for mitigation of ASR under development in field concrete, in particular in the many concrete houses in Reykjavik.

6th ICAAR, 1983, Copenhagen[176]

For this conference, I had organized a special session on the engineering education aspects of ASR. The expectation was that the increasing interaction of university professors (with laboratory research) and civil engineers (with field concrete problems and troubleshooting) would be a fine audience for fruitful debates about updating of engineering education. Besides the invited opening paper by A. B. Poole, UK, the response was one English and two Danish papers – and very little discussion. Presumably, the renovation of university courses, as related to changing engineering technology and structural performance experience, was a subject that the individual professor did not find suitable for peer discussion. At any rate, the subject has not been on the agenda at the subsequent conferences.

As the initiator of the conference and chairman of its scientific programme committee, it was my privilege to present the keynote address, entitled: "Thirty years with alkalis in concrete".[177] I referred to the prolonged global energy crisis, which had gradually alerted technical and industrial authorities to the opportunities in energy savings and concrete improvements by the use of fly ash, blast-furnace slag and, lately, also silica fume in blends with Portland cement. The melting/cooling processes by which these materials are produced have made them reservoirs of hydration energy in glassy, amorphous silica. When used with Portland cement in concrete they are activated by the alkaline pore solution and the released heat of hydration. Their initial hydration in concrete is a mode of ASR and is the fundamental nature of pozzolanic reactions. Consequently, the hydration of fly ash, GGBS and silica fume ought to be acknowledged as potentially *beneficial ASR*. Research had shown, in particular for the industry development for the use of slag in the USA and the UK, that improved workability of the fresh concrete, moderation of curing temperatures, and densification of hardened concrete is obtainable by appropriate selection of the materials' properties, mix design, and monitoring of the concrete processing.

I related these improvements to the primary influence of the alkali ions vis-à-vis the calcium ion on the early hydration of the three materials in blends with Portland cement. The Finnish development of the F-cement, consisting solely of finely ground, granulated blast-furnace slag with a super-plasticizing admixture, was an exceptional confirmation that the doors were opened for further innovations with these recycling resources of reactive silica. I further claimed

193

that, in principle, test methods regarding ASR ought to apply the true reaction kinetics by pre-established, heating/cooling procedures instead of the generally used constant temperature conditions.

In my concluding remarks, I stressed that concrete as a construction material had been radically changed in the course of the 43 years during which the effects of alkalis had been at issue, while research had largely maintained the original concepts and methods, despite its development of instrumentation and basic physico/chemical theory. I therefore proposed an update of the research.

Field investigations and research

P. Poitevin expressed the opinion that nowadays, with so much publicity on ASR, the specifiers and designers are exposed to overestimation of the dangers when new sources of aggregates are evaluated. He reviewed the evidence that exposure environments for structures are often inhibitory for harmful ASR, and that ASR in mortar bar testing is far from being representative of the effects of ASR in field concrete. Also, the initial invalidity of concrete due to thermal stresses during curing was mentioned as an influencing factor in modern construction practice. The effects of ASR-conditioned cracking and expansion in different kinds and elements of concrete structures with and without reinforcement were analysed. It was mentioned that even with dams, no major structural failures with collapse can be attributed to ASR.

G. E. Blight, M. G. Alexander, W. K. Schutte and T. K. Ralph had performed a, presumably, original full loading test on a portal of a major double-deck road structure in Johannesburg, SAR. The concrete structure had suffered severe cracking due to ASR and ultrasonic velocity measurements had indicated deep penetration of the visible surface cracking. The structural displacements prior to loading were calculated, and instrumentation was placed for continuous recording of the actual displacements during loading. The load test supported the hypothesis, *"that deterioration of concrete as a result of AAR is alarming in appearance, but not necessarily structurally dangerous"*.

A. Nielsen found, by analyses of field concrete investigations and comparison with a course of mortar bar tests, that harmful ASR should be divided into an initial, "dormant" phase, the propagation phase, and the "rest phase" towards cessation. Dams in the USA had shown propagations of ASR throughout about 30–35 years, while ASR in Danish highway bridges were approaching termination after about 8 years. H. Mørup and S. E. Petersen described two field cases of harmful ASR in swimming pools in Denmark. In both cases, sodium chloride had been added to the pool water. Even coarse, dense flint particles were affected, and ASR was also evidenced in the interior ceramic tile cladding. The pools were 5–8 years old when repair works became necessary.

C. D. Comberbach, P. G. Fookes and J. Cann described a crack mapping technique as part of field investigations of concrete deterioration in south-west England. I. G. M. Wood and P. J. Wickens discussed and described the structural effects of AAR in general, but did not refer to data from actual investigations.

H. Olafsson described research and development of repair methods for cracking due to harmful ASR in concrete walls of houses and buildings in

Reykjavik, Iceland. The conclusive results emphasized application of silicones/ silanes which allowed "breathing" of the walls and simultaneously prevented ingress of the often severe rain during strong westerly winds.

The conference comprised two reports about the occurrence of harmful ASR in countries which had not earlier identified such cases: Italy and Zambia. G. Baronia described that, from about 1980, ASR had been found to be the cause of cracking in pavements and in an eight-year old building in regions at the Adriatic Sea. N. Thaulow described harmful ASR in the Itezhitezhi dam's intake towers in Zambia. Substantial map-cracking had developed and bending and structural expansion in the order of 40 mm over a height of 30 m was experienced about five years after construction. The coarse aggregate was a granitic rock type from a local quarry and from the tunnel excavations. Veins in the aggregate particles were filled by a brown amorphous material, believed to be opal. The aggregate had passed the ASTM C227 test.

Cement

I. Worning and V. Johansen reviewed the latest developments in cement manufacture technology, especially with a view to the possible reduction of the alkali contents in modern Portland cements. They concluded as follows.

> "*The results attained in practical operation show that Na_2O can be reduced by up to 20% of the Na_2O admitted and that up to some 30% of the K_2O admitted can be removed. Practical experience also seems to show that alkali bypasses become far less efficient once their size exceeds 60%, the alkali reduction in such precalciner kilns being only slightly higher while fuel consumption is increased.*
>
> *The conditions which ensure the most effective reduction of the alkali content in clinker also make kiln operation more costly. It is therefore unrealistic to expect that low-alkali cement will continue to be available at the same price as cement with no limitation of alkali content.*"

GGBS, fly ash and silica fume

Figure 53 is a display which I presented of the hydration of the three siliceous materials in the three phase $CaO-Al_2O_3-SiO_2$ diagram, with either lime or alkali hydroxide as the activator.[177] The display is intended to illustrate that lime activation supports crystallinity of the hydration products, whereas alkaline activation promotes gel-like, amorphous products.

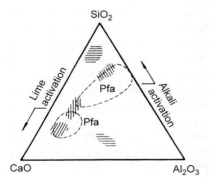
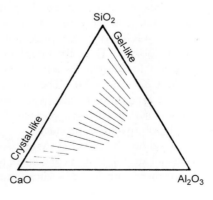

Fig. 53. The three-phase $CaO-SiO_2-Al_2O_3$ diagram showing the well known "lime-activation" range towards the bottom left corner and the less studied "alkali-activation" range towards top right corner, and a three-phase diagram displaying that the "lime-activation" range of cementitious compositions predominantly creates "crystal-like", fibrous or foiled hydrates, while the alkali-activation range of "pozzolanic" compositions predominantly creates sol-colloid, gel-like hydrates, from reference [177]

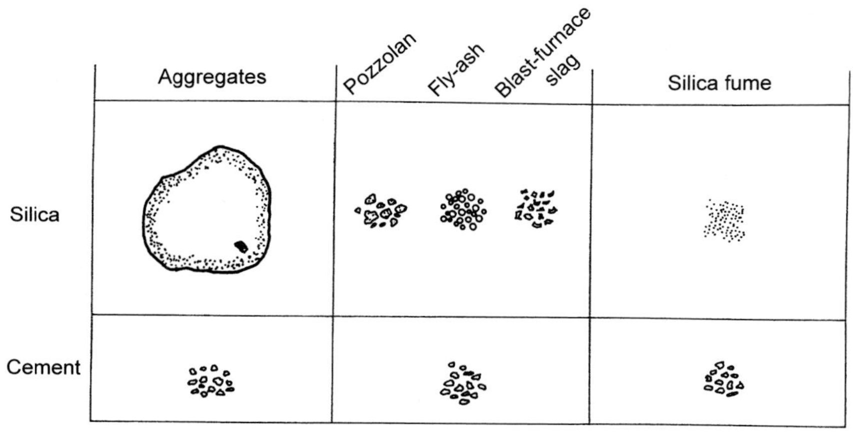

	Aggregates	Pozzolan	Fly-ash	Blast-furnace slag	Silica fume
Silica					
Cement					

Fig. 54. Reacting cement-silica system graded after particle size distribution ranges of the silica supplying constituents

Figure 54, also from reference [177], displays the reacting cement-silica system in concrete as related to the ranges of particle sized distributions of aggregates, natural pozzolans, fly ash, GGBS and silica fume. Harmful ASR can only occur with aggregate particles as the reactive silica supplier. Prevention of harmful ASR is obtainable with the finely ground or manufactured siliceous materials. Beneficial ASR can be attained by intelligent selection of the granulometry, mineralogy, and chemistry of the blends of these materials and Portland cement.

L. Spellman described the investment in a manufacturing plant for 800 000 tonnes a year of GGBS to supplement Portland cement for concrete in the eastern United States. He reviewed the reliance on European and recent, associated American research which confirmed the potential improvements of concrete and the preventive effects against harmful ASR by the use of a 50 : 50% blend of Portland cement and the GGBS, called NewCem. R. I. A. Malek and D. M. Roy had found that the alkaline solution in concrete with GGBS in the cement dissolves not only SiO_2, but also Al_2O_3 in the glassy slag structure, and suggested that this component in the pore solution might also help to mitigate harmful ASR. J. Sims referred to comparable investigations in the UK, concentrating on showing the prevention of harmful ASR in ASTM C227 mortar bars made with GGBS, high-alkali cement and a reactive aggregate.

P. J. Nixon and M. E. Gaze showed by means of ASTM C441 mortar bar tests and concrete prism tests that, with UK materials, a 50% replacement of Portland cement by GGBS or 50% replacement by fly ash effectively prevented damage by ASR. L. Boswell, E. C. Robert, F. G. Buttler and S. R. Morgan confirmed this evaluation for British fly ash by mortar bar experiments in accordance with ASTM C227 and C441. The potentially increasing – but not appearing – effect on expansions by alkalis released from the fly ash during the mortar bar tests was suggested to be prevented by the densification of the cement paste with fly ash hydration products.

G. Gudmundsson and H. Asgeirsson described the effective prevention of the effects of harmful ASR in concrete in Iceland by blending the national, very high-alkali cement with 5–7.5% silica fume, locally produced.

Chemistry and mechanisms

Tang Ming-shu and Han Su-fen acknowledged that ASR is a hydration process, and found, experimentally, that the interdependence of rates of reaction and reaction temperatures could be predicted by the Arrhenius equation:

$$k = K_o \exp\left(-\frac{E}{RT}\right)$$

for narrow ranges of temperatures which were different for different rock types in aggregates. The values of E and K_o had been determined for different aggregates and were presumably also related to the characteristics of crystallinity, composition, porosity, etc. of the reacting rock types.

They established that ASR occurs in three phases:

(*a*) a dormant period
(*b*) constant rate of expansion (not diffusion controlled)
(*c*) decreasing or terminating period of expansion – converging towards threshold values of concentrations of alkalis or silica.

They determined experimentally the activation energy (E) and frequency factor (K_o) for opal, silica bricks, fused silica and quartz sand, and found K_o to decrease from opal ($\log K_o = 5.32$) to quartz ($\log K_o = 0.14$) in this order, with the corresponding E (kJ/mol) varying from 65.024 to 48.538. It was suggested that E and K_o be used for identification of the alkali reactivity of aggregates rather than the conventional mortar bar expansion tests at constant temperatures. The authors had used a new test method of two hours' duration by application of heating to autoclaving temperatures on $1 \times 1 \times 4$ cm mortar bars, stored in 10% KOH at different temperatures, reaching 150°C and 300°C for making quartz reactive, but only 53°C for opal. This paper was a landmark introduction of realistic hydration kinetics in the chemistry of ASR.

S. Diamond presented investigations of the changes in composition of the pore solution in cement paste during early hydration. The pore-squeezing technique was used. It was found that, initially, at mixing, the K^+ and SO_4^{2-} ions went into solution. After a dormant period of around 4 hours (at room temperature), the SO_4^{2-} ions concentration began to decrease linearly, while K^+ ion and Na^+ ion concentration increased slightly, and the OH^- ion concentration sharply. The Ca^{++} ion concentration decreased from minor to almost zero. The experiments suggested that during early hydration of cement paste, the pore solution becomes a strong alkali hydroxide (corresponding to pH values > 13). This was in confirmation of my perception that pozzolanic reaction is, in principle, alkali-silica reaction, albeit not in an expansive mode of development. The consumption of the SO_4^{2-} ions was presumably explained by the corresponding formation of ettringite. The author cautioned that field concrete was a more complicated system than his experimental material. Nevertheless, it seemed to be sustained by other research studies that alkali-silica gel could absorb calcium ions both by diffusion at reaction sites, and subsequently from cement paste during its passage into cracks radiating from aggregates. The author and other workers had found silica fume capable of quickly removing alkali hydroxide from cement paste pore solutions. In conclusion, the author suggested that a threshold value of the alkali hydroxide concentration in pore solution of cement paste of about 0.25 N corresponding to a pH of 13.4 is required to make ASR proceed in concrete.

M. Kawamura, K. Takumoto and S. Hasaba applied quantitative EDX analyses and microhardness measurements to reacted aggregate particles in ASTM C227 mortar bars for measurements of the progressive chemical reaction and changing solution compositions. They found that:

- the intrusion of pore liquid into reacting opal particles reduced the microhardness after seven days
- subsequent solidification of the reacting opaline particle's "rim structure" related to the intrusion of calcium
- expansion of mortars related to the amounts of gel rather than to their chemical composition
- the fly ash used in the study did not inhibit ASR at all, but facilitated the mobilization of calcium in reactive aggregate particles.

M. Regourd described and categorized analyses of evidence of ASR and ACR in drilled concrete cores and correlated petrographic examinations of concrete aggregates by optical microscopy and SEM. Several compositions and morphologies of alkali-silica gel, of deterioration mechanisms of ACR and of secondary compounds found in distressed concrete were identified. The morphological changes of blended cements which mitigate harmful ASR were described.

S. Chatterji, N. Thaulow, P. Christensen and A. D. Jensen had, by petrographic examination of mortar bars, found that expansion with Danish types of opaline limestone and flint required the presence of free $Ca(OH)_2$ and that the complete removal of free $Ca(OH)_2$ prevented expansive ASR.

A. B. Poole and I. Al-Dabbagh examined ASR with UK types of flint by EDX and SEM. They found that crumbled and foiled morphologies of alkali-silica gel depended on the reaction temperatures ($20-50°C$) and related to different chemical compositions, rates of formation and viscosity. A correlation between the reactivity and "impurity levels" of gel could not be established.

L. O. Nilsson had found pop-outs of reactive sand (chert) particles to be a problem in concrete in Sweden. He proposed about 90% RH in the pore space of the concrete to be a "pessimum" moisture content for the pop-out formation. A. Nielsen measured RH in the walls of a swimming pool with ASR damage. He found an average of 80% RH in the concrete and evidence that the ASR contributed to self-dessication of the cement paste in the interior of the concrete.

Xu Huarong and Chen Meiliang described classification of rock types in aggregates along the Yangtse river in China, in order to prepare for avoidance of ASR in the planned construction of a series of hydropower plants.

Test methods

P. E. Grattan-Bellew reviewed the existing examination and test methods for alkali-silica and carbonate reactivity of aggregates, comprising procedures with rock samples and specimens, mortar bars and concrete prisms, cubes and discs. The original ASTM system approach for ASR with petrographic examination plus the chemical and mechanical reactivity test, and the British gel pat test, had now, with the spread of ASR to many countries, escalated as follows:

(a) Petrographic examination by optical microscopy was supplemented by scanning microscopic examination, especially of dolomitic rock types, and by the Canadian undulatory extinction angle determination of crystalline quartz.

(b) Rock cylinder and rock prism expansivity in NaOH, originally developed as alkali-carbonate reactivity tests of dolomitic rocks, were now adapted for alkali-silica reactivity.

(c) A German, modified chemical test of aggregate samples for alkali-silica reactivity was introduced.

(d) Modifications of the ASTM C227 mortar bar test had been introduced in Canada and Denmark.

(e) A new chemical autoclave test with small mortar bars had appeared.

(f) The Canadian concrete prism test CSA A23.2-14 A, originally developed for carbonate reactivity of dolomitic rock types, had been adopted in Canada and was under trial elsewhere for alkali-silica reactivity of slowly reacting rock types.

(g) A concrete cube test for alkali-silica reaction was created in Germany and was on trial elsewhere.

Altogether, two supplements to petrography, several modifications of the rapid chemical test, two rock specimen tests, two new mortar bar tests and two new concrete sample tests were now available. Reference was made to their limited interpretation reliability, but thorough model analyses were not approached. The issues of harmless reaction, reaction kinetics and mass effects were not considered, and no attempt was made to promote joint investigation of the model transfer problems.

The subsequent contributions regarding test methods described applications of the above methods on concrete aggregates from the UK, the Middle East and North Africa. N. Thaulow and H. Olafsen compared the ASTM C227 and a new Danish Technological Institute (T.I.) mortar bar test method, and the ASTM C289 with the German chemical test method. The T.I. mortar bar test used storage of mortar bars in a saturated NaCl solution at $+50°C$, with 8 or 20 weeks' storage duration, dependent on the nature of the reactive rock type. All four methods were checked by petrographic classification of the sand. D. Stark introduced a new procedure for the earlier American osmotic cell test. R. F. M. Bakker analysed the model issue of mortar bar versus concrete prism sizes. He concluded that the mortar bar size may allow reactive aggregates to pass which would be caught by the concrete prism test. D. Lenzner described application of resonance frequency measurements in the "Aachen concrete prism test method".

7th ICAAR, 1986, Ottawa[178]

At this conference, AAR may be said to have been indisputably recognized as a global problem at last, with field cases of harmful ASR reported from five "new" countries: Poland in Europe, India and Japan in Asia, and Brazil and Argentina in South America. Also, increasing research was still being reported from the "old" countries, especially where ASR had been the subject of research already for many years, namely in Canada and England.

New information from these two countries and from Japan supported the lesson from the 1940–60 epoch, that the number of cases of harmful ASR is always small in comparison with the occurrence of harmless reaction in populations of comparable structures. Canadian researchers continued to operate with alkali-silicate reaction and with the UEA measurements in quartz as indicators of reactivity, but with more opposing argumentation than previously. British researchers elaborated on complicated diagnostic and monitoring procedures for field investigations. A large, national research programme was reported to have started in Japan after discovery of ASR in major highway structures. Expansions and deformations of concrete in hydropower structures were reported from Brazil, India and Canada.

Characterization of reactive sedimentary volcanic, metamorphic and igneous rock types with different silica modifications were reported from several countries and more or less related to new and existing test methods. The preventive effects of fly ash, GGBS and silica fume became a high priority topic. But there was again a remarkable tendency towards increasing reliance on expansion test results with mortar bars and concrete prisms, not merely for comparative evaluations of the potential alkali reactivity of aggregates, but also in research for judgements on the ASR preventive potential of blends of various combinations of Portland cements with different types of the blending materials. Model relationships between the laboratory conditions and those of field concrete, and examinations for assessments of what actually happened in test specimens disappeared completely from the scene. In the realm of aggregate reactivity testing, maximum reproducibility of empirical laboratory measurements on test specimens gained preference over studies of the mechanisms and chemistry of the reaction in the specimens as related to comparable field concrete. Chemical shrinkage was introduced as a feature of the chemistry/mechanism of ASR, but it was not correlated with the occurrence of harmless reaction in field concrete. The role of $Ca(OH)_2$ in ASR received vigorous attention. New and existing, revised test methods were discussed.

Comprehensive investigations in Ontario, Canada, had shown that over 130 structures were affected by ASR, ACR, and the stipulated alkali-silicate reaction. The latter was considered the cause of harmful reaction in concrete with argillite and greywacke as aggregates, although with the admission that this reaction was still not "properly understood". In another investigation, 26 structures in the Sudbury region of Ontario had also been found to be affected by the alkali-silicate reaction due to the use of argillite and greywacke aggregates. The recorded evidence of damage was, however, the generally acknowledged symptoms of ASR.

The power house of the Beauharnois hydropower station at the St. Lawrence river, Quebec, had been found to be severely affected by harmful ASR with substantial expansions and deformations of the wet-exposed concrete units. The reactive component of the aggregate was chalcedony in sandstone, and the alkali content of the cement about 1.0%. The structural integrity was not in doubt.

An extensive investigation of concrete structures made with aggregate from limestone quarries in the Quebec city region revealed modest reactivity in 60 structures, with typical evidence of ASR.

In the UK, 40% of 300 structures examined had been found to be more or less affected by ASR, of these some had argillite, greywacke and similar rock types as the reacting aggregate constituent. Cracking was inevitably found to originate within reacting particles and clusters of such particles appeared to act as local expansion centres, generating macroscopic cracking. In older structures gel was replaced by ettringite. An electric substation in the Midlands, England, showed evidence of harmful ASR, despite $2.4-2.9 \, kg/m^3$ alkali content in the concrete, i.e. below the much publicized British $3.0 \, kg/m^3$ threshold value. An investigation which introduced a special "overall structure rating" put damage caused by ASR into five categories. For 63 structures, the proportions in each category (ranging from severe to negligible) were: 10, 19, 47, 22, 2%. As the rating yardstick was rather harsh, the investigation suggests that the general effects of ASR in England were mild to moderate.

From Poland, it was revealed for the first time that ASR had occurred increasingly since about 1970 due to drastic increases of the alkali content in the cements, from an earlier average of about 0.40% eqv. Na_2O (the wet process) to maximum of about 1.5% eqv. Na_2O (the dry process, new plants). No details of affected structures were given.

From South Africa new investigations of ASR in field concrete were reported, emphasizing repair methods and assessments that structural reliability was being preserved.

Figure 55 from reference [179] displays an applied system approach to the investigation of affected structures, and for rehabilitation.

For the first time in its history it was revealed that ASR occurred in Japan. In 1979, fine cracking was observed in concrete piers of the four-year old Hanshin expressway, Osaka. In 1982, the damage was alarming, although comprehensive investigations and stress analyses showed that the structural performance had not been adversely affected. The reactive aggregates were volcanic rocks, which were found to have supplied alkalis to the concrete. In fact, ASR had been identified in Japan as early as 1950, and since 1982 harmful ASR had actually been found at many locations. Depletion of non-reactive aggregates, use of sea-dredged sand, and higher alkali content were referred to as the causes.

In China, ASR had first been recognized in 1953. Later attention was due to concern over new dam constructions.

In India, expansions in the concrete of a penstock gallery in a hydropower plant was identified as caused by ASR. The reaction was causing cracking and operational problems due to the deformation of structural units.

In Australia, a causeway built in 1949–51 at Perth, western Australia, had shown cracking of varying intensity in sections made with granitic/gneissic and quartzite aggregates and high-alkali cement.

In Brazil, harmful ASR was observed in the Motoxó hydropower dam in 1980, three to eight years after construction. Movements in the concrete of the turbine cases had required repairs, and cutting of transversal joints had been necessary at the power house for relaxation of tensions created by expansions in the concrete. The reactive aggregate was granitic, the alkali content of the cement 1.0% eqv. Na_2O, and the cement content of the concrete $350 \, kg/m^3$. Tests with injection of CO_2 to mitigate the reaction were mentioned.

In Argentina, harmful ASR was first recorded in 1958 as occurring in a concrete pavement. A $130\,000 \, m^2$ airstrip, constructed at an airport in 1960, showed deterioration in 1978 in a humid, subtropical environment with opaline sandstone as the aggregate. A few minor cases were also referred to.

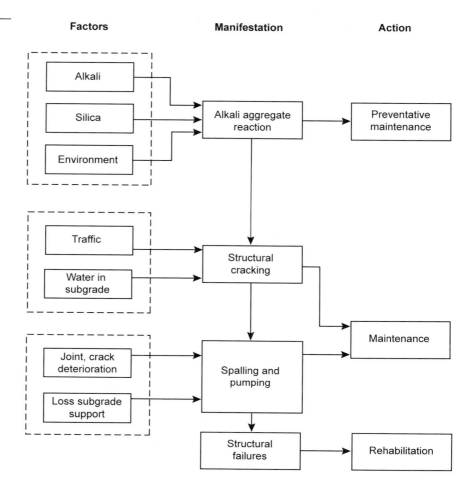

Factors	Manifestation	Action

- Alkali
- Silica
- Environment
→ Alkali aggregate reaction → Preventative maintenance

- Traffic
- Water in subgrade
→ Structural cracking

- Joint, crack deterioration
- Loss subgrade support
→ Spalling and pumping → Maintenance

Structural failures → Rehabilitation

Fig. 55. Factors leading to structural failure and appropriate action

Aggregates

The Canadian UEA method was reported to have been used successfully on granitic and metamorphic rock types from affected structures in south-east USA and India, respectively, whereas there were contributions from Australia and Canada which questioned the reliability of the method.

A new procedure for petrographic examination of aggregates in the UK was said to eliminate the need for supplementary aggregate testing of 70% of the samples in one series and 86% in another.

In Japan, extensive studies had revealed that the younger volcanic rock types (origins in Miocene to Quaternary), which are common throughout most of Japan, are reactive, while the older and altered volcanic rocks (origins before Miocene) are less to non-reactive.

Fly ash, GGBS and silica fume

A study by M. S. Y. Bhatty and N. R. Greening, Portland Cement Association, USA, had, among other things, shown that:

□   considerably less alkali is leached out of blended cement pastes than out of pure Portland cement paste

□   the amount of alkali retained depends on the nature and amount of the blending material

□   the percentage of leached alkali decreases proportionally with the increase of the silica content of the Portland and the blended cement

□   a C/S mole ratio of blended cements of less than 1.5 could effectively inhibit ASR cracking.

Studies of the mitigating effects of the blending materials were also reported by researchers from different countries, using mortar bar and concrete prism expansion test methods. Canadian investigations showed that aggregates which had been found to be deleteriously reactive in field concrete might not cause expansion when tested with the laboratory methods. Most of the reported studies did not, however, make the comparison. There were two exceptions from this practice.

(a)   Large-scale testing, and subsequent successful use of calcined, kaolinitic clays as pozzolan for 7.6 million m^3 concrete in four major dams in Brazil with replacement levels varying from 17–40%. Additional advantages were mentioned:

□   reduction of cement consumption for maintained strength levels

□   reduction of bleeding in the fresh concrete

□   reduction of peak curing temperatures, and

□   reduction of costs because the price of pozzolan was 40% of the cement price.

(b)   Research in South Africa, which had been found to be insufficiently documented by reliance only on laboratory mortar bar testing. The supplementary programme which was now reported comprised $1000 \times 300 \times 450$ mm concrete beams and cubes of 300 mm length edges all stored outside on a site in Cape Town. After four and six years' exposure, respectively, it was found that:

□   50% GGBS as cement replacement appeared to be effective in preventing ASR expansion even with 4.95 kg/m^3 active alkali content

□   15% fly ash as a cement replacement appeared to be effective with 4.07 kg/m^3 active alkali content

□   15% calcined shale or 5% silica fume was not effective in preventing deleterious ASR with alkali contents of 4.07 and 3.87 kg/m^3, respectively.

Mechanisms of reactions and microstructure of reaction products

The most innovative contributions regarding the mechanism of ASR in concrete were those by T. K. Knudsen about a new test method based on the chemical shrinkage concept, and by M. S. Y. Bhatty and N. R. Greening, referred to above, about the influence of the alkali/calcium ratios on the course of reactions. Knudsen mentioned the problems of considering quantitative expansion measurements on laboratory mortar bars or concrete prisms as true expressions of the course of ASR, because the expansion behaviour depends on factors such as the porosity of the reacting specimen, the supply of water, temperature, etc. He drew attention to the fundamental nature of ASR as a hydration process, which means that for a given quantity of the reactants – silica and alkaline solution – the volume of the reaction product – alkali-silica gel – is less than the volume of the reactants before reaction. In other words: *ASR with a given, confined amount of reactants will exhibit chemical shrinkage, and not expansion.* This is important for the distinction between the occurrence of harmless as opposed to harmful ASR in field concrete. The amount of susceptible silica in a given concrete body is fixed, while the amount and concentration of the alkaline pore liquid is variable, dependent on many factors, inherent and external. There may, therefore, easily be regions in concrete structures, even within limited members and sections, with a tendency to develop ASR with shrinkage of the reaction product as well as with expansion. This difference may also change in the course of time, and may even have influenced the course of behaviour of laboratory mortar bars and concrete prisms unnoticed. The universal absence of reports of cases of harmful ASR in indoor, drying concrete can be explained by T. Knudsen's perception, just as the frequent reports about very long-term duration of expansive ASR in hydro-power dam concrete seems explicable by the continuous supply of water which migrates, for instance, through large volumes of concrete from submerged, upstream surfaces to downstream surfaces with high evaporation.

Another Danish study concerned the accelerating effects of NaCl and $Ca(OH)_2$ on ASR. Concrete prisms had been stored in saturated NaCl solution. Petrographic examination of thin sections under an optical microscope showed that crystalline $Ca(OH)_2$ was absent in a narrow zone around affected aggregate grains, suggesting that the calcium hydroxide had been dissolved and engaged in ASR as a partnership reactant. The expansion of mortar bars was found to decrease along with the dissolution of the $Ca(OH)_2$ in the paste, whereas diffusion of SiO^{4+} ions from reacting particles increased with the decrease of free $Ca(OH)_2$ in the adjacent paste. It was stipulated that during storage in NaCl solution, Na^+ ions from NaCl and OH^- ions from $Ca(OH)_2$ in solution enters reactive silica particles, while corresponding amounts of Ca^{2+} and Cl^- ions are left outside the particles in the liquid pore phase. In conclusion, the authors proposed the use of a saturated NaCl solution as storage condition for alkali reactivity test mortar bars, because an inexhaustible supply of alkali ions is thereby ensured.

A French study by means of electron optical microscope and X-ray diffractometry concerned the textures, crystallinity and composition of reaction products of ASR and ACR from two field cases. Both amorphous gels and crystalline calcium alkali-silica compounds were found and analysed. The dolomitic reaction had created de-cohesion of aggregate particles with large cracks and isolated dolomite crystals in the calcitic matric, but also siliceous gel. The AAR as a whole should be considered as a complex reaction giving rise to different reaction products.

Test methods

Seven new test methods were presented at the conference. Five of these were alternatives to the classical ASTM methods for testing the alkali-silica reactivity of concrete aggregates. The Chinese autoclave method had been adopted in

Japan, with amendments, and in China found to be suitable for testing both ASR and ACR reactivity.[180] An Italian investigation repeated the use of the German application of infrared spectroscopy, Hirche 1975.[181] In addition, a new comparative "standard" aggregate was introduced, as was a concrete core test method, and a "round robin" examination of the questionable reliability of the ASTM C227 mortar bar test by prolongation of the test to five years. Knudsen presented an automatic apparatus for simultaneous measurements of chemical shrinkage in six aggregate samples over 20 hours.

J. F. Scott and C. R. Duggan from Canada presented a method for distinguishing between deleterious and stipulated non-deleterious expansions in concrete. They drilled 22 mm diameter × 65 mm long cores out of field concrete structures, heated and cooled, and dried and wetted them with peak heating/drying temperature of 82°C, attained over three periods of one, one and three days' duration, and with cooling to +21°C in between. They related maximum expansion to ASR in the concrete. However, they admitted that the cracking and expansion might be due to the imposed severe physical treatment.

8th ICAAR, 1989, Kyoto[182]

The 885 pages of the proceedings, with 133 papers, made the 8th ICAAR by far the largest conference in the series, so far. Of the contributed papers, 65 were about recent Japanese research illustrating the recent national concern about AAR. This cause of concrete deterioration had not been considered worthy of much attention before 1985, when severe cracking development was observed in the piers for the elevated Hanshin expressway, and thereafter also in major structures in the infrastructure system elsewhere in Japan. The relatively high risk of earthquakes and the enormous traffic intensity in and between the major cities in the country justified concern about the possible degradation of structural safety as a consequence of AAR and research for methods for monitoring and repairs to affected structures. The general increase of the alkali content in cement and the predominance of reactive volcanic rock types as the prevailing national resource for concrete aggregates made also preventive measures, such as the cement replacement materials and chemical admixtures, hot topics for the research. The conference showed that the recognition of AAR had launched substantial research investments in Japan, with preceding experience elsewhere as the planning basis. The accomplishments from the unusually concentrated realization of the research was an important asset for the conference.

Structural research into the effects on the structural load-transfer capability of harmful ASR was now in progress in several countries, as was research into repairs and mitigating treatment of affected structures. The misconception that gel may cause expansion after having exuded out into cracks caused by the bursting, reacting aggregate particles, apparently still had supporters. Chinese and Danish studies definitively showed that UEA measurements should be rejected as reflecting alkali reactivity. A Canadian study of concrete cores from eight dams in eastern Canada revealed that they all possessed the typical evidence of ASR, although only two of the dams showed visual signs of damage, and the strength of the cores from the interior was apparently unaffected by ASR. This study questioned, in conclusions about AAR: *"is it always harmful?"*

205

Table 26 shows how the Japanese organizing committee had integrated its national comprehension of the state of the art and the record level of solicited papers into the chosen structure of conference sessions.

There were now enough countries with accumulated experience about the occurrence and effects of AAR to justify the arrangement of the special opening session containing national reviews. These included as "new countries", north-eastern Australia, Taiwan, France and Belgium. A special case of ASR in ceramic tiles was reported in Session 1, mechanisms, from Norway as another "new" country.

National reviews

S. Nishibayashi reported in the review of the AAR history in Japan, that comprehensive testing of Japanese aggregate sources had been made by the ASTM methods in the 1950s, resulting in the assessment that a few types of river gravel with chert and shale were potentially reactive. A single case of harmful ASR had been identified in 1965 with andesite as the reactive rock type. Since then nothing had been done about AAR until the development of cracking in the new Hanshin expressway piers due to ASR caused concern in the early 1980s. The depletion of the traditional river-deposited gravel aggregates caused changes to quarrying of rock outcrops together with the use of dredged marine sand, and increasing alkali contents in Japanese cements had apparently taken the authorities, the industry and the engineering community by surprise, without any, or perhaps a neglected, forewarning from the research.

The New Zealand review similarly illustrated the features of delayed recognition of ASR in that country. The New Zealand and Japanese reviews showed that, in both countries, the younger volcanic rock types are the predominating reactive rock types.

The review from Iceland, where the same younger volcanic rock types have caused problems, confirmed that the national ferro silicon production has offered the country an effective preventive measure, with 5–7% of the silica fume added to the local cement.

The Australian review referred to the identification of about 100 structures in

Table 26. *Survey of disposition of sessions and number of papers at 8th ICAAR, including keynote papers in sessions 1–6*

Sessions	Number of papers
General	3
Opening – national reviews	9
1. Mechanisms	13
2. Mineral and chemical admixtures	15
3. Test methods and criteria for aggregate reactivity	25
4. Reaction products and petrographic examination	21
5. Environmental influence and preventive measures	9
6. Assessment and repair to damaged structures	38
Total	133

North Queensland with ASR, which was severe in eight of the cases. The cases with harmful ASR concerned high strength, prestressed, steam cured concrete beams, while two ordinarily reinforced structures were found to display harmless ASR, which was judged to be commonly occurring. Volcanic rock types of rhyolitic (and andesitic) compositions were stated to be the reactive aggregates. A dam structure (not located) and a causeway bridge in western Australia had previously been identified as harmful ASR cases.

The South African and the Canadian reviews confirmed their common situations with slowly reacting metamorphic rock types, and in Canada also igneous, granitic and gneissic rock types, as the cause of harmful ASR. In South Africa, surface treatment with monosilanes as a surface coating was found to be effective for termination of ongoing ASR. In Canada, the special slow alkali-silicate reaction was still stipulated to occur with metamorphic and granites as the reactive rock types. The poor correlation between testing-based evaluation of aggregate reactivity and field performance of concrete was still subject to research – primarily funded by the government and public technical agencies. A total of 32 locations of harmful AAR cases in eastern Canada (Quebec and Ontario) and 2 cases in western Canada (British Columbia) were shown on maps, and over 160 reports and papers were referred to as describing the Canadian research accomplishments.

In the UK, somewhere between 100 and 300 concrete structures, built between 1931 and 1975, had been found possibly to have harmful ASR as the cause of cracking. In south-west England, chert particles in sea-dredged sand were reported to be the cause of ASR. Different mitigating techniques were applied in affected structures. In the Val de la Mare dam, Jersey, vertical post-tensioned steel anchor bars were placed in holes bored into the bottom foundation in order to impede gross expansions in one block. In other structures the performance capability was unaffected. No British test method for aggregate reactivity had yet been accepted. Fly ash and GGBS were reported to be acceptable for preventive measures, provided that the alkali contents of these materials were taken into account, with a total of $3 \, kg/m^3$ alkalis in the concrete as an acceptable maximum for concrete with reactive aggregates.

From Belgium and Italy, the national reviews concerned the recent identification of one structure with harmful ASR in each of these countries. The Italian paper referred to the local warm, humid climatic exposure in the Adriatic coastal region as a contributory factor.

The reviewer from Denmark made a new distinction between two phases of national research into ASR. The first being the period before, and the second after, his transfer from abroad to the country, and referring to observed cases of harmful ASR in highway pavements, which had been de-iced with sodium chloride during winter seasons. This gave rise to studies, by laboratory testing of mortar bars, of the impact of the chloride and calcium ions on the development of harmful ASR.

There was no national review from the USA. An individual paper from France acknowledged that a few cases of harmful ASR had been identified in 1986, but no further information was given.

Effects of AAR on structural performance

At the conference, three papers from the UK and six from Japan were given about laboratory studies of the effects of harmful ASR on structural models, such as slabs, columns, beams, tubes and cylinders, and one paper from Canada on the mechanical properties of unreinforced concrete. These papers reflect a conscientious response to the growing concern about the possible degradation of the structural reliability of AAR-affected concrete buildings and structures. As a whole, applied loading tests substantiated that even severe harmful ASR generally has little effect on the performance of structures, thus substantiating that AAR is not, *per se*, a likely cause of structural collapse.

There were eleven papers about investigations of cases of harmful ASR in field concrete. Four of these concerned cases in Japan, including the Hanshin expressway piers. Two papers were about the power house of the Motoxó hydropower structure in Brazil. This structure was among the relatively few in which structural expansions were part of the problem, due to heavy moisture loading exposure conditions. A Norwegian case concerned ASR in ceramic tiles used as coatings on concrete walls in swimming pools and shower cabinets, similar to Danish experience reported at the 6th ICAAR. A Belgian study revealed, for the first time, the occurrence of harmful ASR in 18 structures of 6–28 years of age in the country. The reactive aggregates were chert, volcanic porphyric rocks with siliceous groundmass, sandstones and other rock types with strained quartz. Crystalline ettringite occurred as secondary compounds in cavities, etc. both in steam cured and in situ concrete.

A severe case of harmful ASR was reported in a 5.76 km long jetty at Lucinda, Queensland, Australia. The jetty consisted of 288 prestressed box girders, each 20 m long. The coarse, reactive aggregate was a rhyolitic tuff with varying degrees of secondary silicification. The extent of cracking in the girders varied from severe to zero. The prestressing prevented longitudinal expansion, but some sections exhibited considerable transverse expansion, which was still in progress. There was copious exudation of alkali-silica gel where cracking was severe. The location was at 18° south of the equator, i.e. tropical, with about 3000 mm rain in the wet season and with splashing of sea water over the structure during storms and typhoons. Statical calculations showed that the structure still possessed satisfactory performance reliability.

One Japanese report concerned a three-storey school building in which ASR had caused expansion of the concrete roof slab during the first ten years. The expansion and crack development ceased when the roof was covered with sheets. Thermal expansion of the roof slab during the summer seasons was a contributory factor. Expansive ASR was also found to occur in a prestressed concrete railway bridge in central Japan, constructed in 1978–79. Differential expansion of the upper slab due to heavy moisture loading caused the anomalic behaviour of the camber of the girders. Epoxy injection, silane surface treatment and cement coating were applied as remedial treatment.

Experimental laboratory and outdoor testing of the environmental influence on the course of AAR was the subject of several Japanese and one South African paper. One American paper presented a new method for identification of alkali-silica gel in field concrete by application of an uranyl acetate solution which shows fluorescence under UV illumination. A Japanese paper suggested laboratory expansion measurements of drilled cores from affected structures as a means of structural investigation, and other papers presented experimental tests by wetting/drying and ultrasonic spectroscopy on laboratory specimens. A British and a Japanese contribution outlined a sort of normalization of diagnostic investigations.

The preventive measures adopted by the Japanese Ministry of Construction as the consequence of the national research efforts since 1982, were reported to be alternative use of innocuous aggregate, low-alkali cement, or blended cement (with fly ash or GGBS). The total alkali content should be limited to $3 \, kg/m^3$ concrete. Two British papers contributed philosophical views on investigation methods and principles regarding ASR in concrete structures, based on experience in the UK. Several Japanese contributions referred to experience with and testing of the effects of repair to concrete affected by AAR by surface coating and/or injection of epoxy compounds in cracks in field concrete.

Aggregates

The conference offered three papers on the microstructure of reactive rock types with emphasis on the role of micro-crystalline quartz, two contributions on reactive volcanic rock types, five on siliceous sedimentary rock types, and one paper on the geology and mineralogy of limestone formations in the Quebec province of Canada.

Tang Mingshu, Wang Meihua and Han Sufen had studied the variety of microstructure of minerals from opal to quartz and the related reactivity, and suggested positron annihilation as a suitable method for characterization of the degree of reactivity. They refuted the undulatory extinction angle as being unsuitable for measuring the reactivity of micro-crystalline quartz in igneous and metamorphic rock types. A Danish contribution substantiated this evaluation, whereas an Indian paper, which showed reactivity of a granitic rock type with micro-crystalline quartz, implied that the UEA measurements correlated with the reactivity.

Correlation between the geology, microstructure and mineral composition in volcanic rocks and their alkali-silica reactivity was presented in two contributions which made New Zealand and Japanese volcanic rock types of various geological ages the subjects of investigation. (There was no emphasis on characterization, or descriptions of occurrences of non-reactive, silica-poor basaltic rock types, which in some volcanic regions might be predominant and safe to use with any high alkali content of cement.)

Five papers, of which three came from Japan, one from Italy and one from the UK, described the occurrence and characteristics of siliceous rock types, such as often occur in alluvial sediments, and which are therefore easily accessible as aggregate resources.

Cement

Hung Chen and P. E. Grattan-Bellew presented the only paper at the conference on the influence of the properties of cement on the course of ASR. They examined the effects of Portland cement of different clinker compositions on ASR in ASTM C227 mortar bar tests with a Canadian reactive reference aggregate material. They found that the total acid-soluble alkali content was the decisive component which influenced the mortar bar expansion.

Fly ash, GGBS and silica fume

The conference contained nine papers, one being the session keynote, covering the effects of the three available siliceous cement replacement materials. Three papers dealt exclusively with fly ash, one with GGBS, and two with silica fume. All the papers concerned empirical laboratory specimen testing without any characterization of the reaction kinetics, the attained degree of hydration in the tested specimens of the Portland cement or the replacement materials, or of the mass effects for model transfer considerations. The British paper on the effects of slag on the course of ASR, relied on an assumed contribution from the slag component of one half of its alkali contents in the concrete, and used a new calcined flint material as reactive aggregate. One Japanese paper observed release of alkalis both from the syenitic aggregate used and from fly ash. Another Japanese paper was unique in characterizing the fly ash both by particle size and chemical composition. None of the papers applied thin section petrography for examinations of the microstructural features of reacted specimens.

Chemical admixtures

Five papers contributed information about empirical laboratory testing of the possible inhibiting effects of chemical admixtures on expansion of mortar bars and concrete prisms, such as super-plasticizers, phosphate solutions, air entraining and water-reducing agents, lithium salts and a latex compound as a cement modifier. No references to comparable experience with field concrete or cost-effectiveness analyses were presented.

Mechanisms and chemistry

The keynote paper by S. Diamond, and nine solicited papers, four of which came from Japan, two from the UK, one from the USA, and one from France, summarized the state-of-the-art knowledge about the mechanism and chemistry of ASR.

It was an opportune reconfirmation by S. Diamond that "*ASR reactions can take place without damage to the concrete*", although this was not explicitly related to the frequency of harmless ASR occurrence in concrete structures. The emphasis of the presentations was on the chemistry of the reaction. Osmotic pressure development was related by the authors to expansive pressure growing with the swelling of gels during the breakdown of amorphous to micro-crystalline siliceous components of rock types in aggregates. The authors did not clearly identify that the swelling pressure develops within individual reacting aggregate particles, and that the subsequent cracking of such affected particles represents expansions simply by the added volume of the internal fractures. In the contribution by G. West and R. G. Sibbick, their Figure 1 explicitly illustrated this mechanism, albeit repeating identical observed features in numerous previous studies since 1940. Classical observations of the dissipation of low viscosity gel out from reacting particles into adjacent cement paste without any development of expansive pressure were also confirmed by some authors and related to the compositions of the gel. Still, some authors implied that the alkali-silica gel is able to exert pressure in cracks in the cement paste after having exuded from its origin in reacting particles. However, no one presented a possible mechanistic explanation for such a reaction course, and the uptake of calcium in the gel with increasing viscosity as the consequence observed by previous authors was not referred to. The necessary presence of calcium in the pore liquid for the reaction to proceed was acknowledged, albeit apparently with somewhat different perceptions of its role, by Chatterji and colleagues and other workers, respectively.

The ability of fly ash, GGBS and silica fume in concrete to reduce the penetrability of the cement paste for pore liquid migration was reconfirmed by one contribution, although without explanatory analyses of the nature and effects of the modified alkali-silica hydration of these materials in Portland cement paste. Basic chemical perceptions of the kinetics of ASR were not dealt with in the presented studies.

Test methods

The keynote lecture by P. Grattan-Bellew reviewed the available test methods for the reactivity of alkali-silica reactivity of concrete aggregates.

Table 27 summarizes the most used methods, comprising the classical and the later moderated mortar bar and concrete prism methods, which apply linear expansion as a measure of the reactivity, the different chemical methods, and the few recently adopted autoclave tests of mortar or concrete test specimens. Petrographic examination methods were also reviewed. The undulatory extinction angle method was dismissed as being unable to disclose the reactivity of aggregates with crystalline quartz as a component.

The summary presentation showed that the basic principles from the original American creation of the ASTM methods had prevailed. Later methods developed elsewhere had also aimed at simulation of the mechanical effects of ASR, expansion and cracking of mortar or concrete specimens, or of the chemical reaction *per se*. The summary did not give any indications of application of thin section petrography of mortar or concrete specimens after testing – whether failed or passed. Moreover, the original cautionary advice from the ASTM in C33, that comparable experience with field concrete behaviour is essential, was left unmentioned. In other words, the indispensable modelling quality of the testing had passed into oblivion.

New methods

New procedures for acceleration of the test methods based on expansion measurements of mortars or concrete were presented in six Japanese, two Canadian, and one French contribution. The methods included the application of very sensitive measurement instrumentation, such as acoustic emission, pulse velocity, Young's modulus of elasticity, electrical conductivity and triaxial stress development at early ages of specimens. Moreover, means for accelerating the chemical reaction, such as supplementary alkali supply, and heating including autoclave conditions, were applied. The new Canadian test by R. Duggan and F. Scott induced arbitrary harsh crack development in the test specimens by which the stipulated relevance of the test results was obscured.

Refinements to existing methods

Six contributions concerned critical, comparative studies of the procedures and

Table 27. *Available test methods for alkali reactivity of concrete aggregates as surveyed in keynote address, session three of 8th ICAAR*

Mechanical effects: expansion		
Mortar bar		Conditions
ASTM C227	2.5 × 2.5 × 25 cm	100% NH; 38°C
NBRI	2.5 × 2.5 × 25 cm	1MNaOH; 80°C
Japanese	2.5 × 2.5 × 25 cm	1MNaOH; 80°–20°C cycl.
Nordtest	4.0 × 4.0 × 16.0 cm	NaCl sol.: 50°C
Concrete prism		eqv. $Na_2O = 1.25\%$
CSA A23.1	7.5 × 7.5 × 35.0 cm	$C = 310\,kg/m^3$
		100% RH; 38°C
Autoclave		
Chinese	1 × 1 × 4 cm	100°C, 4 hr, 10% KOH, 6 hr,
Japanese	4 × 4 × 16 cm	150°C
GBRC	4 × 4 × 16 cm	
Chemical reaction		
ASTM C289	Silica dissolution, alkaline reduction	
VDZ	Weight loss by silica dissolution in alkaline solutions	
Osmotic cell pressure	Swelling pressure by dissolution	
Chemical shrinkage	Hydration densification	
Gel pat	Visual, qualitative gel development	

accuracy of the methods of measuring linear expansion of mortar bars and concrete prisms. Two of these were by Japanese, two by Canadians, one by an Australian and one by a French delegate. The ASTM C289, quick chemical method, was critically examined in three Japanese papers, which proposed improvements similar to the evaluations by K. Haulund Christensen in 1957.[167] One American contribution reported further changes of the osmotic cell test, previously presented at the 6th ICAAR, 1983.[183] Three Japanese contributions described correlating examinations of the mortar bar and the quick chemical test methods, and one American paper suggested calcined flint as a suitable reference standard aggregate material. One contribution dealt specifically with the petrographic examination method. This was a Danish "round robin" test of the UEA of crystalline quartz in aggregate rock types as a measure of alkali reactivity. As mentioned above, the results confirmed that the method does not provide a reliable basis for evaluation of the alkali reactivity of aggregates.

9th ICAAR, 1992, London[184]

The 1128 pages comprising the proceedings of the 9th ICAAR in London, 1992 made this the most voluminous of the conference reports, so far. A special feature was the French participation, with 22 papers. These appeared as evidence of the delayed recognition in France of AAR as a national cause of damage to structures which needed serious attention. The major public technical agencies such as Ponts et Chaussées, Electricité Générale, and the French cement industry had apparently now found national investments in AAR research to be required, and the French papers comprised the whole realm of AAR issues, including the development of new, national standard test methods, and regulations for the use of preventive measures.

A pronounced satiety of the international research was also now evident. New, younger research workers, with national rather than international scope and backgrounds, presented studies which were repetitive, or added second order adjustments to the state-of-the-art knowledge.

The ever-increasing number of new test methods advanced different national regulatory test and acceptance systems, while paradoxically the uniformity of ASR over the globe became better documented. Most of the research into test methods concentrated also now on improvements of the reproducibility, with the result that the original ASTM caution about the missing transfer knowledge was still ignored. In other words, the testing development approached the broader concrete "testing accuracy syndrome" which does not concern itself about transfer from laboratory to real concrete. The conference also revealed that many research institutes and university research groups which had formerly operated with long-term financial basis and corresponding independence, had now been forced to operate on piecemeal funding and consultancy bases; and also with advisory service to lawyers in litigation cases.

Major cases of harmful ASR had now become the subjects of legal conflicts regarding the responsibility for causes of damage. The degree of thoroughness in case investigations and in detailing regulatory requirements for concrete and concrete materials had apparently, in such cases, been increased by the legal professions. This broadening of the scope of investigations also affected the research. Additionally, settlements in major legal suits had included requests for total and permanent confidentiality for experts' reports, hence keeping the results of the research out of reach for open judgements and also for progressive utilization. The free international exchange of ideas, intermittent accomplishments, and innovative discoveries among a special cast of researchers with singular dedication to the creed was beginning to become only a nostalgic memory for the old-timers in the field of ASR research.

Table 28 is a survey of the conference sessions as structured by the organizers, and of the number of papers belonging to each session. In many ways, this survey reflects the national British priority evaluation of the issues of AAR.

Guidance and specifications

The contributions to the 9th ICAAR about guidance and specifications with the aim of averting harmful AAR in field concrete, reflects the level of knowledge achieved by the investments in research in many countries since 1940, in total 52 years, with the nine ICAARs as exceptional opportunities for the sharing and accumulation of knowledge. In some of the countries involved, research, industries and civil engineering have been involved in the development of the knowledge bases during most of the past half century; USA and Denmark are

Table 28. *Survey of sessions and number of papers at the 9th ICAAR, London, 1992*

No.	Session subject	Number of papers
1.	Reactive aggregates	11
2.	Undulatory extinction of quartz	4
3.	Testing aggregates by standard methods	22
4.	Testing concrete	13
5.	Evaluation of structural effects	13
6.	Damaged structures, evaluation, management, repair	14
7.	Chemistry and mechanisms of reaction	19
8.	Review of guidance and specification and regional reviews	10
9.	Cement replacements and additions	22
Total		128

among these. In other countries, AAR was not recognized as requiring serious attention until the 1980s, and then new research with modern analytical instrumentation was commissioned. The UK, Japan and, as the latest addition, France fall within this category. The conference illustrated that, despite the uniformity of AAR, its source materials, nature of reaction, and structural effects all over the world, the attitudes to preventive measures and investigation methods are nevertheless at considerable variance from country to country.

Contributions from the USA, the UK, South Africa, and France (and from Japan at the 8th ICAAR in 1989) illustrated these different approaches.

I. Javed presented a survey of the American programme: "Eliminating or minimizing alkali-silica reactivity", launched in 1988 by SHRP (Strategic Highway Research Program) for a five-year operation with an approximately 2 million US$ budget. It is remarkable that in the country which pioneered a cost-effective approach to ASR in the 1940–60 period, it was not acknowledged before now that harmful ASR is widespread in highway structures, and that the classical test methods, acceptance criteria and application of preventive measures no longer suffice. The influence of the environmental conditions on the course of the reaction has been recognized, but the decisive parameter is merely found to be RH = 80% in concrete, with no clarification of the related properties such as the w/c ratio and the permeability, or of the external exposure, including freezing and thawing in winter seasons combined with hot summer seasons, etc. No causes of harmless ASR are sought. The apparently low priority given to the preventive effects of pozzolans and GGBS is peculiar in view of the early pioneering American studies. But the most astonishing item of the presentation, was the highlighting of the simplistic uranyl-acetate-fluorescence (UAF) method for demonstration of ASR in concrete. Considering the early, pioneering American introduction of thorough methods for diagnostic investigations of field concrete by geologists/mineralogists at WES, USBR and PCA, the UAF method is apparently designed for SHRP as a means for ordinary highway engineers to make simple judgements on whether suspected ASR has actually occurred in highway structures. It does not provide any quantification of harmful or harmless ASR, or observe evidence of alternative causes of damage, if any, but just determines the occurrence of alkali-silica gel as a symptom of the chemical reaction.

Therefore, while confirming the development of the gel which is easily identifiable without the use of the special treatment, the method seems to be simply redundant. The presentation did not represent a structured renewal of the past American leadership in ASR research and transfer to civil engineering practice.

In the UK, the conference year saw the resulting outputs of the comprehensive investments in British research on ASR since the first recognition in 1976 of the occurrence of harmful ASR in the south-west of England. In the course of the subsequent 16 years of intensive investigations all over England and Scotland, "more than 200" structures had been identified as being affected, more or less seriously, by ASR. Notwithstanding this modest overall occurrence of ASR, the British contributions showed that research and engineering and the journalistic investments in the research and its transfer have grown comparatively high, both for diagnostic purposes, for monitoring and management of affected structures, and as efforts meant to increase the general knowledge on ASR. The resulting committee documents [185] and [186] represent a corresponding emphasis on detail and regulatory method descriptions for examination and management of affected structures, and for analytical approaches to the selection of preventive measures. The apparently high ratio of harmless ASR, and the reassurance that the safety of affected structures is never seriously at issue, have not engendered economic analyses of the effects of harmful ASR vis-à-vis the costs of the research, the committee work and the resulting investigations and precautions. In summary of the British achievements, three matters of policy prevail. First, that despite the exceptional regulatory requirements for diagnostic investigations, the need for these has not been substantiated by published reports of such undertakings on specific structures. Secondly, that reliance on empirical mortar bar testing has been consistent throughout the British research and laboratory storage behaviour of drilled cores has been favoured in the concurrent development of diagnostic and structural monitoring methods without thorough modelling analyses. Thirdly, that despite the investment levels in the ASR activities, the summary paper: "Specification of major projects" by I. G. M. Wood refers to the need for more research on practically all the issues dealt with in the two concluding consensus reports.

In France, the discovery of ASR as a cause of cracking in some one hundred bridges in northern France dates back only to about 1985–86, i.e. only a few years before the discovery was referred to at the 8th ICAAR in 1989.[187] The 22 French contributions to the 9th ICAAR reveal concentrated research and transfer efforts in France since the first discovery, with the research groups of the cement industry and the major public technical agencies primarily engaged. With access to magnificent analytical instrumentation, the French contributions add significant new knowledge about the chemistry and the submicroscopic phenomenology of ASR. However, these new achievements cannot be related back to the microscopic and megascopic evidence and course of development of ASR in northern France, because no information about locations and identification of the structures, the concrete and concrete materials, the exposure conditions, or of the extents of the effects of ASR was released for publication.

The justification for the magnitude and priorities of the investments in new French test methods, new theoretical hypotheses, and for the detailed complex of optional preventive measures was therefore not established for international comparison and exchange. In any case, the concentration of cases of harmful ASR in the "limestone regions" in northern France means that the silica-bearing limestone formations and the aggregates produced from them must be similar to the Danish and English types of limestone with interstitial, reactive silica. Information on the geology, mineralogy and reactivity of this kind of aggregate deserves to be compared with the classic Danish and later British investigations of the reactivity of flint types.

The attained French national ASR policy operates after the German model in reference [173] with:

□ three categories of structure with levels of risk acceptance for harmful ASR
□ four exposure classes for field concrete, related to the risk of progressive ASR
□ three levels of preventive measure, none being the lowest requirement, five optimal solutions the next, and categorically non-reactive aggregates the strictest requirement.

This logical and clear system has some imperfections inherited from the established ASR policy abroad, and some derived from specific French views. However, the French standard test methods are, although improved with regard to reproducibility, still empirical, simplified models without scientific and model law-based transfer to field concrete conditions. Therefore, the French testing system is, despite inherent qualifications compared with older systems abroad, still not realistically reflecting the course and effects of ASR in field concrete. Its defect in this respect is related to the absence of available information about harmless or negligible ASR in populations of individual structures with varying extents of harmful ASR. Without such information, the cost-effectiveness of the rigorous system for selection of preventive measures is still in doubt, and it leaves little flexibility for more progressive solutions for individual engineering projects.

National and regional reviews

In Ireland, a national committee study of the possibility of harmful ASR occurrence had been carried out since 1987, prompted by an average alkali content of Irish cements of about 0.85% eqv. Na_2O and common use of reactive aggregates, such as chert with crypto-micro-crystalline quartz, and basaltic and rhyolitic volcanic rock types with siliceous glass contents. Recommended preventive measures had been elucidated based on the experience and research abroad, albeit with the reservation that no cases of harmful ASR had been encountered in the country. Apparently, the occurrence of harmless ASR had not been considered.

In northern France, 140 bridges had been investigated in the 1970s. Of these, 5% had shown severe deterioration probably related to harmful AAR; 24% had shown minor evidence of AAR; 57% had shown only little evidence of damage, and 14% of the bridges had been without damage. Two bridges north of Paris had been demolished due to harmful ASR. Comprehensive petrographic mapping of French aggregate resources had been made and numerous chemical analyses of exuded alkali-silica gel in affected concrete had been carried out.

Apparently, the north of France had been the region with the largest number of concrete structures affected by ASR. Considering the figures given, a high frequency of harmless ASR in field concrete seems certain to occur among the identified individual cases of harmful reaction.

In the Netherlands, ASR had not been believed to occur in field concrete until a few cases were identified in 1991 during management inspection of 700 structures in the Zuid-Holland province. Reference is, however, made to an isolated investigation of a case by R. A. J. Bosschart in 1957,[188] which at that time was contested and, apparently, widely disbelieved and defiantly opposed. The occurrence of about 25 cases of harmful ASR in Belgium was mentioned. Test methods and recommendations for preventive measures were referred to as being studied by a working party.

In Norway, the possible occurrence of harmful ASR was proposed as early as 1962 by H. B. Museus,[189] and identified in the Rjukan hydropower plant by A. Kjennerud in 1981,[190] sustained by Idorn and Thaulow in 1982.[191] Since 1989, field inspections of 483 structures and detailed investigations including geological surveys and mineralogical studies have disclosed widespread occurrence of volcanic and metamorphic reactive rock types, which have occasionally caused harmful ASR with the usually high-alkali Norwegian cement. Like elsewhere, the early investigation of the Rjukan hydropower plant had revealed deformations and expansion of concrete in the turbine areas of the structure where water saturation was high. The occurrence of the reactive rock types over large areas of southern Norway suggests that, in this country too, cases of harmless ASR occur among the harmful ones, but do not attract the attention of investigators.

Recent investigations in China had shown that harmful ASR occurred in many concrete structures in the Beijing area, comprising prestressed railway sleepers, industrial buildings and bridges. The industrial development in the country had necessitated intensive exploitation of aggregate resources and rapid increase of the cement manufacture capacity. In the Beijing area, aggregates with reactive chert were accessible along with high-alkali cements. The rapid autoclave test method was used to determine the alkali reactivity of the aggregates. Railway sleepers, in which severe cracking appeared in the course of a few years as map-cracking in end sections and longitudinal cracking between rails, contained $470\,kg/m^3$ Portland cement with 1.10% eqv. Na_2O (i.e. $5.23\,kg$ Na_2O per m^3 concrete) and coarse chert aggregate. In the northern region of China, the major part of the increasing cement production must accept alkali contents up to 1.2–1.4%. Some plants return the alkali-enriched dust to the cement as additive, and in some places alkali sulphates or carbonates are added as accelerators. For winter concreting, sodium nitrate or chlorides are added as antifreeze-additives without considering the alkali reactivity. More widespread occurrence of harmful ASR was reported to be probable.

Survey reports from the Western Cape province in South Africa and from New Zealand sustained and added details to reports at the previous conferences. Mutual representation of the relevant professions in the research programmes were reported to have practically eliminated the problem of harmful ASR in the country.

In New Zealand, many years of research was concluded by limitation of the alkali content in concrete to $2.5\,kg/m^3$ eqv. Na_2O with reactive aggregates. The alkali limitation was referred to as reasonable due to the general alkali content of 0.6% eqv. Na_2O or less of the national cement brands.

Structural research

Several projects were reported about the structural effects of expansive ASR on reinforced concrete beams and columns in large-scale laboratory models. Generally, the reduction of load-bearing capacity by provoked ASR and shear capacity was found to be negligible. Drilled cores showed negligible reduction of compressive strength and E_{dyn}, when the direction of the imposed stress was at right angles to the predominant cracking, i.e. usually at a right angle to the concrete surface. Bond strength failure was found in elements with substantial expansions. A Japanese study based on testing of reinforced concrete prisms with provoked ASR, indicated that expansions were effectively mitigated by more than 0.7% reinforcement, while there were no significant effects of less than 0.3% reinforcement. The long-term Danish study, which was preliminarily reported at the 7th ICAAR,[192] concerned reinforced beams with provoked ASR (by storage in a saturated NaCl solution at $+50°C$) and had shown that the punching shear strength, even with serious ASR, had not been reduced, that the affected concrete behaved in a more ductile manner than unaffected, and that anchorage strength was 20–30% reduced. In general, the undertaken research corroborated many years of field investigations, that harmful ASR is not a likely cause of structural failure. A special case from India concerned damage by expansive ASR in the mortar with which cable ducts had been filled.

Diagnostic investigations

A comprehensive South African field and laboratory investigation was the first to deal with harmful ASR in prestressed, steam cured concrete railway sleepers during the series of conferences. Cracking and expansions were observed in sleepers made with reactive quartzite and granite, although after some ten years of field service, still only about 10% or less of the sleepers, depending upon the type of aggregate, showed damage. Exposure with protection against moisture had mitigated cracking, and this effect was also obtained by treatment of sleepers with a water-repellent agent. There were no cracked sleepers among the series cast with a non-reactive dolerite aggregate. Application of the Duggan test gave expansions in the drilled cores both from damaged and undamaged concrete, and the required structural strength was preserved both in cracked and uncracked sleepers. Ettringite was found in the interfaces of cement paste with aggregates and reinforcement, and the typical formations of ettringite were found both in damaged and undamaged sleepers. ASR was concluded to be the cause of cracking. It was stipulated that delayed ettringite formation might have contributed to the overall expansion of cracked sleepers, but with harmful ASR as a prerequisite for this to happen. No evidence of such a possible mechanism was presented.

Three French papers by three different groups of researchers described the recent acceptance of the occurrence of harmful ASR in France. Actually, the first case was the Chambon Dam in which evidence of ASR had been detected in 1976 (the year of the 2nd ICAAR in London), but not publicly revealed. During the late 1980s, examinations of 860 bridges in northern France had shown that 123 (35%) showed slight to intense effects of harmful ASR. All were built after 1970, and the occurrence of ASR was related to increase of the alkali contents of the cement and a change to a type of siliceous limestone aggregate. Also, a metamorphic, porphyric rock was found to be susceptible. Apparently, structures built before 1970 were without evidence of harmful reaction. The detailed field and laboratory investigations described did not include any of the 65% which had not shown evidence of harmful ASR. The occurrence of harmless ASR-affected structures can therefore not be estimated. It was observed, in agreement with classic information from other countries, that even visibly affected concrete in the structures showed considerably varying extents of cracking and also of amounts and types of the reaction products in the microstructure. The French studies increased the knowledge bank regarding harmful ASR, in particular by refined instrumentation which had made possible more observations than hitherto of the sub-microscopic varieties of ASR evidence.

An Australian paper described cracking due to harmful ASR in precast columns supporting the water ponds for a power station cooling tower. The cracking was observed in 1990 at about eight years of age. Thin section petrography showed that harmful ASR with chert as the reactive aggregate was the cause of the cracking. The pond water was 26–42°C warm and the combined heat and moisture was considered to be an aggravating factor.

One of the above mentioned French contributions presented three methods for the monitoring of ongoing ASR in field concrete: crack width measurements, overall deformation by infrared distance meter, and residual expansion of cores.

A Japanese contribution presented application of vibration with measurements of the response of the concrete as an indication of its inherent monolithic structure.

An American paper illustrated alternative application of measurements by the acoustic emission technique.

A Danish contribution described the determination of the capacity for residual ASR in affected concrete structures by calculation of the attained degree of reaction as the amount of already reacted alkali over the sum of available plus reacted alkali. The residual reactivity is one minus the attained degree of reaction. The amount of available alkali can be determined by pore solution analyses, while the amount of reacted alkali can be determined by petrographic measurements of the amount of reacted silica. The total alkali in the system can be determined as acid-soluble alkali. Available alkali below a threshold concentration of 0.2 N hydroxide is innocuous.

Pre-demolition and repairs of affected structures

One paper from South Africa described partial demolition for reconcreting of a portal supporting an overhead section of the motorway system at Johannesburg. Expansion and crack widening was occurring in the concrete even at 15 years of age of the concrete. Alkali content up to 2.6% eqv. Na_2O was calculated from concrete analyses. Compressive strength of drilled cores showed an average of about 31 MPa, i.e. the design strength, but there were locations with strength well below this value. A Japanese experimental study described the adherence by anchor bolts and epoxy resin of steel plates to the web and compression bottom of ASR-affected T-shape bridge piers, when the bridge concerned had to be kept operational during repair periods. Five papers described projects for inhibiting the progress of ASR in affected structures, comprising field and laboratory tests, by injection of cracks and surface coatings. Silane monomers and polymer cement were found to be promising candidates, because surface coatings with these types of chemicals allowed for the evaporation of water from the interior of the concrete, while the coating concurrently prevented water ingress and penetration from outside. All tests and field experiments were of recent origin, and did not disclose longer term effectiveness.

One single paper from Japan described the influence of two different climatic exposure conditions on concrete affected by ASR. Experimental massive cubic block specimens were exposed in outdoor test fields, one on the seashore facing the Sea of Japan and the other on the roof of a university campus building far from the sea. Prismatic control specimens were stored in laboratory conditions and measured monthly. An andesitic aggregate with reactive volcanic glass was used along with cement contents varying from $300-700 \, kg/m^3$ to give alkali contents from $2.9-6.8 \, kg/m^3$ concrete. Expansion measurements and crack pattern observations during three years' storage showed acceleration of ASR during summer seasons relative to winters, but no definite difference between seashore and rooftop exposure. Concrete with less than $4 \, kg/m^3$ alkali content did not develop harmful ASR, and surface coating with a highly elastic, acrylic rubber type material reduced cracking and expansions.

Aggregates

The major part of the papers concerning alkali-reactive rock types and their characterization, contained information supplementary to knowledge previously acquired and reported at the preceding conferences. A few special types of aggregate were reported for the first time to have caused harmful ASR.

A French paper reported that the mineral Wollastonite ($CaSiO_3$) had caused harmful ASR in a concrete structure on the St. Martin Island in the French Antilles (the Caribbean). The mineral was found as a constituent of metamorphic limestones. Volcanic rocks such as porphyric basalts and andesites also present in the aggregates had not reacted in the concrete. An Argentine contribution suggested that aggregates containing montmorillonite in some types of basalt and in dolomitic rock types were alkali-reactive. Mortar bar testing after the NBRI method had sustained this assumption, which was stated to confirm that ASR (and ACR in the case of dolomitic aggregate) was the cause of observed damage to certain structures. A Chinese study reported site investigations and laboratory analyses which had shown that magnesium-rich rock types were the cause of concrete deterioration due to delayed hydration in the concrete of the MgO component of the aggregate. Apparently, in one case, the aggregate was a steel slag with about 80% MgO and in the other case an MgO-rich zinc slag.

A British paper presented a study of the microstructure of flint as related to alkali-silica reactivity. Unfortunately, the study is without references to prominent, previous mineralogical and geological investigations of flint types, such as [133] and [193–196].

P. Grattan-Bellew presented a thorough review of more than a decade's intensive research in many countries on the nature of alkali reactivity and, in particular, of the slowly reacting metamorphic rock types such as greywacke, quartzite, etc., and of the earlier promoted reliance on the undulatory extinction angle of crystalline quartz as mineral in susceptible rock types as a measure of alkali reactivity. It was concluded that the reactive component in the slowly reacting metamorphic rock types is micro-crystalline quartz, strained during the metamorphosis, and that a special "alkali-silicate" type of reactivity is purely arbitrary and non-existent. Furthermore, UEA measurements are not reliable for characterization of alkali-silica reactivity of the metamorphic rock types. A British study presented a thorough review of the characterization of potentially reactive aggregates. This British study is also without reference to previous research about flint and chert.

Preventive effects of fly ash on ASR

Two British and one Italian paper described the effects of fly ash on ASR in concrete. The British contributions concerned concrete in dams with reactive greywacke as aggregate. Both dams were of about 30 years of age. In one dam – without fly ash in the concrete – severe cracking due to harmful ASR had developed, in the other – with about 25% fly ash in the cement – no damage had developed. A related experimental research study gave corroborating results. The Italian paper concerned only laboratory expansion measurements on ASTM mortar bars and concrete prisms with an artificial, fused silica reactive aggregate, with and without fly ash additions.

Preventive effects of GGBS on ASR

Three British papers described laboratory examinations by expansion tests with mortars and concrete specimens of the preventive effects on ASR of GGBS in blends with Portland cement. The three investigations used different reactive aggregates, different cement: slag mixes, and different test conditions, which altogether eliminate the validity of the results for direct transfer to engineering practice. A study of the kinetics and thermodynamics of the reaction of slag in alkali-poor and alkali-rich Portland cement paste would have given better opportunities for analyses of the observations in the presented papers.

Preventive effects of silica fume on ASR

Two Canadian papers discussed the possible combined preventive effects of silica fume and entrained air, and of silica fume in the long term, respectively. Both studies relied on laboratory conditioned measurements of expansion mitigation without correlating examinations of comparable field concrete behaviour. The stipulated combined effects of silica fume and entrained air relied on the assumed function of air bubbles as reservoirs for alkali-silica gel which has exuded from reacting aggregate particles. This assumption is not substantiated by investigations of affected field concrete. The other paper stipulated that the preventive effects of silica fume on ASR may not be permanent. The accelerated tests were, by their very nature, incapable of showing long-term effects in field concrete.

221

Preventive effects of other materials on ASR

A British study suggested that 15% replacement of ordinary Portland cement by metakaolin would cause conversion of the $Ca(OH)_2$ in the concrete to cementitious C-S-H and calcium aluminium silica hydrates, and make the concrete resistant to expansion by ASR, even if immersed in saturated sodium chloride solution. The study also offered a revised explanation of the chemistry of ASR.

A Chinese report informed that about two-thirds of the national cement production, 200 million tonnes annually, is made in vertical kilns, and one-third of this is blended with natural zeolite which causes long-term increases of strength and density of concrete due to pozzolanic reaction with the high amounts of reactive silica and alumina in the zeolite. On the other hand, the high alkali content of zeolites might be thought to cause harmful ASR. Mortar bar tests confirmed the preventive effects of using the zeolithic cement with reactive aggregates.

An American study resumed classical findings by researchers in the USA and Australia that lithium salts may be used to inhibit expansions due to ASR in concrete. The study applied the ASTM C227 mortar bar test and the tentative P214 mortar bar test. Different dosages of different lithium salts were required for effective inhibition. A trial application of lithium hydroxide in a highway project where reactive aggregates were used was mentioned but was, however, not advanced enough to provide evidence of possible effects.

A Canadian study examined the possible inhibiting effects on ASR of chemical compounds such as sucrose, lactic acid, EDTA and oxalic acid. The ASTM C227 test was used with 2% reactive opal in the non-reactive limestone aggregate. Sucrose was found to decrease expansion of mortar bars. Tests with added $CaCl_2$ showed increase of expansion.

A French study indicated that ASR can be inhibited by chelating the cations adsorbed by SiO groups of alkali-silica gel. Continuation of the study with ASR developed in concrete with reactive aggregates was mentioned to be in preparation.

A Japanese study concerned the effects of air entraining, water-reducing, super-plasticizer agents, and NaCl vis-à-vis NaOH on ASR by concrete prism expansions. Air entrainment was found to reduce expansions, whereas water-reducing agents and super-plasticizers only had little effect. NaCl increased expansion more than NaOH.

Chemistry and mechanisms of the reaction

H. Vivian from Australia summarized the state-of-the-art knowledge on ASR in a brief review, based on fifty years' association with the research on the subject matter. In its generalization, his review presented a still valid overall framework to which the ten other papers in the session belong. One fundamental matter of the ASR was unequivocally stated by Vivian: "*The simple expansion mechanism involves the swelling of reacted siliceous aggregate particles as they absorb water and the disruptive expansion cracking of the concrete. Although the swelling forces are not excessively large they are sufficiently great to exceed the cohesive strength of hardened cement paste and concrete*". This statement, which represents knowledge from back in the 1940–60

period of ASR research, is essential, because there were still conference contributions which relied on the assumption that alkali-silica gel when exuded into
cracks in the cement paste, actually swelled there and caused the expansivity of
the reaction. These contributions in 1992, like those of the same perception at
previous conferences, seem to consider the measurement of linear expansion
per se as the evidence of the reaction, while actually it is, as observed by
McGowan and Vivian in 1952,[145] the accumulated widths and interconnec-
tions of cracking in and radiating from the reacting particles which represent
the expansion.

By means of new instrumentation, several contributors provided further detail
to information obtained from previous research, for instance about the ranges of
the chemical compositions of alkali-silica gel, e.g. as related to the distance from
the originating reaction sites in aggregate particles. Also, regarding the relative
role of $Ca(OH)_2$ vis-à-vis the alkali hydroxide and the presence of ettringite,
there were new data which essentially confirmed the earlier observations
previously referred to by Powers and Steinour, K. and B. Mather, Mielenz and
colleagues, and myself.

A study by T. Uomoto, Y Furusawa and H. Ohga introduced a kinetic-based
model for predicting ASR, adopting the Arrhenius equation for determination of
the alkali diffusion coefficient, dependent on the reaction temperature. The use of
this realistic model parameter is mitigated by the authors by other assumptions
for the model approach, *inter alia* that the volume increase of gel in the cement
paste of mortars gives rise to the expansion of mortar bars. Another modelling
study of ASR applied calculations incorporating the specific surface of reacting
particles and the viscosity of the gel products as related to pore solution compositions, but did not present experimental or field investigation back-up data.

One French paper, by F.-X. Deloye and L. Divet, was remarkable in several
respects. By application of thermogravity, the lime content in the examined
concrete was used as pilot oxide for calculation of the cement content and,
from that point, to determine the silica in the aggregates which had reacted.
Examinations of sound and affected mortars and field concrete samples were
concluded to show that about 1% of the silica in aggregates (which in all cases
were the northern France siliceous limestone types) was involved in the reaction
in affected concrete. It also appeared that clay minerals and pyrite (secondary
constituents of the limestone aggregate) delivered alumina and ferric oxide to
take part in the reaction. The paper deserves attention because it deals with quantification of the reaction – and its effect in concrete. It may contain a lead for
further exploration of the frequent occurrence of harmless ASR (apparently
also in northern France), although it is handicapped in this respect, because it
is a basic assumption that the "silico-calco-alkali" gel exerts pressure "at the
paste–aggregate interface" (p. 25). The paper is also impaired by only having
nine references, of which the one to T. E. Stanton's opening paper in 1940 is
the only representation of 54 years of work on the subject, besides eight
papers related to the recent French acceptance of the existence of ASR.

New test methods

Eight "new" methods for testing of the alkali-silica reactivity of aggregates were
presented at the conference. Three of these concerned the chemistry of the

reaction, and the other five the mechanical effects. All eight exposed the aggregates to specific laboratory treatments and conditions.

A new French method applied dissolution of susceptible silica by ester hydrolyses of reactive particles in cement paste, rapid gelling of the pore solution, and consequent mechanical degradation of the aggregate/cement paste system. Another new French chemical test used different modifications of the ASTM C289 chemical test and introduced reaction time as a supplementary parameter. An Italian test method combined the ASTM C289 method with psammographic (i.e. modified petrographic) methods. A new Japanese, mechanical method, employed cylindrical test specimens which, after four days' storage at $+20°C$, were boiled for two hours at 0.049 MPa gauge pressure. After this treatment, the E_{dyn} was measured and, if reduced, taken as a measure of reactivity. A French test method operating with $7 \times 7 \times 28$ cm concrete prisms measured accelerated expansions after four days' heating to $+60°C$. Three methods, one Canadian and two French, applied autoclave treatment of mortar bars and further acceleration by arbitrary increase of the alkali content of the concrete. The Canadian test appeared as a development of the ASTM C227 method, and alternative to the proposed ASTM P214 accelerated mortar bar test. One of the French methods used microbar ($1 \times 1 \times 4$ cm) as in the original Chinese autoclave test. The other French method used $4 \times 4 \times 16$ cm mortar bars as previously introduced by Japanese researchers. In all three tests, observations on the reacted specimens showed that the reaction products were identical with those produced by the conventional tests and in affected field concrete structures with aggregates of the tested origins and compositions.

Standard and other test methods

An introductory RILEM TC-106 committee report presented a survey of tests for alkali reactivity of aggregates in different countries. The paper also surveyed the preventive measures specified in different countries. Several other papers discussed different modifications of the generally used mortar bar and concrete prism test methods. In principle, these changes have aimed at the following improvements:

- introduction of concrete prisms for testing of coarse aggregates without crushing down to sand particle sizes
- intensification of the reaction by increasing the alkali contents of the concrete or mortar
- acceleration of the reaction by increase of the storage temperature.

The first of these changes is a rapprochement with reality, while the other two are the opposite, at least as generalizations. Incidentally, none of the test methods considers the frequent occurrence of harmless ASR in almost all countries in which cases of harmful reaction have been reported. In this connection, the Danish test method applying chemical shrinkage is of general interest, as an illustration of one likely cause of harmless ASR in many cases of field concrete with reactive aggregates. The American method for demonstration of the occurrence of ASR in field concrete by UV-illumination of fluorescing uranyl acetate sprayed onto concrete surfaces was also reported to have been applied in France.

10th ICAAR, 1996, Melbourne[197]

The events and the course of the 10th ICAAR suggested that the conference will appear in the future as a turning-point gathering for international ASR research and practice. The holistic concept of past research needs to be re-adopted with new approaches to the issues of the energetics and fracture mechanics of ASR in concrete. The development of empirical test methods and of field concrete failure case investigation methods have reached levels of satiation, and reasonable rehabilitation technology for affected field concrete is available.

The cost-effectiveness of further research needs serious attention in view of the uncertain ASR situation in the continents predominated by developing countries.

H. E. Vivian honoured

The 10th conference was unique in being the first during which an award for outstanding research on ASR was made, namely to Vivian for his eminent achievements in the long-term Australian CSIRO programme from the early 1940s. The award was introduced in the keynote address: "Systematic ASR research – Australian research 1940s to 1958" by G. M. Idorn. Vivian's work in those days was exceptional in several respects. It pioneered the assessment of ASR as the conversion of chemical energy in the reaction between cement and aggregate constituents to mechanical work in concrete. It contributed to the distinction between harmless and harmful ASR and became an indispensable data-bank for the contemporaneous, explanatory research by Powers and Steinour in the USA. The experimental planning, skill of operation, and the common sense intelligence of the interpretation of the results of different series of laboratory studies by Vivian and his colleagues were second to none. His early, clear comprehension of the holistic nature of the issues was remarkable, and still represents an important lesson for present-day ASR research.

The award was also bestowed because this remarkable service to his country and to the general progress of concrete technology has never been formally acknowledged by the sponsoring, national agency, CSIRO. The recognition by the 10th ICAAR stands out further because the collegial type of informal, organizing leaderships of the conferences have otherwise carefully avoided interfering with award policies of concrete research authorities in the different host countries, and therefore also abstained from the trend of issuing "discount awards", commonly made at commercially orientated conferences.

Fortunately, Vivian was able to attend the conference and receive the well deserved tribute. But it was inevitable that, from close to 60 years of ASR research history, only two people from the international research cooperation 1940–1960, namely B. Mather and G. M. Idorn, were in attendance besides the awardee. Quite a few colleagues who shared the work of the Phase II conferences since 1974 have also terminated their positions or work with ASR, and others are coming close to joining them. The effects of these personnel changes are even more remarkably signalled by the decline of participative interest in the western European (including the North American) and South African cement industries since the 5th and 6th ICAARs. In contrast, Asian cement companies have moved in, in accordance with the general industrial development in their regions. Many new industrial and academic researchers have entered the work with new impetus from national needs to ensure the durability of concrete.

It is unfortunate that, after so many years of investment in ASR research in the developed parts of the world, the 10th ICAAR could not transfer a holistic concept of the global ASR challenges to the developing countries. The conference showed that such an international front-line R & D leadership position has not been established as an achievement of the six decades of the research investments.

Keynote addresses

In contrast to the emphasis on the early conceptual approach to ASR research which is described in the keynote address to H. E. Vivian, the five other keynote lectures illustrated the present-day policy of fragmentation of the research:

- Professor S. Diamond – "Alkali-silica reactions: some paradoxes"
- Dr P. E. Grattan-Bellew – "A critical review of accelerated AAR tests"
- Professor D. M. Roy – "AAR investigation of concrete for storage of radioactive wastes"
- Professor R. N. Swamy – "Assessment and rehabilitation of AAR-affected structures"
- Professor M. Moranville-Regourd – "Modelling of expansions induced by ASR: new approaches".

Professor S. Diamond – "Alkali-silica reactions: some paradoxes"

S. Diamond described four laboratory modelling investigations of the chemistry of ASR which question conventional perceptions and were presented as paradoxes:

- Paradox 1: Addition of NaOH to cement increases the sulphate ion concentration of the pore liquid rather than the hydroxide concentration.
- Paradox 2: Partial drying of cement paste reduces rather than increases the alkali hydroxide concentration of its pore liquid.
- Paradox 3: Silica fume in blends with Portland cement may, if agglomerated, engender harmful ASR rather than prevent it.
- Paradox 4: Lithium treatment of concrete for prevention of harmful ASR usually involves increasing the OH^- challenge to the reactive aggregate of concrete.

The first two paradoxes mentioned are founded on chemical analyses of pore liquid squeezed out of laboratory produced hardened cement paste. They have no congruent measurements of the mechanical effects of the observed chemical changes of the pore solution composition. In many ways, they constitute "one-dimensional" chemical equivalents of the mechanical linear expansion philosophy with no bridge building between the chemistry and the mechanical effects of the reaction.

The third paradox refers to laboratory observations and a few field observations, suggesting that agglomerated silica fume particles in cement paste may provoke harmful ASR in mortars and concrete.

The pozzolanic effect of silica fume is commented upon as follows:

"Furthermore, silica fume is known to function as an extremely efficient pozzolan, reducing or even eliminating the calcium hydroxide normally formed by cement hydration. Many studies have shown calcium hydroxide needs to be present to 'stabilize' the ASR gel. Lacking access to calcium hydroxide, the ASR product tends to be too fluid to exert much mechanical effect and, in extreme cases, it may simply dissolve into the pore solution."

This statement is confusing in view of the general knowledge that the Ca^{++} ion from the pore solution is absorbed by alkali-silica gel when expelled from the cracking in reacting particles, thereby making the gel rigid and non-swelling. When the reacting aggregate is present in pozzolanic size ranges the Ca^{++} ion absorption must take place without causing flowing or swelling gel at all. Hence, the "third paradox" seems not to be a real paradox, but rather a case of incomplete data compilation.

The fourth paradox refers to a classical American suggestion by W. J. McCoy and A. G. Caldwell,[198] that addition of lithium salts to concrete with reactive aggregates mitigates cracking and expansion due to ASR. The investigation results suggest that lithium entrance into alkali-silica gel reduces its swelling and expansion capability and thus creates harmless reaction. Concurrently, the OH^- ion concentration in lithium treated samples remains unaffected or is increased by the addition, and the sulphate concentration in the pore-squeezed solutions remains high under some of the investigation conditions.

In the concluding comments on the paradoxes, it is stated as a general theme running through the examined matters that: *"the internal workings of concrete are complicated, and sometimes influenced unexpectedly by admixtures and chemical treatments"*. This is indeed a classical, omnipotent truth, requiring additional information in order to become educational guidance for research planning, namely that special experimental methods (such as e.g. the pore-squeezing technique) and model transfer conditions influence the validity of data from analytical experiments.

The paper represents an academic approach to studies of the chemistry of ASR. The designated paradoxes are interesting new fragments of knowledge on the chemistry of ASR, but difficult for the reader to place in the chemical-mechanical holism of the reaction and its effects in concrete.

Dr P. E. Grattan-Bellew – "A critical review of accelerated AAR tests"

P. E. Grattan-Bellew presented a review of the approximately 40 different existing methods for characterization of aggregate reactivity (including both ASR and ACR) with emphasis on mortar bars and concrete prisms and terminal, linear expansions as criteria for the reactivity. The keynote lecture failed to define it as a fundamental misconception that linear expansion, only one selected evidence of the mechanical effects of ASR, has, over the years, become widely adopted as the predictive modelling measure of the complex, non-linear dynamic mechanisms of the reaction in field concrete.

Considering the magnitude of research investments in many countries on refinements for the original ASTM C227 mortar bar test, the keynote statement:

"Blindly following standards may lead to acceptance of an aggregate which may be potentially expansive in a particular structure, or rejection of an aggregate which would

perform satisfactorily in the field, leading to unnecessary expense with finding and possibly trucking an alternative aggregate"

[author's emphasis] implies basic reasons for the erratic modelling represented by the following:

□ Accumulated knowledge about the widely differing compositions and properties of reactive aggregates even within laboratory samples makes it futile to aim at one single test as representative for all aggregate rock types.

□ Maximum attainable reproducibility of linear expansion tests entails utmost homogenization of the test objects and conditions, i.e. systematic elimination of the parameters of the real non-linear, dynamic mechanism of the reaction.

□ Arbitrary acceleration of linear expansion tests distorts the actual kinetics of the chemical reaction in unknown ways and with incalculable effects on measurable expansions. None of the standard test methods incorporate detailed recording of the rates of measured expansions over the course of test duration for enumeration of the kinetics of the reaction.

□ The persistent emphasis on linear expansion limits as criteria for acceptable/ unacceptable aggregate reactivity engenders disregard of investigative attention to cement-aggregate combinations which have passed in test series, thereby forfeiting the inherent information about conditions causing harmless ASR. The equally persistent drive for improved reproducibility within test series has obviated the inherent information of spread as evidence of the complexity of the reaction and its course and effects which characterize ASR in field concrete.

The keynote paper reveals the prevailing preference of the expansion methods – over chemical test methods and, therefore, the general loss over the years of the holistic concept of the chemical reaction and mechanical effects.

The briefly mentioned, chemical shrinkage test, first presented at the 7th ICAAR, 1986, by Knudsen, [199] does measure mechanical effects of the reaction, albeit not expansion but chemical shrinkage, as the result of the process when the amounts of reactants constitute a closed system. As a test, the method is merely an inexpensive empirical alternative or supplement to the linear expansion methods. However, interpreted with regard to ASR in field concrete, it does illustrate one reason for a harmless course of the reaction in field concrete.

The keynote paper is in harmony with the submissiveness of much concrete research to the market attractiveness of crude empirical testing, with the disregard of realistic model transfer. The paper also implies that, *per se*, the test methods cannot be "made better", i.e. more reproducible; hence it justifies, as far as testing goes, that in this respect the ASR research has reached a turning-point.

Professor D. M. Roy – "AAR investigation of concrete for storage of radioactive wastes"

D. M. Roy presented an investigation of the AAR reactivity of a dolomitic rock type for aggregate, used in a concrete structure for radioactive waste storage in Tennessee, USA. The approach is unusual in the use of a large fraction of the spectrum of the Canadian and USA test methods, primarily those relying on linear expansion for modelling of the reactivity. The chosen aggregate was found to be marginally reactive and apparently accepted for utilization. The paper confirms the academic preference for the linear expansion, empirical test methods over a science-based approach integrating the chemical conversions and the mechanical effects. It does not refer to considerations of purchase of alternative, proven non-reactive aggregates to match the given high-performance requirements of the concrete.

Professor R. N. Swamy – "Assessment and rehabilitation of AAR-affected structures"

R. N. Swamy reviewed methods for assessment and rehabilitation of AAR-affected structures. He represented a rather popularized AAR knowledge base by reviewing a long series of past, personal articles and conference contributions. The fundamental theoretical concepts of AAR were not included, and it is tempting to see the styling and visualizing analogies used as means of introducing the subject matter into a civil engineering student course.

Professor M. Moranville-Regourd – "Modelling of expansions induced by ASR: new approaches"

M. Moranville-Regourd's new approach to modelling of the expansion in concrete induced by ASR attracted much attention in the conference audience by the application of reaction kinetics and thermodynamics for calculations of the progressive development of concrete cracking and expansion in the course of advancing ASR; hence the paper was judged to bridge the gap between conventional specimen testing and the course of reactions in larger concrete bodies, i.e. presumably in entire structures.

The applied integral chemistry-mechanism modelling is a dramatic, long overdue progress which inadvertently reaches back to the early research in Australia and the USA. Hence, the keynote paper and the associated new French studies referred to, and those presented at the conference, support the designation of the 10th ICAAR as a turning-point in ASR research and development.

The new modelling idealizes the established ASR knowledge base reality in some respects which require further studies as follows:

□ It assumes that swelling – and cracking – in the ASR process happens when alkali-silica gel expelled from reacting aggregate particles fills the pores in the cement paste surrounding the particles. Numerous studies, pioneered by Vivian in the 1950s, have irrefutably shown that swelling of alkali-silica gel happens in the reacting particles until the swelling causes cracking which continues out into the surrounding cement paste. The subsequent transfer of the "surplus volume gel" out into the cracks causes Ca^{++} ions to be absorbed and the gel to lose its expansivity. Brown,[128] Powers and Steinour,[115, 116] Idorn,[36] Farrouto and Haynes,[200] and others have substantiated this perception of the swelling-cracking mechanism. Thaulow and Knudsen,[201] Kawamura et al.,[202] Thaulow et al.,[203] Laing et al.,[204] French,[205] Katayama and Bragg[206] have further documented that gel absorbs Ca^{++} ions when it precipitates into the cracks opened by the swelling pressure in reacting aggregate particles. The model by Dent Glasser and Katauka,[207] to which the new French theory refers, assumes that the gel is disseminated to isotropic occupation of the cement paste pore volume (or, perhaps, created there), and while still swelling in situ causes further expansion and cracking.

☐ It accepts the classical pessimum perception that there is a pessimum ratio of reactive to innocuous aggregate particles which warrant maximum expansions. It ignores the fact that this perception is only valid for mortar bars as closed reacting systems, Idorn *et al.*[158]

☐ It does not take the chemical shrinkage of the reaction product in a closed system into consideration, Geiker and Knudsen,[208] Knudsen.[199]

☐ It seems to have been based experimentally on a high-amorphous or glassy, reactive aggregate material, such as opal, porous flint, pyrex glass, obsidian, etc. At least, it has no parameter reservations relating to modelling of poly-mineralic rock types in which the reactive silica is a minor constituent in strong, crystalline or amorphous, non-reactive matrix phases.

☐ It fails to address the issue of harmless ASR.

☐ It does not yet include the basic fractal character of the reacting system which says that the "increment reaction", such as seen in microscopic evidence of ASR and theoretically calculated by Fick's second law and Arrhenius' law, etc., cannot be "scaled up" as such to cover extended macro- and megascopic courses and effects of the reaction.

Nevertheless, the new French approach to modelling represents an innovative avenue for further research – more in conformance with reality than the linear expansion models.

The acceptance of the Glasser-Kataoka hypothesis of the swelling mechanism of ASR does have early, supporting suggestions by Vivian[142] and Idorn.[36] Both indicated that under certain circumstances alkali-silica gel might cause supplementary swelling and expansion in concrete after having been expelled from reacting particles. The basis for this suggestion was, for Vivian, that profused gel formation was observed on surfaces and in cracks in mortar bars, while Idorn observed the same phenomenon on surfaces and in cracks in field concrete and on wet preserved, reacting aggregate surfaces in drilled cores of affected concrete. With today's knowledge base, these early observations are explained by the fact that both workers studied concrete with opaline, reactive aggregates apt to react violently and to produce profuse amounts of gel, which is initially movable and swelling before absorption of Ca^{++} ions from the cement paste takes place. Both of them also observed that low-viscosity gel is capable of seeping out from affected particles into the porous structure of adjacent cement paste without causing expansion and cracking, but is apparently transformed to an impregnating, densifying cement paste component in the course of Ca^{++} ion absorption.

The keynote paper's reference list includes 28 early and contemporary published studies. Sixteen of these are by French colleagues who produced the basic inputs for the new modelling in the course of the 1992–1996 period. Besides the other twelve references, which go back to 1981, those mentioned above by Vivian and Idorn, and especially the crack-propagation mechanism by Krogh in 1975,[168] should have been mentioned as preceding the Glasser-Kataoka hypothesis (although Krogh also failed to consider the stiffening effect on gel in cement paste of Ca^{++} ion absorption). Likewise, the introduction by Tang Mingshu and Han Sufen, in 1983,[180] of application of the Arrhenius equation deserves to be remembered in further progress with the new theoretical approach.

More turning-point issues

The socio-economic importance of ASR, and the quest for a knowledge base for the elimination of its deleterious effects in field concrete, was conveyed to the conference in a strong appeal made in ten papers by the four delegates from the People's Republic of China.

With a population of 1200 million and an exhausting 10% annual increase of the cement production capacity, in 1996 approaching 450 million tonnes per year, the country is in a tremendously challenging race to match the demands for industrial, housing and infrastructure development. Concrete production still has to rely on a majority of cement of inferior quality from older, primitive plants, on high-alkali cement from newer plants, on the use of aggregates of unknown compositions and performance quality, of chemical admixtures to substitute for adequate materials and craft skill, and on excessive heat-curing to accelerate precast concrete element production.

Recognising harmful ASR as a serious threat to the durability of new concrete, the research has chosen a dualistic scientific and engineering approach. The researchers have, since the 6th ICAAR in 1983 and at the following conferences – including the 10th – contributed important achievements regarding the kinetics and thermodynamics of ASR, about ACR, and the introduction of autoclave-based, rapid test methods. At the same time, the progress of studies for national use of aggregate characterization, investigation of affected structures, etc. has been made available to the international knowledge base.

Hence, in terms of matching the research needs and the obstacles which have to be overcome, China is setting an admirable yardstick for the developing continents of the world, such as Asia in general, Africa and Latin America.

T. Wang, S. Nishibayashi, and K. Nakano from Japan, introduced the fractal analysis method as a means of quantifying the visible surface cracking in concrete affected by harmful ASR. The early ASR research in the USA adopted the designations pattern and map-cracking as an initial, visual indicator of the occurrence of ASR (in contrast to crumbling and scaling in surfaces affected by frost, sulphate attack, etc.). The terminology did imply that a certain systematic order exists between the elementary formation of cracking at individual ASR reaction sites within concrete bodies and the accumulated surface macro-evidence of the internal mechanism.

The new study confirmed the fractal character of surface cracking due to ASR, with lower limits of fractality corresponding to the maximum size of reactive aggregates. Fractal values were found to characterize the cracking features. The study needs to be extended to incorporate different conditions for the ASR cracking mechanisms, such as the effects of combined reactive and non-reactive aggregates, supplementary surface cracking due to drying shrinkage,

231

etc. Furthermore, it does not yet associate the fractality of surface cracking with the chemistry of ASR and the basic "micro-fractality" of increment cracking and volume increases at the individual reaction sites. Such further accomplishments require:

(*a*) integration with the further development of the new French concept of modelling of the ASR chemistry and mechanisms

(*b*) application of the new chaos theory to bridge the gap between the increment fractality and the macro-mass effects of the reactions.

The turning-point for the ASR research will be passed when, in the overall picture of industrial and science applications of the new chaos theory,[209] the absence of the many years of ASR history has been rectified. The likeliness that this will happen is due to the obvious applicability of fractal analyses, reaction kinetics and thermodynamics, and the chaos theory due to:

□ the complexity of the course of ASR in field concrete which is obvious to experienced field investigators

□ the inability of the homogenized, linear expansion test methods to make predictions regarding the development of harmless versus harmful ASR in field concrete

□ the fractal features of crystalline precipitates in concrete with ASR, and of accumulated, fractal cracking due to expansive pressure in reacting aggregate particles

□ the experience that, in country after country where harmful ASR in field concrete has been recognized, sooner or, with more reluctance, later, the visible symptoms − cracking patterns, gel-exudations and occasional expansions − are the same, whereas we are aware that different reactive rock types each set each their mark on the course and effects of the reaction, in the same way that environmental conditions do.

The costs of ASR

The presentation in Melbourne of Iceland's 16-year successful reliance on the mixing of 5–7% silica fume and high-alkali Portland cement, suggests that attention to the cost-benefit ratio of ASR research, which Iceland, as a country of very limited resources, has mastered, ought to become a primary target of forthcoming ASR research planning and management, as continents containing the majority of the world's populations begin to need the services of the research.

The contribution by R. E. Oberholster, "Case studies of the practical and economic impact of alkali-silica reaction in South Africa" is a promising, albeit still rare, study of the costs of rehabilitation of concrete affected by harmful ASR. The economic analyses in the paper are confined to structures in the South African Cape area, where harmful ASR has been common. Some bridges have been demolished; they are not included in the survey. For a 27 km stretch of highway with bridges and pavements, the present worth estimate brought forward to 1996 was Rq 540 million[1]. Including other affected structures, an overall excess of Rq 2 billion is estimated (US$ = 550 million).

Tables 29 and 30 summarize the more specific analyses of the costs of construction, investigation, analyses and monitoring, repairs and replacement costs and,

[1] Rq = US$ 0.2743 (1996 rate)

in one case, the loss of production, for four categories of structure:

- ☐ 27 km highway pavement and bridges
- ☐ 1.4 million railway sleepers
- ☐ a city centre building in Cape Town
- ☐ the Stenbras hydroelectric power plant and dam.

The repair/replacement costs are apparently partly real and defrayed, and partly prognosticated for the future needs of continued repairs during the total period of ASR activity. The limited background information suggests cautious interpretation of the data; nevertheless, the figures are noteworthy. The repairs and rehabilitations of the highway bridges and pavements may witness that the case happened early after the discovery of ASR and that traffic safety was an ultimate request. The 1.4 million railway sleepers have in ways been a tremendous series of "concrete bars" under field exposure to one deleterious cause, ASR,

Table 29. Construction, investigation and rehabilitation costs in four different categories of structure in the Cape area, South Africa (after Oberholster)[197]

Operation	Cost: Rq × 1000			
	Highway	Sleepers	City centre	Power plant
Construction	2 000	8 400	12 000	75 000
Investigation and monitoring	4 100	500*	48[†]	340
Repairs and rehabilitation	12 700	34 000[‡]	250	12 000[§]
Revenue loss				12 000[§§]
Total	18 800	42 900	12 298	99 340

* Including rehabilitation 1987–96
[†] Rehabilitation and replacements 1996–2006
[‡] 10×10^3 Rq hereof for annual monitoring
[§] Alignment, etc., 15 years
[§§] Loss of revenue, 15 years

Table 30. Comparative costs for construction, investigation and monitoring, repairs, and power plant only – loss of production for the analysed highway and bridges sector, the railway sleepers, the city centre and the power plant figuring in Table 29 (after Oberholster)[197]

Construction	Cost: Rq × 1000			
	Construction	Investigation and monitoring	Repairs and rehabilitation	Revenue loss
1970 Highway	2 000	4 100	12 700	
1973–76 Sleepers	8 400	500	34 000	
1976–77 City centre	12 000	48	250	
–1979 Power plant	75 000	340	12 000	12 000
	97 400	4 988	58 950	12 000

of grades from harmless to severe, and the railways have had to request maximum performance safety. The dome in the city centre seems to have been a "mild" case. The power plant structures exhibit the typical features of disalignment of machinery foundations and gross expansions of the dam.

The typical range of categories of concrete structures with exposures to ASR are thus represented in the article, and the case of the railway sleepers represent an exceptional opportunity for comparison, namely with the − litigation − cases of ASR in railway sleepers in Canada and USA in the 1980s and 1990s. In South Africa the total costs (for 1.4 million sleepers) are reported to 42.9 million Rq, or about 12 million US$.

In Canada and the USA, respectively, about 0.35 and 0.3 million similar sleepers which were affected by ASR were summarily discarded by the railway companies and replaced by new ones (of wood in Canada). The costs of investigations have not been published, for legal reasons, but can be estimated to have run to something in the order of 35−40 million US$ plus the legal expenses, which with certainty have not been less. Hence, it seems justified to imagine that, for the two cases in the USA and Canada together, instead of a theoretical maximum of 12 million US$ costs for investigations and repairs, more than 100 million US$ have been spent, besides unknown expenses for the replacement operations.

More general interpretations of this kind of comparison should also take into consideration the fact that the research on ASR in South Africa, which commenced in the mid-1970s, was organized under the auspices of a national committee which included both public and private engineering and industrial leadership commitments. It accepted a strong aim for applicability of the research and for consensus implementations. In the USA and Canada no such superior, national leadership commitments existed in the 1980s and 1990s (while, during the early 1940−60 phase of ASR history in the USA, there was a strong, voluntary drive for consensus implementation of the multifaceted research).

It is inevitable that the contrasting "railway sleeper" experience in South Africa versus that in the USA and Canada will bring the issues of structural rehabilitation expenses due to harmful ASR and to associated research programmes into focus during the turning-point changes for future development.

Diagnostic investigations

The now refined methodology of diagnostic investigations into field concrete deterioration was the subject of contributions from many parts of the world in the 10th ICAAR.

As mentioned earlier, many authors have shown that cracking due to ASR takes place in reacting aggregate particles, and some authors have demonstrated that alkali-silica gel absorbs CA^{++} when precipitated in concrete after being formed during the conversion of silica in reacting particles. A few have also further observed that after long-term field exposure (in cold, wet climates), unhydrated clinker components still remained in the cement paste.

Supplementary studies from "new" countries confirmed that field concrete investigations made for assessment of the cause or causes of deterioration including ASR are now approaching standardization of methods and procedures.

In such "failure case studies" the amount of alkali-silica gel versus the amount of precipitated ettringite, traumasite, calcium carbonate, brucite, gypsum, etc. still engenders controversial disputes about the causation of damages. Among other things, this is because the available data about the initial concrete processing and the environmental exposure are usually scarce and uncertain, while the basic research into deleterious reactions in concrete is primarily undertaken by science-orientated specialists relying on idealized laboratory model examinations.

Papers about failure cases in Newfoundland, South Korea, India, China and Australia did not, as examples, include characterizations of the environmental exposure conditions which could make it possible to identify different impacts in the concrete, graded in accordance with the ranges of latitudes, inland/marine situations, etc.

The introduction of failure case studies in Australia in the 1980s, W. F. Cole *et al.*,[210] A. Shayan and C. J. Lancucki,[211] and Thaulow *et al.*,[203] has not yet brought the continent's range of excessively aggressive inland and marine exposure conditions into focus and their influence was not mentioned in the review paper by A. Shayan and colleagues. The above paper by Thaulow *et al.* about the Lucinda Jetty case in Queensland, 1986–1988, was sorely missed in the review, because the published records of the case investigation:

□ illustrated the range from severe, harmful to harmless ASR within one structure composed of about 300 prestressed, standard concrete beams in a tropical, marine environment
□ substantiated the absorption of Ca^{++} ions in alkali-silica gel expelled from reacting aggregate particles, and the rigidity of calcium-rich gels, approaching the composition of cement paste vis-à-vis the swelling capability of low-calcium alkali-silica gel which exuded on the undersides of severely affected beams of the structure
□ by stress analyses confirmed that the prescribed 40-year performance lifetime of the structure was not in issue
□ included monitoring equipment and procedure for recording of the further development of harmful ASR in the affected parts of the structure.

K. Okada, M. Fuji, Y. Yamaguchi and K. Imada described the effects of the Hyokoken Nanbu earthquake in Japan of 17th January 1995 on structures with and without harmful ASR. The internal cracking in the concrete affected by ASR did not appear to have increased the damage caused by the earthquake; it rather looked as if the concrete without ASR had been the most susceptible. This indication concurs with earlier studies of the effects of harmful ASR in reinforced concrete, e.g. F. Bach *et al.*[212] at the 9th ICAAR which suggested that interior cracking due to ASR may lead to increased ductility and thereby more efficient stress distribution in shear zones. They further envisaged that the shear capacity may be increased by prestressing of reinforcement due to expansion caused by ASR.

Social development is urgently required in future years in many regions where earthquakes are common and most traditional buildings possess little earthquake resistance; hence observations relating ASR to earthquake resistance of concrete deserve goal-orientated, integrated ASR and structural design attention.

235

Smaller east Asian countries, South Korea, Taiwan, Hong Kong, joined the global "ASR club" in Melbourne with reports about field cases of harmful ASR. Their contributions were, in many ways, yardsticks of the incomplete transfer of the total ASR knowledge base when ASR becomes recognized in "new" countries. The professionals engaged in the research cannot start by screening the entire pre-existing knowledge and making judgements on its inherently differing opinions, protective regulations and test methods. Nevertheless, general geological-mineralogical expertise with petrographic equipment, usually now including SEM-EDX, and acquaintance with the classical ASTM methods, have made the available researchers in such countries capable of identifying and diagnosing cases of harmful ASR, classifying the types of reactive aggregates used, and proposing adaptation of initially reasonable, preventive measures.

Cost-effectiveness of the research

Lingering uncertainty among the producers of the source materials for concrete was discussed by A. Leshchinsky, J. Pattison, I. Dumitru, and G. Smorchevsky They referred to the general use of laboratory test methods for aggregate reactivity as adding possibly unnecessary costs for concrete production. They suggested a system established for critical analyses of field concrete failure cases. They did imply that cases of harmless ASR in field concrete made with reactive aggregate-cement mixtures, yet showing no damage, ought to be incorporated in such an overall analysing system. Leshchinsky and co-authors were remarkably isolated at the conference as contributors from the operating industries concerned, considering the persisting uncertainty about the real extent of harmful versus harmless reaction in field concrete.

The UK, for instance, was represented in Melbourne by 14 delegates contributing 21 papers, in a continuation of the high profile research effort ever since the discovery of harmful ASR in south-west England in 1976. Meanwhile, the number of structures in which the cause of damages has been established to be harmful ASR has remained a very small percentage of the amount of concrete in structures, road pavements and buildings in Britain. The occurrence of reactive aggregates is confined to a few areas as an inconspicuous proportion of the available aggregate resources, and fly ash and GGBS are available nationwide, along with low-alkali cement to make even reactive aggregates acceptable with negligible risks.

It seems to be a special British development that public pressure, acting both through the technical press and the news media, in the later decades has raised several antagonistic campaigns against concrete due to unexpected kinds of deterioration. This has happened concurrent with declining investments in strategic cement and concrete research. At first there was a problem with incompetent uses of structural concrete made with high-alumina cement in the 1960s. Next came the populistic ASR "concrete cancer" period in the 1970s, reinforced by the reluctant professional recognition of the problem. There then followed in the 1980s the misconception, even in the engineering professions, that increased C_3S contents in Portland cement had made the British cement industry responsible for early concrete dilapidation, especially in precast concrete housing. These repeated "affairs" appear to have created the prevailing, pessimistic trouble-shooting research with emphasis on extraordinary refinements of investigation methods and procedures, and of protective regulatory restrictions regarding materials properties, concrete compositions, etc.

In Canada, the occurrence of harmful ASR and of ACR was recognized and engendered research as early as 1960. As in the UK, the number of failure cases due to ASR has, since then, remained small compared with the number of concrete structures in service. Nevertheless, the Canadian ASR research has, over the years of the ICAARs, been profusely funded, with emphasis on petrographic characterization of aggregates, failure case diagnoses and, in particular, national and international refinements of the empirical, linear-expansion model testing methods. With 8 delegates in Melbourne presenting 18 papers, it appears that academic and public institutions remain capable of continuing the research with the linear-expansion model testing applied in pragmatic, experimental studies of second-order ASR problems. The absence of cost-effectiveness analyses of the research investments and accomplishments is striking. With a building and construction sector for 28 million people, Canada possesses sufficient resources of low-alkali cement, non-reactive aggregates, fly ash, GGBS, and silica fume to eliminate any risk of harmful ASR in field concrete using the already established knowledge base.

The French participation in Melbourne included a review by A. le Roux and B. Godart of the recently adopted, national system of preventive measures for AAR (i.e. including alkali-carbonate reaction). The system: "Recommendations for the prevention of damage by the alkali-aggregate reaction" includes characterization of the environmental exposure for a given concrete structure, careful identification and monitoring of the production quality of given, acceptable aggregates, and five new French test methods. It is a novelty that "potential reactive pessimum (PRP)" aggregates, such as flint, are acceptable if used in proportional amounts which have been found to be higher than an agreed "pessimum". Considerable efforts have been spent on development of a system which minimizes the risk of harmful AAR without unnecessary rejection of available French types of aggregates, or enforcement of changes in the national cement production technology. The system is an industry-public authority consensus achievement, and was apparently introduced to put a final stop to the occurrence of harmful AAR in France. It is an interesting paradox that with this consensus, achieved in the course of the last 6–7 years of intensive research in France, there has concurrently been launched a long-term explanatory study of the basic chemistry and mechanisms of ASR, from which the French cement and aggregate industries appear to have withdrawn.

The USA has its own story with respect to the current international ASR research exchange. The brief review by I. Jawed of the 1987–1992 SHRP programme at the 9th ICAAR in London,[213] was one of four USA contributions to that conference, whereas there was no mention in Melbourne among the four papers from the USA of the substantial follow-up implementation programmes, run since that time by the Federal Highway Administration and many States' highway administrations. Considering the past, superb leadership in the 1940–60 international ASR research exchanges, the reduced present American participation is evidence of the pronounced transfer of scientific research leadership within the USA to the high-technology industries and away from cement and concrete. In other words, building and construction have become low-technology enterprise areas, with insufficient returns on the investments to attract private investors and therefore also unable to provide sufficient funding for the research to make it effective in modern industrial terms.

In Australia, the pioneering explanatory ASR research in the 1940s and 1950s apparently passed into oblivion on the continent when CSIRO decided to call a halt to it. It was never followed up by comparative investigations of the possible occurrence of harmful ASR in field concrete. A single case of harmful ASR was identified in Victoria in 1981. Thereafter, the recognition of the occurrence in western Australia by Shayan followed in 1986, and in the Lucinda Jetty in 1988. The Australian participation in Melbourne showed that, since then, the international methodology for diagnosing field investigations has been adopted, whereas the past investments in basic studies of the chemistry and mechanics of ASR have not yet been communicated to present-day researchers and academic engineering education.

Scrutiny of the accomplishments of the ten ICAARs

The second phase of ASR research commenced in the early 1970s because the effectiveness of the American and the Danish precautionary solutions had been undermined by the changed conditions, which also forced a few new countries to concede that they had experienced harmful ASR as an impediment to the progress of concrete usage. The subsequent, gradual spread of the recognition of ASR as a serious problem throughout the world is chronicled in the proceedings of the International Conferences on Alkali-Aggregate Reaction (ICAAR) which together form a unique narrative of 22 years of unprecedented continuity of international research exchanges and contacts.

The achievements attained in the course of the period of the ten ICAARs are identifiable within the categories of the research efforts:

- ☐ ASR in field concrete
- ☐ concrete materials
  - — aggregates
  - — cement
  - — fly ash, GGBS, silica fume
  - — water
- ☐ mechanisms and chemistry
- ☐ examination and testing methods.

The long-term, gradual development of the ASR research and the spread of ASR occurrence has set its mark on the accumulation of the acquired new knowledge. The engagements over many years of new research staffs from different cultures have contributed towards bringing many different conditions for the occurrence of ASR and for the research within the overall picture, but have also mitigated approaches towards a holistic concept of ASR and its effects in concrete. Likewise, progress towards transfer of the acquired knowledge into global guidance for engineering practice has been ineffective and lacking in mutual, goal-orientated leadership.

The course of the 10th ICAAR illustrated that the research has, in many respects, reached "turning-point situations" with the need for a thorough scientific renaissance and determined mutuality for the final eradication of harmful ASR from concrete building and construction.

ASR in field concrete

The paramount experience which the ICAARs have provided is the global occurrence of harmful ASR as a serious cause of damage to concrete structures. With hindsight, it is still astonishing that the occurrence of the reaction was ignored in western Europe until:

- □ 1976 in the UK, with a forewarning from Jersey in 1971
- □ 1983 in Italy
- □ 1989 in Belgium and France
- □ 1992 in the Netherlands, Norway and Sweden
- □ 1996 in Portugal

since all these countries had potentials for ASR similar to those identified in Denmark in 1951 and studied by us under a policy of open exchange of information during the following decades. The astonishment may, however, deserve to be moderated. In the northern continental European countries, and also in Spain and Italy, blast-furnace slag cements have been widely used since the early 1900s. In the Mediterranean countries, notably Spain, Italy, Greece (and also Turkey), pozzolanic cements have been commonly used since antiquity. Hence, inadvertently harmful ASR may have been effectively prevented, albeit unnoticed, over large parts of Europe. The reluctance among the industries concerned to recognize ASR as national problems may therefore also have been motivated both by occurrence of harmless ASR and by the uses of pozzolanic cements as an unconscious preventive measure.

From Japan, the first mention of occurrence of ASR in field concrete came at the 7th ICAAR in 1986, where also western Australia, Brazil and Argentina reported cases as "new countries". North-east Australia joined in 1989 with about 100 cases of harmful ASR. Norway and Sweden appeared as "new countries" at the 9th ICAAR in 1992 with volcanic and metamorphic rock types, e.g. greywacke and phyllites, as reactive types and severe field cases of harmful ASR.

It is virtually undeniable that the countries with deferred recognition of ASR must have had visibly developing ASR in field concrete several years before the problem attracted serious attention and funding of investigations. Some countries, notably South Africa and Japan, have continued the 1940–60 open-door research policy in the ICAAR epoch of research and exchanges. They have identified important field cases, described them in detail, and made them accessible for visits with the purpose of exchanging knowledge. From other countries, notably some of those with very delayed recognition of the ASR problems, the proceedings of the 7–10th ICAARs provide limited or no available information about field cases. The structure of the ICAARs has not made the conferences suitable for discussion of such policy issues, although experienced research professionals can see the loss of mutual benefits in comparison with free exchange.

The series of ICAARs reveal implicitly another, even more serious, hindrance to realistic assessments of the engineering implications of ASR, namely the overriding frequency of harmless over harmful ASR in field concrete. This should influence engineering practice worldwide due to the effects on construction economy, resource consumption and preservation strategy, and should also change the scientific research modelling of ASR for reliable transfer of empirical research results. It may seem hazardous to claim that ASR occurs in a harmless modification in by far the largest number of concrete structures in the world today, which have the potential for ASR: *How can one justify such a stipulation when close to 60 years' publications are full of descriptions of harmful ASR, while harmless reaction has nowhere been explicitly detected and quantified as an existing alternative to the harmful reaction?*

The insistence, that the harmless cases are the large majority has, nevertheless, the strong support of circumstantial evidence. The evidence was already appearing during the 1940–60 phase of the ASR history with experience from field investigations. (Incidentally, the laboratory experimental research with mortar bar testing disclosed higher probabilities for obtaining non-expansive, reactive aggregate: cement combinations (i.e. harmless) than harmful combinations. The conceptual problem was that non-expansive reaction was mentally interpreted by most researchers as no reaction, instead of harmless.)

The failure to identify harmless reaction as the major mode of occurrence appears to be continuing in the ICAAR proceedings, despite the fact that common sense implicitly informs us, with regard to every "new country" that any individual case of harmful ASR is within populations of structures with several or most cases being harmless reaction. Moreover, field investigation reports inevitably tell that within affected structures there are always different grades of severity of the cracking and, if present, also of expansion, and zero effects, i.e. harmless ASR. This is, in fact, why modern field investigation methods have adopted the rating system which I introduced in the 1950s.[36]

From South Africa, Canada, and England, which are countries with substantial investments in ASR research since the mid 1970s, the number of structures demonstrating harmful ASR amounts to no more than a few hundreds per country (see the 4th–8th ICAAR proceedings). At the 9th ICAAR, more figures are given, such as reports detailing grades of damage to railway sleepers examined in South Africa and on damaged bridges in northern France. The reports comprise ratings of the damage which show that figures for the number of affected structures are overestimating the seriousness, in other words they incorporate harmless reaction. Notwithstanding that a stage of no-cracking ASR may represent an incipient early phase of later harmful reaction, it is also apparent from this information that harmless ASR is the predominating modification of the reaction in field concrete.

In recent years, field investigations of concrete with ASR have engaged a growing interest as a commercial enterprise in their own right, not least for the consulting engineering profession; and the methodology for such investigations has been made correspondingly more complicated[186] and expensive for the client. However, the 10th ICAAR indicates that, at least in North America and western Europe, most existing field cases of harmful ASR have now been identified and investigated sufficiently to enable adequate rehabilitation. Unfortunately, the motivation is negligible for building owners to sponsor balancing investigations of comparable cases of harmless ASR.

It is a lasting reassurance that almost 60 years of ASR case discoveries in many tracts of the world have not included a single case of structural collapse caused by cracking or expansion due to harmful ASR. Hence, the experience and associated research in South Africa, the UK, Japan, Denmark and France since the 5th ICAAR, certifies that harmful ASR is not a safety issue in structural concrete engineering; but it may incur unanticipated expenses for structural rehabilitation.

South African, Japanese and Icelandic civil engineering and research programmes have, in particular, contributed investigations of ASR-damaged structures associated with the development of reasonable rehabilitation methods.

Aggregates

The most significant accomplishment of the ASR research into alkali-silica reactivity of aggregates during the period of the ICAARs is the gradual clarification of the reactivity of rock types other than the classical siliceous, sedimentary and glassy, volcanic rocks, which were those found predominantly to cause harmful reaction in the USA and Denmark in the 1940–60 period. Actually, R. C. Mielenz,[214] in 1958, made the predicative statement; "*Convincing evidence has recently been obtained to demonstrate that coarsely crystalline quartz which is intensely fractured, strained and granulated internally as the result of metamorphic processes during geological time . . . can cause a deleterious degree of expansion of mortar or concrete containing a high-alkali cement*". Based on cases of harmful reaction with phyllites and quartzites in the eastern States of the USA and in the 1960 review[114] the reactivity of phyllites was referred to with the suggestion that the reactive component was micro-crystalline quartz. Canadian experience with harmful reaction in the Nova Scotia region, reported by M. A. G. Duncan *et al*.[215–217] revealed that low to medium grade metamorphic rock types, such as greywacke, argillites, phyllites and schists with minor or negligible contents of amorphous to crypto-crystalline silica were the cause of harmful reaction in which mica was somehow believed to play a part.[218] Mineralogically, these rock types were designated silicate rocks, corresponding to the special designation alkali-silicate reaction by Gillott. The indices for this hypothetical stipulation were:

- □ lack of correlation between expansion of test specimens, and field evidence of the reaction, including amounts of gel
- □ slow and long lasting expansions of mortar bars
- □ absence or negligible content of hitherto known reactive minerals
- □ presence of strained quartz (although of unknown implications).

The "direct" evidence for the stipulation was:

- □ phyllosilicates (phyllites and argilites) in the aggregates exfoliated at alkaline treatment, and there were peak changes with X-ray diffractometry.

D. Mantuani found phyllosilicates from the Canadian shield without mica which exfoliated at alkaline treatment, and stipulated that strained quartz in the rock types, also found in gneissic-granite rocks was the particular reactive

241

component. She characterized the diminished or delayed expansive reaction as a dilution effect with the silicate rock types.

As referred to in the present reviews of the ICAARs, the Canadian alkali-silicate reaction hypothesis and the undulatory extinction of quartz as a reactivity measure reappeared, albeit increasingly opposed, at the subsequent conferences until finally dismissed as unreal and unreliable at the 8th and 9th ICAARs, respectively.

The recognition of harmful ASR in Norway and Sweden in 1992 added a substantial region to the world map of occurrence of susceptible metamorphic and igneous rock types in aggregates, although a forewarning for Sweden had appeared in the late 1950s when T. Hagermann had found phyllites to be the cause of harmful ASR in dams in northern Sweden.[114] Reports from India, see discussion by R. R. Hattiangadi to reference [114], and contributions to the 7th and 9th ICAARs by H. C. Visveswaraya *et al.*, and by A. K. Mullick *et al.* at the 8th ICAAR, and Mullick *et al.* at the 9th ICAAR, identified the areas at and to the south of the Himalayan mountain chain as a third region containing the metamorphic/igneous rock types. The geological perspective of the overall picture is significant for potential occurrence of harmful ASR where it has not yet been recognized.

Iceland was the first country outside the USA which, during the late 1960s, was forced to realize that the high alkali contents of their national cement brand, combined with the frequent occurrence of acid, glassy volcanic rock types, constituted a risk for harmful ASR. In the early 1970s, New Zealand had made similar observations,[219] with a volcanic geology similar to that of Iceland. Subsequently, Japan and South America and, during the 1980s, also eastern Australia, experienced harmful ASR due to the reactivity of acid, glassy silica in syenites, andesites and dacites. The "ring of fire" of active volcanoes running from the south-east Pacific archipelago, Japan, north-east Asia over the Aleutians, Alaska and down the Pacific mountain chains of North, Central and South America, along with the volcanoes along the East African rift-valley, Mediterranean Europe, and the Atlantic Islands have, since pre-history, been consistent producers of reactive, volcanic rock types; but also of natural pozzolans, such as the Greek Santorin earth, the Roman Puzzooli sand, the French gaize and the German Trass.

The classical knowledge about the reactivity of opaline modifications, chalcedonic flint and chert in sedimentary limestone formations has not been significantly extended during the nine ICAARs, primarily because so much of the 1940–60 research had concentrated on these as the primary reactive materials and suitable for the explanatory research. Because they could be obtained in relatively pure, mono-mineralic and homogeneous samples, they were even adopted as standard reference reactive materials, such as Australian opal, Californian opaline-magnesium limestone, American Beltane opal, and Danish and British flint types. For the latter materials, the early Danish investigations still represent the bulk of basic information. This has, in the course of the nine ICAARs, been supplemented by the north German experience around 1970 and the much delayed recognition of harmful ASR with the similar types of flint and chert from the cretaceous and older limestone formations in southern England, northern France, Belgium, the Netherlands, and eastern Italy. Tang Mingshu *et al.*, at the 9th ICAAR, confirmed that the Beijing region in China has cases of harmful ASR with aggregates of siliceous limestone types. The occurrence of comparable geological formations elsewhere, such as in the CIS countries and Eurasia, supplements the ASR perspective for the extension of concrete utilization in further global development.

Table 31 is a summary display of the primary identified alkali-silica reactive rock types in the four categories: sedimentary, metamorphic, extrusive (volcanic) and intrusive (igneous), and – by deduction rather than explicit documentation – also the rock types which can reasonably be designated non-reactive.

The table requires supplementary comments.

- ◻ It refers to materials retrieved from quarries. Aggregates from secondary, sedimentary formulations such as sea beaches or sea bottoms, and from glacio-fluvial gravel and sandpits, may consist of more than one of the four categories.
- ◻ Natural rock formations are inevitably heterogeneous, and identification of species in loose gravel and sand and in solid rock outcrops or mines does not suffice for characterization of such materials for production of concrete aggregates without comprehensive, thoroughly planned sampling with geological and mineralogical examinations.
- ◻ Natural rock formations are subject to alterations due to weathering, wear and tear, tectonic stresses and foldings, and gradual convergence towards thermodynamic equilibria.
- ◻ Coupling of the established knowledge about the alkali-silica reactivity of the different rock types and a geological world map sustains the experience that ASR occurs all over the world – even where it has not yet been recognized.

In other words, Table 31 implies that several decades of work for the compilation of an international knowledge base on the alkali-silica reactivity of concrete aggregates has created an apparent paradox of worldwide implications: *Most of the available aggregate resources consist of potentially reactive rock types. Most field concrete made with such aggregates does not give rise to harmful reaction.*

Table 31. Survey of alkali-reactivity of rock types

Reactive			
Sedimentary	Metamorphic	Extrusive (volcanic)	Intrusive (igneous)
Siliceous limestone Chert Flint	Greywacke Shale Phyllite Shist Quartzite Granite-gneiss	Syenite Andesite Dacite	Granite
Non-reactive			
Pure calcareous limestone	?*	Basalt Diabase	Granite Gabbro

* No definite "non-reactivity" classification can be given for metamorphic non-reactive rock types.

For the ASR year 2000 situation, both aspects of this issue must be approached in terms of advisory guidelines for concrete engineering practice and for the research community.

Cement

The first ICAAR in Denmark, 1974, was arranged in accordance with Aalborg Portland's policy that the research operations were a service to the cement users, providing knowledge about the effects of cement in concrete. The R & D department of F. L. Smidth & Co. (FLS) made their contributions as a result of their interest in and knowledge about the implications of alkalis in the cement manufacturing process. Politically, the acknowledgement of the seriousness of the ASR problems by this manufacturer of – at that time – one-third of the world capacity of cement manufacturing equipment, was an encouragement for the attending researchers. That alkalis in cement increased the rate of early strength development in concrete (at the expense of decrease of ultimate strength) was general knowledge within the cement industries. After World War II, concrete engineering came to favour high early strength in order to support the desirable acceleration of concrete processing. Cement industries with high-alkali contents could therefore save expenses on grinding as a means of achieving the increase of the early strength of concrete. At the same time, reduction of the alkali contents in naturally high-alkali cements was possible with the predominant wet process manufacture technology, but required waste of the alkali-rich kiln dust, and of the corresponding part of the fuel for calcination. Consequently, in many countries with a substantial amount of high-alkali cement production, the high early strength issue was a marketing asset, and all talk of ASR and requirements for low-alkali cement was an inconvenience. In the first epoch of the ASR history, 1940–60, naturally low-alkali cement was so widely available in the USA that companies with high-alkali cement had to reckon with competitive pressure. In Denmark, one factory produced a low-alkali cement which was sold at premium prices in order to restrict its use.

During the 1960s, the first dry cement kilns came into use, and with this technology the reduction of alkalis during the burning process became more expensive. The reduction of heat consumption from about 1450 kcal/kg cement in wet kilns to about 800 or less by the new dry kiln and pre-calciner systems was a progressive step which, in the general perception and as a survival means for cement companies in depressed market situations, represented an indispensable trade off vis-à-vis the disadvantages of higher alkali contents.

However, during the same decade, harmful ASR had been found to occur, or to attract more attention than previously, in new countries. This made it impossible to continue to ignore the trend of increasing alkali contents in cement. The USA was in a special situation, in that its economically impoverished cement industry caused prolonged preservation of the wet-processing technology with sufficient supply of low-alkali cement and correspondingly reduced interest in ASR development. The ICAARs reflect this development, with presentations by delegates from cement industries and cement production equipment makers. At the 6th ICAAR in 1983, I. Worning and V. Johansen, FLS, predicted the trend of further increase of alkali contents in Portland cement.[220]

The prevailing trend in the development of cement technology is also unfavourable with regard to ASR because the increasing CaO/SiO_2 ratio means decreasing capability of the cement paste to retain the alkalis.

However, blended cement paste (with fly ash or GGBS) retains more alkalis than does pure Portland cement paste. These findings by Greening and Bhatty (4th and 7th ICAAR) reflect both problems without offering opportunities for selection of preventive measures against harmful ASR, dependent on particular, relevant circumstances.

The 7th to 9th ICAARs illustrated a gradual change towards increasing attention to ASR issues in cement industries in many affected countries, although without any visible prospects of further development in increasing production of low-alkali cement. On the contrary, new issues of environmental protection policy gained influence. Restrictions on emissions of SO_2 in the stack gas from cement plants leads to increased alkali-sulphate contents in cement. Concurrently, depositing of alkali-rich waste dust from precipitators is increasingly prohibited, meaning that the kiln dust must be incorporated into the cement. Moreover, any depositing of the dust is a loss of semi-produced raw materials. Meanwhile, concrete engineering still tends to increase the cement contents per m^3 concrete, and new chemical admixtures, some of which contain alkalis, are being introduced.

Some of the eastern European countries and the former Soviet Union were in special situations with regard to ASR and the alkali contents in the national cement brands. B. Penkala admitted, at the 7th ICAAR, the occurrence of harmful ASR in concrete structures in Poland.[221] The former Soviet Union has never had delegates at the ICAARs and did not publish information about attitudes to ASR elsewhere, despite geological conditions for their occurrence. It has now been disclosed by the former East Germany, that the cement industry did not use dust precipitators and produced high-alkali cement for use in concrete with reactive, metamorphic rock type aggregates in about one-third of the DDR territory. Eleven million prestressed railway sleepers were earmarked for replacement after the fall of the Berlin Wall, and it was disclosed that the occurrence of harmful ASR had been declared a "Staatsgeheimnis" by the DDR government.[222]

The prospect of increasing alkali contents in cement and concrete in the developing countries, as described for China by the Chinese delegates to the 10th ICAAR, ought to attract high priority attention in the major cement-producing corporations which are leaders in the current investment boom for increase of the global cement production capacity in the developing countries. The use of fly ash, GGBS and silica fume for neutralization of the alkali contents is one aspect of this situation.

Fly ash, GGBS and silica fume

A review of the 1940–60 epoch of ASR research shows that sufficient knowledge was attained for application of pozzolanic additions to cement as a preventive measure. There was no commercial basis for such development in the USA. This placed the Danish cement industry in the pioneering role as the first and only industry to market a pozzolanic alkali-resistant cement for use in the only country outside the USA which acknowledged harmful ASR as a serious problem. Not surprisingly, the issue received scant attention at the 4th Symposium on the Chemistry of Cement in Washington DC, 1960. The situation was changing when the ICAARs began in 1974. The Icelandic Building Research Institute, in conjunction with the national cement company, launched the quest for suitable natural pozzolans due to the volcanic geology of Iceland and the excessively high-alkali content of the national cement.

The energy crisis in the 1970s made power plants in many countries change their fuel from oil to coal, which made fly ash an inevitable by-product in search of applications. I introduced this new situation at the 4th ICAAR in 1978 in two contributions in which I made a pledge for innovative research to combine the ongoing energy conservation development in the cement industries with utilization of the power plant by-product, fly ash.

At the 5th ICAAR, 1981, in South Africa, the recognition of harmful ASR as a serious problem in the Cape Town province resulted in realistic openings for industrialized manufacture and utilization of fly ash from the power production and GGBS in blends with Portland cement as effective preventive measures, and the Icelandic research presented the first successful utilization of silica fume as a preventive measure. In the keynote address of the 6th ICAAR, I described the obtainable benefits of the blended cements. Other contributions covered different aspects of this new development, including the industrial progress and research studies, in particular regarding GGBS in the USA. Also, the special Finnish "F-cement" innovation of GGBS made cementitious with sodium hydroxide and lignosulphates, but without Portland cement, was introduced.

Chemistry-mechanism dilemma

The inherent, holistic concept of the original ASTM approach to the methodology of testing:

☐   conversion of chemical energy (C289) to mechanical work (C227)

with its caution regarding simplistic model transfer from laboratory to field concrete, was neither realized as conceptual by engineering practice nor subsequently by the research.

Perhaps the civil engineering educational emphasis on structural, i.e. mechanical matters made C227 the most popular test and experimental method, while analytical chemistry schools in academia preferred the challenges of exploring the complex silica-chemistry aspects of the reaction. In any case, fundamentally, it must be the absence of industrial innovation incentives for constructive utilization of the energy conversion, which left the ASR research with the lasting dilemma:

☐   Investigations of harmful ASR in field concrete offered comprehension of the expansive fracture-mechanics of the reaction by means of macro- and micro-observations of the structural effects on the material: the aggregate particles as reaction sites, the cement paste and the concrete as an entity.
☐   The chemistry became analytical, colloid and stoichiometric silica-chemistry, but bereft of the energetics of the reaction (in accordance with the prevailing trend in academic concrete research), and therefore not applicable for realistic model transfer.

In the early days, McGowan and Vivian in Australia[145] summarized their numerous observations of expansions and fracturing in mortar bars with harmful ASR as follows:

"*In a series of papers . . . the swelling of a gel was suggested as causing mortar expansion. In these papers evidence was presented to show that reacted aggregate particles absorb water and, while swelling in the gel condition, cause cracks and expand mortar. Further it was suggested that swelling aggregate particles caused mortar expansion by the widening of cracks, not by the elastic distension of the specimen. If this is true it follows that the magnitude of linear expansion at any instant and in any given direction should be equivalent to the sum of the appropriate directional components of the widths of all the cracks in the mortar specimen. The correlation between the expansions of mortar in the mortar bars obtained by calculation from the numbers and width of cracks and those obtained by overall measurement is discussed in this paper*".*

The American studies, notably those by Powers and Steinour which concentrated on the chemistry of the reaction, were also dealing with conversion to swelling (alternately non-swelling) alkali-silica gel in the interior of the reactive aggregate particles, and associated this swelling with mortar bar expansions – but not explicitly with the illustrated cracking mechanism. However, they did not contest the Australian perception of the mechanism of expansion and fracturing. Thin section microscopy observations were not yet available for their study, and they did not correlate the measured bar expansions with the "summary of incremental cracking" of individual reactivity particles, or the overall expansion as the integral of "crack widths originating at each particle". Concurrently, G. Verbeck and C. Gramlich in reference [223] had shown that the chemical reaction might cause the development of substantial osmotic pressure, albeit without any experimental correlation to cracking in reacting aggregate particles.

Figure 56 (shown as a photomicrograph in Figure 43) is a display of both the Australian perception of the swelling-cracking mechanism, the early Danish and American exploratory ASR studies, and the tremendous amount of later petrographic investigations of affected field concrete published in the ICAAR proceedings and elsewhere. It is a sketch made by hand in 1956 while I observed, in the optical microscope, the features of cracking of a dense flint particle, of sand size, in a thin section of concrete from a pier of the Oddesund Bridge, North Jutland, severely affected by harmful ASR. The sketch shows that the reaction mechanism consists of cracking in the interior, solid rock substance. This causes volumetric increase (swelling) represented by the widths of the cracks, which have opened fractures out into the adjacent cement paste. The cracks penetrate weaker aggregate particles (with weakness "planes" in the paste) and pass alongside stronger, unaffected particles. Alkali-silica gel from the reaction in the particle has solidified in the crack extensions in the adjacent cement paste, and exhibits shrinkage cracking. The widths of the cracks in the particle and the cement paste represent incremental volume increases, in other words expansion. The depicted feature of cracking is the same as is shown in Figure 42 (reproduced from contemporary American observations) and in Figure 44 with a Danish opaline flint in a progressed stage of conversion of its mineralic structure to swelling gel (however, showing subsequent drying-shrinkage cracking). Figure 45 extends the features of cracking to modifications in rock types of which the reacting silica is only a minor rock constituent, such as in reacting metamorphic rock types, etc.

The chemistry of ASR

Unfortunately, the long spell of ASR dormancy, with that period's declining long-term cement and concrete research investments, caused the ASR research's potential for a holistic development to vanish. Alkali-silica chemistry moved in as a research discipline in its own right, with hypothetical assumptions about the swelling of alkali-silica gel in the pores and cavities of hardened cement paste after expulsion from the reacting particles, disregarding the fact that cracking and increment expansion in reacting particles must happen prior to the expulsion of gel into the created cracks in the adjacent cement paste.

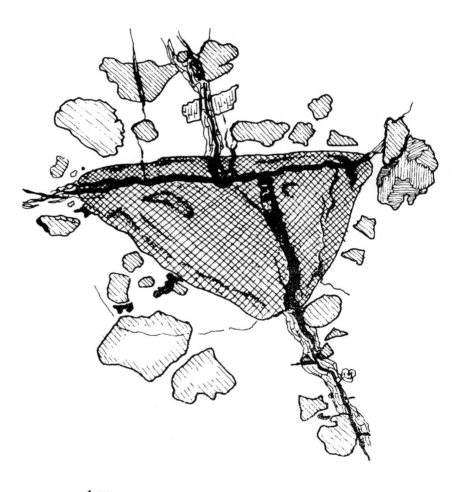

Fig. 56. Freehand sketch made at the optical microscope of sand particle of dense flint in thin section of concrete of a core from the Oddesund Bridge, Denmark

1 mm

In many ways, it is characteristic of the development of ASR research in the period of the ICAARs that the Glasser-Kataoka hypothesis[207] won acceptance even by field investigators, despite the consistent presentation of observations of affected concrete during the subsequent conferences which by nature were strong, visual arguments against the perception. One reason for the prevalence of the hypothesis may be that the kind of professionals who were engaged in the 1970–1980s boom of diagnostic field investigations did not need the subtlety of silica-chemistry and fracture-mechanics expertise while, on the other hand, the physical chemists did not need to be much concerned about the behaviour of field concrete. Hence, throughout the ICAAR period, the classical Powers-Steinour theoretical elucidation of the chemistry of ASR has also remained uncontested or, perhaps, rather unknown by an increasing number of the researchers concerned. Studies by S. Chatteri et al.,[224] did suggest more importance of the Ca^{++} content of cement paste as decisive for the cause of ASR, but their work was especially related to concrete exposed to excessive ingress of alkalis in solution, for instance due to application of sodium chloride as a de-icing agent for highway pavements and bridge decks. The introduction by Diamond of pore-squeezing analyses has sustained that the pore liquid in ordinary, hardened cement paste is a high-alkali concentration solution with pH about 13.5, fully capable of reacting first in an acidic-basic and subsequently a hydration reaction with silica. However, the consequential thorough revision of the classical perception of pozzolanic reaction as exclusively a silica-calcium hydroxide reaction remains to be seen to break through the barriers of conventional creeds for acceptance, in fact to be designated beneficial ASR.

The prevailing "room temperature syndrome" of academic concrete research and testing methodology in the industrial world, was probably the reason why it was the Chinese researchers, Tang Mingshu and Han Sufen[180],[225], who were the first researchers to examine the energetics of ASR by application of Arrhenius law for examination of the kinetics of ASR. This pioneering innovation in the research did not engender follow-up studies to appear at the subsequent conferences, notwithstanding the following implications:

- Field concrete has experienced higher heat development during production and, in warm environments, performance temperatures higher than at laboratory room temperature handling.
- The chemistry-mechanics of the reaction at room temperature is a two-dimensional projection of a multi-dimensional conversion of energy to work.

The new French approach to studies of the energetics of ASR and the Japanese adoption of fractal analyses for investigation of the fracture mechanics shows some promise of a change of direction towards a holistic concept of the reaction and its effects in field concrete. This must evidently incorporate two different aspects of the holism: namely, revelation of the basic conditions which make it possible to predict whether future reaction in field concrete will become harmless or harmful; and also elucidation of methods to assess the accumulation of the energy conversion in big concrete masses which may cause long-term structural expansions and deformations besides map- or pattern cracking.

Testing methods

Notwithstanding the fact that the ASTM testing system has never been applied with the purpose of obtaining integrated mechanical, chemical and mineralogical databases for risk evaluations of potential ASR damages in field concrete, the C289 rapid chemical test has won some recognition in construction and precast practice for its rapidity and low cost, while the C227 test has been eminently suitable for testing and research laboratories because the need for it coincided with the post World War II development of empirical testing equipment and technique. It also had appeal because it could justify extensive testing technique research for high levels of test accuracy with statistical data analyses. Petrographic examination of aggregates for identification of alkali-silica reactive constituents in special rock types was implemented as routine in aggregate examinations later than the two above test methods, due to limited employment of geologists and mineralogists in concrete research and testing institutions in many countries.

The reviews of the 3rd to 5th ICAARs show that the slow rate of ASR with the polymineralic Canadian, and later the South African, rock types made the changes in the mechanical test procedures necessary. This led, in time, to acceleration of the tests by increasing the storage temperatures and to aggravating the reaction by external supply of alkalis with storage in an alkali hydroxide solution instead of in water. The reactive rock components were common in the stone fractions in the two countries, but not in the sand, such as in the classical Californian cases, which were the basis for the mortar bar test. This difference prompted the Canadian research to adopt the concrete prism test, in which the reactive silica is often primarily a minor constituent of the coarse aggregate particles. The subtlety that the quantity of the reactive material in many cases in Canada probably amounted to less than in the classical Californian reactive sand is a matter of complication for the model transfer. The storage of test specimens in a NaOH solution adds a further model complication, because the external supply of alkalis enables the reaction to proceed expansively beyond the threshold value of alkali concentration, which in field concrete would cause expansion to terminate.

The Nordic procedure for mortar bar tests with storage in a saturated NaCl solution at $+50°C$, N. Thaulow and H. Olafsson,[226] had its origin in harmful ASR in highway pavements, which were de-iced by NaCl during winter seasons. Also, with this procedure, the aggregate is in some ways made to appear more deleteriously reactive than in the mortar in real concrete and the reaction is accelerated by the elevated reaction temperature.

The Chinese autoclave expansion test[180] actually operates with a changed energy activation level in test specimens.

Altogether, the mechanical specimen test development during the ICAARs has emphazised:

☐ reproducibility and comparability of test results by strict control with constancy of materials compositions, preparation of test specimens, storage conditions, and measurement techniques

☐ intensification of test procedures – chemically and thermal – in order to ensure that slowly reacting aggregates do not pass due to unsuitability of the classical test methods for high levels of susceptible silica per reactive particles

but neglected to consider the model transfer from laboratory to field concrete performance conditions. Consequently, "blindly following standards" may still lead to unjustified rejections or acceptance of aggregates, as concluded by the keynote speaker on test methods at the 10th ICAAR.

ASR research management, 1940–1996

The research into ASR in the first two decades had, for several reasons, accomplished its mission with remarkable effectiveness:

- □ In the four countries involved, the superior goals of the research were held in awe: to explore the nature of ASR with the purpose of preventing its occurrence as a cause of damage to field concrete.
- □ In Australia, the UK and Denmark, ad hoc leaderships representing the national top-level public and commercial interests had been in charge of the strategies and overall management of the research programmes. In the USA, the contemporary research had been so rich and pluralistic that many independently managed programmes were run simultaneously but with a strong drive towards complementarity.
- □ New groups of young researchers were engaged. They belonged to a breed of people who, under the impact of World War II circumstances, were dedicated to conducting innovative research under the panoply of a greater cause.
- □ Free, international exchange among peers was a ubiquitous feature of the research; often with essay-length discussions by correspondence in the preparations of individual publications and at conferences.
- □ The leading USA research was of outstanding integrity and intellectual brilliance and demonstrated effective transfer of the research through the ASTM consensus authority and the ACI communication efforts.

It is remarkable that the 1960 review of the international ASR research in reference [114], with presentation and discussions in the presence of the global top-level leaders of the cement and concrete industries and research institutes, did not cause any concern about the problems beyond the four countries involved. The attitudes behind the apparent ignorance of the problem restrained the new research in one country after another in the 1970s and 1980s. The deferred, gradual spread meant that strategies and policies for the programmes were dependent on widely different interests and attitudes.

The organization and management of the ICAARs has been placed, ad hoc, in the hands of those individuals and local back-up associations, institutes and industries, who have been dedicated to making them happen. This has kept the conferences free of public, commercial and institutional contingencies. The different, national preferences for conference structure and topical priorities have therefore also reflected the demands of the situations and the available research capacity regarding scientific responses and applicable guidance to the engineering professions.

The succession of the conferences has coincided with the contemporary development of analytical research instrumentation and the general progress of laboratory techniques and facilities. Our Danish approach to a diagnostic system for field concrete investigations with core drilling, thin section preparation, and optical thin section petrography in the 1940–60 phase of the ASR research, preceded the later access to X-ray diffractometry, flame-photometry, DTA-DTG, pore-squeezing and electron microscopy, which became generally available during the 1970s, along with refined, mechanical testing methods.

The autonomy of each of the conferences means that only a few of them comprised any synthesis of the attained state-of-the-art accomplishments, and none of them presented any kind of strategic consensus regarding "needs for further research". It is therefore useful to extract from the records just how far the ICAARs have brought us in furtherance of the 1940–60 accomplishments and what, if anything, we still need to do in order to enter the twenty-first century having eradicated harmful ASR from new concrete throughout the world.

In the making of such an evaluation, one should keep in mind that the ASR research is an integral fragment of the general development of concrete research. Therefore, its merits and problems in ways of operation in scientific research interaction, engineering practice and industrial technology also offer guidance for planning and management of forthcoming research and transfer beyond the particular realm of ASR.

The retrospective knowledge of the accomplishments attained through the relatively modest 1940–60 research efforts in four countries, see Tables 16–19, is a suitable yardstick for evaluation of the achievements during the much broader and deeper second phase efforts. The ASR situation in the year 2000 and the world perspectives are deducible from this extended knowledge basis.

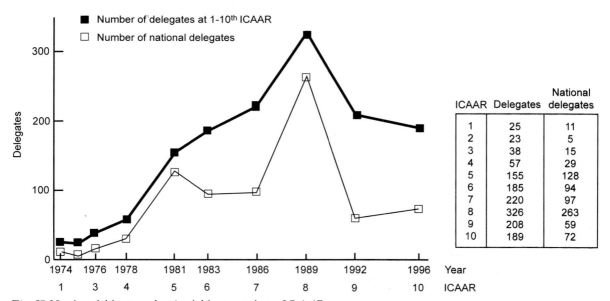

ICAAR	Delegates	National delegates
1	25	11
2	23	5
3	38	15
4	57	29
5	155	128
6	185	94
7	220	97
8	326	263
9	208	59
10	189	72

Fig. 57 Number of delegates and national delegates at the ten ICAARs

Attendance at the ICAARs

The stepwise increasing numbers of delegates at the ICAARs reveal information about the eclectic character of the management interests in the course of the period of conferences.

Figure 57 shows the total number of delegates and of delegates from the countries hosting the conferences at each of the ten ICAARs.

Figure 58 shows the number of papers presented at the ICAARs and the number of pages of the proceedings. The accumulated number of pages is 5533.

If one adds to this figure papers on ASR published elsewhere in the same period, and the number of papers previously published, it is likely that more than 20 000 pages of information exist today as a knowledge basis for ASR.

Figure 57 shows that the 5th ICAAR (in South Africa), the 6th (in Denmark), the 8th (in Japan) and the 10th (in Australia) attracted high national attendance. The South African local civil engineers made pioneering introductions of the structural implications of harmful ASR. The later Japanese upgrading of the structural ASR research prompted a very high national attendance from numerous public and industrial research groups and from the civil engineering sector. Probably, the nature of the indigenous aggregate resources, the cement technology development, and the susceptibility of the infrastructure function to earthquakes also motivated the large attendance, since the integrity of highway structures was highlighted.

The growth of the research in the UK from 1976, when the first case of harmful ASR on the mainland was reluctantly recognized, caused the creation of "special service groups" within the major consulting engineering firms. Subsequently, litigation cases about the responsibility for damages to structures caused by ASR and other kinds of deterioration created a prosperous market for "harmful ASR expertise".

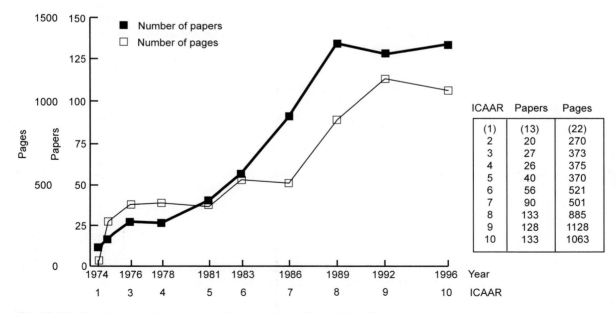

ICAAR	Papers	Pages
(1)	(13)	(22)
2	20	270
3	27	373
4	26	375
5	40	370
6	56	521
7	90	501
8	133	885
9	128	1128
10	133	1063

Fig. 58. Number of papers and pages of proceedings presented at the ten ICAARs

In Denmark, the ASR activity peaked with the 6th ICAAR in 1983. At that time, the engineering community and the public were alerted to the general "durability crisis", which also included premature corrosion of reinforcement in precast, steam cured concrete in many multi-storey buildings from the boom period, 1960 to 1973. The established "low risk" ASR policy from our earlier research period now became untenable. The BFL was no longer in existence and the residual concrete research was fragmented and reduced. The political authorities imposed a rigorous "triple" preventive measures policy by specifying simultaneous use of low-alkali cement, fly ash and non-reactive aggregates in concrete for public buildings and structures. The science-based, forward-looking ASR research was therefore left without public funding interest and was dismissed. Iceland, of all countries, had successfully established an effective preventive measures policy. In Norway and Sweden, ASR was acknowledged by the major research institutes as late as at the 1989 and 1992 ICAARs, despite the earlier identifications of the occurrence of reactive aggregates and cases of harmful ASR. Acknowledgement of ASR as a national problem in the Netherlands, Belgium, France and Italy was deferred until the 1980s. The sudden French participation in the 9th ICAAR in 1992 with 22 papers, but only scant information about the apparently large number of affected structures, is conspicuous.

Throughout the considered period, a low level of interest in the subject matter prevailed in the USA, while in Canada considerable interest has been generated since the 7th ICAAR in Ottawa.

The conference proceedings and supplementary articles in publications, such as references [226] and [227] show that in some countries concentrated research programmes as the basis for national guidelines and specifications regarding preventive measures have been accomplished in the course of a few years. This has happened where, as earlier in Australia and Denmark, consensus orientated management boards with all interested parties involved have run the programmes and prepared guidelines, etc. for adaptation within their broader framework of concrete construction and technology specifications. These countries are:

- Germany (West) 1969–73
- Iceland 1974–81
- United Kingdom 1983–89
- South Africa 1977–81
- Japan 1983–89
- France 1989–94.

In most countries, other than these six, the 1974–1992 phase of the ASR research has been managed by less representative, institutional hierarchies or individual, academic researchers, and public funding has been the primary source of finance.

As the research has progressed, the amount of duplicating studies have also increased, not least in the growing numbers of studies confined to empirical laboratory experimental testing. In accordance with much other research, the "reductional" philosophy has assumed the position as the governing planning principle, leaving unsystematic overlapping and large "holes" in the overall jigsaw picture.

8

ASR year 2000

The 60th anniversary of the history of ASR coincides with the commencement of the twenty-first century. The ICAAR conferences have substantiated that ASR occurs in field concrete all over the world, that the majority of available concrete aggregate materials are alkali-reactive, and that, nevertheless, the majority of ASR occurring in field concrete is harmless. The fact that the multinational ASR research has not yet established why the harmless reaction has predominated in field concrete is now the most crucial issue left for the research to resolve, because the classical preventive measures are not available in sufficient quantities for worldwide no-risk policies, and widely unavailable in the developing countries, where construction and building is going to intensify.

This situation is, in view of the potent impact of ASR on the world's concrete production economy, so precarious that a global, industrial/public leadership initiative is desirable for formulation and realization of an overall ASR research strategy, with a programme for scrutiny and finalization of the many years' eclectic, national-minded research history.

The amount of research investigations and studies about ASR since about 1970 is truly of exceptional magnitude and represents enormous expenditure on one single subject in the history of concrete research.

The concepts of strategy, cooperation and science-engineering interaction which developed among cement and concrete research professionals and their sponsors after World War II, engendered an effective intrusion of applied science into the 1940–60 phase of ASR research. Cost-effective engineering and industrial precautions against the harmful nature of the reaction were the result, along with the creation of a formidable new knowledge base and far-reaching innovations of research methods.

The geographical "spread" of the occurrence of the reaction in the second phase of ASR history has caused corresponding engagements of new research units and individuals in many countries. Meanwhile, social and technological developments have reduced the financial basis for general societal influence of cement and concrete research in comparison with the situation in the first epoch.

Hence, ASR research has, despite its remarkable growth and global outreach as the back-up for the ICAARs, lost a corresponding joint industrial/public leadership, which could have imposed a convergent, joint global strategy for a cost-effective precautionary policy. Besides, there has been no collegial engagement for a holistic, scientific concept of the basic nature of ASR, which could have reduced the disproportionate investment in continuous refinements of the empirical laboratory test methods.

The achieved knowledge base

Figure 59 displays my stipulation of the relative value of the ASR knowledge as it has accumulated since 1940. Phase 1, with only four countries involved, has provided about 60% of the entire 1996 knowledge base.

This evaluation rests on several observations:

☐ The presentation of available preventive measures at the 8th ICAAR in 1989, as adopted by the Japanese Ministry of Construction, in reality represents not more knowledge than was achieved in Phase 1, as reviewed in reference [114], 1960, and that has not changed since then. In other words, the global spread of the research, with remarkable increases in new research investments, has not given improved guidance for cement industry and engineering practice in return.

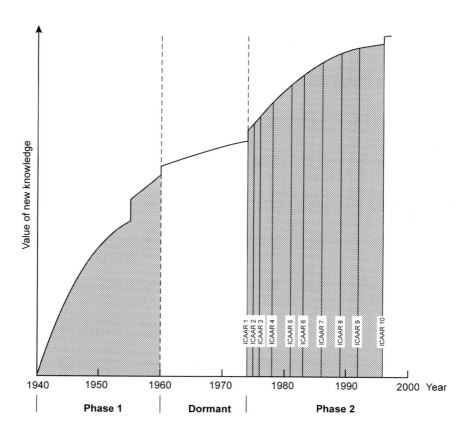

Fig. 59. Qualitative perception of the increase of knowledge about ASR, obtained by research and field experience from the identification of the reaction in 1940 until 1996 with the 10th ICAAR in Melbourne

- During the "dormant ASR period" 1960–1974, research methodology and instrumentation were subject to remarkable progress. Conference publications resulted in broader implementation during Phase 2, which, consequently, has added considerable value to the current knowledge base in these respects.
- The "rate of value increase" by new research is distinctly decreasing in the later part of Phase 2. This is a logical consequence of the successive incorporation of new researchers in one country after another. The focus of all new "start-up" operations on the same problem as predecessors and contemporary workers in many other countries does increase the incidence of repetitive investigations.
- The general trend in concrete technology research since the 1960s towards increasing reliance on pragmatic, empirical standard testing rather than on conceptual, explanatory study principles has inflicted the "reductional" philosophy on most of the ASR research.
- The research does not possess a problem matching holistic paradigm encompassing:

  — materials science – materials engineering
  — engineering design – construction technology
  — societal needs and resource economy

  for coordinated investments in a final, cost-effective, cooperative programme.

The figure suggests a distinct knowledge progress in 1955 due to the appearance of the Powers/Steinour's theory, coupled with Vivian's input. The 1960 international review[114] and the start of the ICAARs in 1974 represent further steps forward. There are also distinct "individual up-turning peaks" of accomplishment in the smoothed curve of knowledge progress between the highlighted events. The parent workers might feel that many such individual accomplishments should have been made visible. However, the figure is meant to be a qualitative depiction of the overall progress of accomplishments.

The display is invalid in one important respect, namely that the ordinate axis does not reveal the money spent on the many years' research programmes, or, rather, the return on the capital investments, but merely represents a qualitative estimate of the value of progressive knowledge. The reason for this deficiency is that concrete research publications on ASR research practically never include any information about the expenses, let alone estimates or calculations of the values of accomplishments in terms of profitability for the users.

No multinational, manufacturing industry would be able to survive if their management accepted substantial investments in R & D over half a century for the preservation of customers' confidence in their products, without regular budgeting and critical accounting of the cost/benefit ratio of the expenditure. But the separate ASR research groups and individuals, mostly in public employment in many different countries, have had no background or incentives for the creation of a common strategy with a return on investment

(ROI) philosophy for the ASR research, even though it must have dawned on them that we are facing a problem of serious, global implications.

Hence, the concrete resource materials industries, the engineering and construction enterprises, public agencies, financial investors and insurance corporations are forced to impose competent management systems for the ASR research investments which are still required.

Table 32, which presents a summary review of the ASR research achievements from 1940 to 1996, is presented as a basis for the creation of a strategic programme for a final settlement of the remaining ASR issues.

Concluding ASR research investments

The current prospects for increasing concrete utilization in the global urbanization development requires a distinct improvement of the ASR knowledge base. The experience from the Phase 1 and Phase 2 research suggests that a competent leadership, appointed by industrial and public investors, is desirable for the creation and supervision of a new paradigm for interactive materials science, industrial and engineering research. Such a management hierarchy would be able to release visionary energy in the currently hidebound research. It could fuse and mould new efforts into a common, dedicated undertaking, and under a panoply of global interests and responsibility it could re-establish a strategy, including knowledge of the consequences of the applicable solutions.

The primary, overall heavyweight issues for joint undertakings are:

☐ satellite-supported classification of reactive vis-à-vis non-reactive concrete aggregate resources in the world
☐ classification of the occurrence of harmless ASR in field concrete in all countries where the cases of harmful ASR have been intensive
☐ classification of the resources of natural pozzolans and the perspectives for the production of GGBS, fly ash, and low-alkali cements in the world
☐ an updating, omnifarious scrutiny of the established ASR knowledge base.

Scrutiny of the existing knowledge base is bound to reveal that the high priority of remaining ASR research concerns the long overdue classification of the energetics and fracture mechanics of ASR with the chaos theory as a vehicle for attaining a holistic system. Only this approach can harmonize descriptive clarification of increment reactivity in reacting aggregate particles with mass effects, whether beneficial, harmless or harmful, in field concrete.

A conspicuous amount of the data and observations from laboratory studies and field case investigations produced to date are likely to "fall into place" in the course of the suggested scrutiny and new approach. Hence, cost-effectiveness of the remaining research and of the use of preventive measures can be achieved and results issued for implementation.

Table 32. The ASR knowledge base 1996

ASR in field concrete

ASR has been found to occur universally, except in polar regions.

Harmless ASR is the predominant mode of occurrence.

Harmful ASR has not been found to cause structural collapse

The typical, visible field evidence of harmful ASR is pattern cracking in concrete surfaces.

Structural expansion may occur in mass concrete with external supply of water.

Moist and warm climatic exposure and external alkali supply are favourable conditions for harmful ASR.

Aggregates

There are two different modifications of alkali-reactive constituents in concrete aggregates:

□ Siliceous, amorphous or glassy, volcanic and low-order crystalline mineral phases in sedimentary and volcanic rock types and in tropical regions also in devitrified volcanic and igneous rocks. This category of reactive aggregates is likely to show reactivity when tested by the classical methods, such as ASTM C227 and C289.

□ Distorted, crypto- to micro-crystalline quartz as components in polymineralic, metamorphic and igneous rock types. Reactive aggregates in this category are likely to pass the classical test methods, but to reveal reactivity with aggravated test conditions, e.g. by elevated temperatures and/or external supply of alkali hydroxide.
(Concrete test specimens are preferable to mortar bars because the reactive components are only partial constituents of the aggregate particles.)

Cement

Low-alkali Portland cement (i.e. $\leqslant 0.6\%$ eqv. Na_2O) is not an unconditional safe, preventive measure.

There is a general trend of increasing alkali contents in cement.

Fly ash, GGBS, silica fume, natural pozzolans

Fly ash, GGBS and silica fume may, in blends with ordinary Portland cement, effectively inhibit harmful ASR in concrete with alkali-reactive aggregates. Natural pozzolans with the same effect may be found.

The reaction of these materials in concrete is a beneficial mode of ASR and, in principle, a hydration reaction akin to the hydration of Portland cement.

Effective inhibition of harmful ASR by the use of these materials in concrete requires mix design based on analyses of granulometry, mineralogy and chemical composition of the blend components.

Water

Alkali content in mixing water for concrete, and in moisture affecting field concrete during performance are favourable for the development of harmful ASR.

Table 32. (continued) The ASR knowledge base 1996

Chemistry and mechanism

Powers' and Steinour's theory for the chemistry of ASR and the effects of pozzolans is virtually unopposed and generally valid.

The pore liquid in hardened cement paste is a saturated alkali hydroxide solution which acts as a vehicle for migration of the alkali and hydroxide ions to reaction sites in alkali-reactive aggregate particles in concrete.

ASR is, in principle, a hydration reaction. Kinetically, it follows Arrhenius's law and, in closed systems with given amounts of the reactants, the resulting reaction product, alkali-silica-gel, will exhibit chemical shrinkage, and not expansive swelling.

Expansive swelling in reacting aggregate particles may create internal pressures large enough to cause tensile rupture of the particle, and to cause developed alkali-silica gel to issue out through created fractures in adjacent cement paste.

The space occupied by created cracks in and from a reacted aggregate particle is an increment enlargement in concrete. Surface pattern cracking and, under certain conditions, also structural expansions, result from accumulation of such incremental enlargements.

Alkali-silica gel which exudes from reacting particles absorbs calcium ions from the pore liquid of cement paste and thereby looses mobility and the capacity to swell. Eventually, the composition of such gel approaches that of cement paste.

Harmless ASR is logically the most frequent mode of the reaction in field concrete, *inter alia* because:

☐ the reaction exhibits chemical shrinkage when the supply of alkali hydroxide and water to reaction sites in reactive aggregate is limited
☐ the reaction may produce low viscosity gel which disseminates out into adjacent cement paste without exertion of expansive pressure
☐ swelling pressures developing in aggregate particles must exceed the fairly high tensile strength of many reactive rock types
☐ increment enlargements and cracking at individually reacting aggregate particles can only accumulate to visible fracturing in concrete under conditions favourable for the reaction
☐ creep of cement paste and autogenous healing of cracks caused by expansion prevents crack propagation and closes cracks in the long term
☐ low permeability of the cement paste, low concentration of alkali hydroxide in the pore liquid and limited amounts of pore liquid are inhibitors for the progress of ASR in field concrete.

Examination and testing of aggregates

Geological and mineralogical (petrographic) classification makes it possible to disclose the presence of alkali-susceptible phases of silica in rock types, and thereby to classify aggregates as reactive or non-reactive.

Identification of reactive rock types also makes it possible to classify them as either slowly or "classical" reactive.

Table 32. (continued) The ASR knowledge base 1996

The approximately 40 test methods developed for the reactivity of aggregates can be used to substantiate the geological/mineralogical classification.

The methods cannot establish whether a reactive aggregate will cause harmful or harmless ASR if used in field concrete.

INTERNATIONAL CONSULTANT

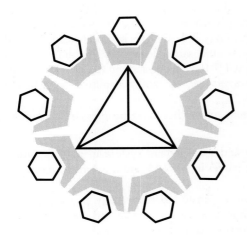

G.M.Idorn
Consult ApS

The general decline of cement and concrete research in western Europe and North America in the 1970s forced me, among many others, to face the profound changes from employment situations in research institutes which we had believed to be secure, to individual consultants' private enterprises — free and independent but only to the extent that there were enough clients to keep such operations alive.

I was 58 years old when I took up this new way of making a living in November 1978. I had not been trained to be a commercial salesman while in Aalborg Portland's service, and definitely not in my previous public employment. Moreover, the prospects for the sale of cement and concrete R & D know-how were not very rosy at the time.

The potential customers among industries, construction and engineering firms, and public agencies were in a deepening recession. Besides, they were accustomed to obtaining their special services free of charge. Nevertheless, it soon appeared that my past international promotion of Aalborg Portland and, earlier, of building research in Denmark had developed a hibernating capital of commercial goodwill which brought calls for assistance from many countries.

9

The consultancy basis

A systematic expertise

Figure 58, after reference [226], is an illustration of how we had made the BFL a player in the public debate in Denmark in the 1960s and 1970s on the ways of advancing cement and concrete technology R & D. This had been accomplished in conjunction with contributions to the same debate for the international audiences in Cembureau, EIRMA, ACI, RILEM, etc. and, on frequent occasions, invited lecturing at conferences, universities, etc. and committee work in the above mentioned organizations.

The figure presents the two different approaches to the progress of technology in which I was involved:

□ the classical R & D planning and management system in manufacturing industries, such as member companies in EIRMA and the American equivalent IRI

□ the fragmented and much slower transfer to technology in the building and construction sector, including most of the cement and concrete industries, engineering and construction companies, and public engineering departments.

Our work at the BFL, as described above in Part I, had managed to overcome some of the conventional barriers against effective application of cement and concrete research within the small community in which we operated. Our

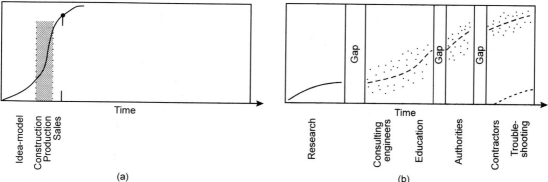

Fig. 60. Model configuration of the course and interaction of R & D in manufacturing industries and in the building and construction sector

long-term strategy encompassed the undertaking of innovative research, implemented in cooperation with Danish entrepreneurial firms under broad, public support and intense interaction with engineering and blue-collar education. Hence, we had made a contribution towards advancing the international competitiveness of Danish concrete technology know-how. At the end of 1978, I therefore felt well equipped to offer the acquired know-how for sale to clients in a consultative capacity; albeit at the same time prepared to be informed that the market for such services might be virtually non-existent.

I was aware that the depiction in Figure 60 of the building sector and concrete technology R & D process was an idealized configuration in comparison with the system in industries. The omnipresent system – if one can use the term "system" at all in this context – was that funding agencies and industries preferred to sponsor individual or group-operated research on themes or subjects which appeared attractive because they had already engendered support and funding elsewhere, or subjects such as problems with public appeal which were given news media attention. Within each forum for concrete progress one therefore found at any given time smaller or larger clusters of uncoordinated and even duplicating research projects. Conference organizers had also commenced an escalation in the number of conferences, which promoted uncoordinated duplications and did nothing to stimulate a convergent approach towards systematic technology innovation. The hegemony of the laboratory specimen testing syndrome and the wave of investments in new, high-power analytical instrumentation also drove research in the direction of fragmentation. As a consultant, I was forced to learn how, among the bulk of research publications and presentations, one identified those of merit for incorporation or cooperative arrangements in problem-solving work for clients.

I was directly confronted by the animosity towards our holistic BFL concept of R & D management during advisory service in the USA in the late 1970s, such as at the US Department of Commerce (DOC)/National Bureau of Standards (NBS) conference "Possible contributions of cement and concrete technology to energy conservation" in 1977,[230] for the National Research Council (NRC) study "The status of cement and concrete R & D in the United States", chaired by Professor D. M. Roy, Pennsylvania State University, 1977–80,[65] and as consultant for the Electric Power Research Institute (EPRI) in 1981–82 regarding development of fly ash uses with cement in the USA.[231] Actually, these undertakings investigated the implications of strategic goal-setting for the national cement and concrete R & D. The DOC/NBS conference emphasized all aspects of energy saving in cement and concrete production; the NRC, National Materials Advisory Board (NMAB) committee prepared a thorough analysis of the degradation of American cement and concrete research since the 1960s, and the EPRI project sought means of reducing energy consumption and environmental pollution by increase of the very low level of utilization of fly ash in cement and concrete. However, there was no superior leadership in the Department of Commerce, the National Research Council or the Utilities Association with overall strategy commitments and sponsorships to further the analytical efforts with master plans for interactive research and means to pursue implementation programmes.

The technology developments which actually did appear in the 1970s and early

1980s, such as the massive introduction of new chemical admixtures, the gradual increase of the uses of fly ash, the intrusion into the Portland cement market of GGBS and the exaggerated promotion of the use of silica fume. These developments came about where the economic advantages in the short term were attractive, in easily accessible market sectors such as, for instance, the ready mix concrete industry. The accompanying public research was primarily post-assessments by laboratory specimen testing, bereft of rational model transfer to the effects in field concrete masses and structural elements, and thoroughly discussed some years later in a keynote paper at a RILEM/NATO workshop.[232]

As invited speaker at different conferences and symposia, I assumed the lonely task of promoting the holistic concept of cement and concrete research. My intention in this, sometimes very time-consuming, unpaid activity, was to appeal to the general research community for strategic planning and effectiveness, especially in public research. In effect, this voluntary work happened to act as a form of marketing, appealing to the kind of clients for whom I wanted to work.

Figure 61 from reference [233] is a typical example of a contribution to the advance of the above mentioned philosophy (in this case with Niels Thaulow, a former BFL team member and future associate, as co-author). It sketches a model of the improved dispersion of fresh cement paste with fly ash. The advantageous effect on the compactness of the hardened paste and the beneficial role of the alkalis in the pore liquid by their reaction with the fly ash particles are implied.

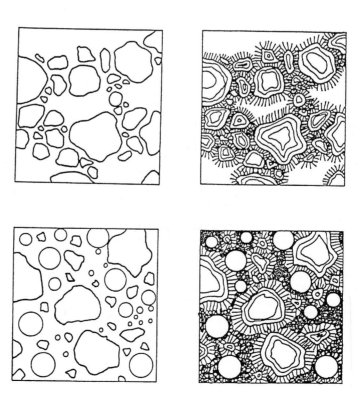

Fig. 61. Models of cement paste, with and without fly ash, fresh and hardened

Note also the function of unhydrated fly ash particles and residual, unhydrated cement particles as "microaggregates" with strong bond adherence to the hydrated fraction of the paste. The figure is, incidentally, also a principal illustration of the basic issue in the rheology of fresh concrete – effective dispersion vis-à-vis coagulation or flocculation of the cement paste. The paper further suggested a coordinated strategy for research with the aim of making the increasing use of fly ash with cement in concrete more effective.

Tables 33 to 36 (also from reference 233) are configurations of a holistic planning and management concept for this field of research. As a consultant, I was therefore able to make use of repeated opportunities for promotion of such a philosophy. The ACI committee work for updating guidelines for the uses of fly ash in concrete was one such opportunity, where my fingerprints became visible at least on some essential issues.[234]

Table 33. Matrix for a research strategy for production of fly ash of suitable qualities for use in concrete. The acquisition and production conditions must be considered decisive for the relevant characteristics of the fly ash: chemical composition, mineralogy (including glass content) and granulometry

Characterization	Coal resource	Production Combustion	Collection
Chemical composition	X	X	
Mineralogy	(X)	X	
Granulometry	X	X	X

Table 34. Matrix for the research strategy with distinction between the exploration of the impact of fly ash characteristics during concrete processing and effects on concrete performance, illustrating the interdependence of the intermediate reactions and phenomena and the final effects – i.e. a holistic approach

	Processing		Performance
Characterization	Rheology Surface chemistry	Hydration Energetics	Strength Longevity Microstructure
Chemical composition Mineralogy Granulometry Testing			

Table 35. Model depiction for explanatory research about the hydraulic reactivity of fly ash in concrete

Objective	Boundary conditions	Solids	Liquids
Explanatory research	Granulometry	X	
	Mineralogy	X	
	Chemistry	X	X
	Mass	X	X
	Temperature	X	X

Table 36. Parameter identification and quantification of characteristics for transfer of laboratory research to technology for the use of fly ash in concrete

Objective	Boundary conditions

Application in engineering technology	Mass
	Geometry
	Temperature
	Humidity
	Processing
	   Mixing
	   Fresh
	   Curing
	Load
	   Static
	   Dynamic
	Exposure
	   Physical
	   Chemical

Commencement of the consulting services

One of the first contracts for the new G. M. Idorn Consult ApS of 11 November 1978, was to assist with the preparation of concrete specifications for the construction of the Faroe Bridges in Denmark. This entailed, with P. Freiesleben Hansen's special assistance, the first systematic application of the curing technology system invented by the BFL in a major construction job. Tendering firms were requested to document their competence to precalculate and monitor the curing process for the concrete substructure and pylons of the bridge.[100, 101] The application of this technology was an outstanding success. However, in the larger outside world where I marketed consulting services, the existing specification systems and the "monopoly" of room temperature hydration in research and concrete production quality control were insurmountable barriers against such iconoclastic novelties from a small country.

I was next asked, by an international construction joint venture, to investigate the cause of severe cracking and corrosion of reinforcement in a power plant under construction at the coastline of one of the Arabian Gulf States. The concrete specifications were written in the same way as for construction works in the UK (i.e. relying on British Standards) with special requirements for sulphate-resistant cement – supersulphated or low C_3A brands – and with conventional curing clauses.

Figure 62 first published in reference [235], depicts existing records of the temperature development in a concrete pier from the time of mixing through the first days of curing under the given external climatic conditions. It was possible to calculate and demonstrate by thin section examination of concrete cores that the excessive early temperature rise during the curing had caused initial internal fracturing and high porosity of the cement paste, allowing easy

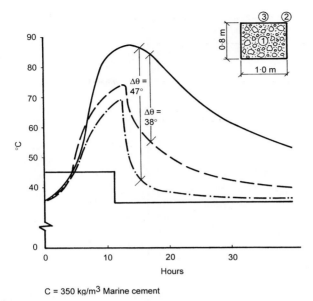

C = 350 kg/m³ Marine cement

Fig. 62. Temperature development during concrete curing in the interior (1), mid-face (3) and corner (2) of column in basement of building in a hot country

access for chloride ingress and with high activation levels of early corrosion in the reinforcement. My investigation showed that the specification writers had relied on transfer of the technology and quality control which was customary in the climatic environments of the UK; they had not taken precautions against the profound impact of the external heating of cement paste in addition to the release of the heat of hydration during the early phase of curing.

Management contacts in this Arabian Gulf area led to informal contacts within the USA about the tragic collapse of a cooling tower in West Virginia during construction in the 1978 winter season.[236] The support of the working platform in the newly cast concrete some 30 m above the ground had not reached the required strength during a cold night, and the whole platform fell to the ground, killing 51 workmen. I offered to apply the maturity calculations for examination of the deferment of cement hydration and the rate of strength development as a potential cause of the accident. However, the specified procedures for the testing of the concrete strength had been complied with and the tests had passed. It was therefore claimed that the operating party was not guilty, and that a further diagnosing analysis would be of no benefit within the given framework.

Figure 63, from references [237] and [238], illustrates the effects of excessive, external heating during the curing of a precast 50 tonne concrete dolos for a marine construction site at a northern-temperate climatic location in Europe. The figure shows the cross-section of a dolos with the temperature profile of the heating/cooling situation six hours after casting. This was also an early case in which I was engaged to diagnose tensile fracturing in the majority of a series of about 2000 doloses. They were cast for a breakwater slope, as the barrier against the power of 12 m high ocean waves, and the requirement of the shortest possible construction period had enforced an accelerated curing

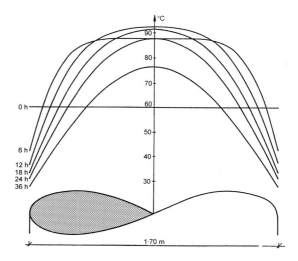

Fig. 63. Temperature development during concrete curing in shaft of dolos, cast in steel mould with concrete heated to +60°C by steam injection in the mixer. After 6 hours the concrete surface is in an almost isothermal room temperature situation, corresponding to the procedure with quality control test specimens. In contrast, the centre of the concrete body is in an almost adiabatic situation at +90°C from 6–24 hours, and in between there are intermediate time-temperature conditions (after [237] and in [238])

method by injection of steam into the fresh concrete during its mixing. This raised the initial, precuring temperature of the fresh concrete to +60°C and caused the concrete temperature in the centre of the cross-section to peak at +97°C, six hours after mixing. The steel casting forms were without insulation; this caused the concrete surface temperature at six hours to decrease to about +30°C with an average external temperature of about +15°C. Calculations made it obvious that the simultaneous interior expansion versus surface contraction of the concrete with +60°C temperature difference caused initial, deep tensile fractures across the dolos bodies. The fracturing was visible in doloses in the stockyard before placement and the tremendous power of the surf left broken doloses in the breakwater slopes after the first exposure to gales.

The durability crisis

Heat and concrete

The early 1980s made the alarming extent of rapid deterioration of new concrete buildings and structures in the Middle East a serious problem for American and western European consulting engineers and construction firms who had been awarded the contracts at a time when requests for services in their homelands were plummeting, not least due to the depression caused by soaring fuel prices.

Simultaneously, the wave of early deterioration of post World War II concrete highway bridges and pavements appeared in North America and some countries in western Europe, and also in precast, multi-storey apartment complexes from the 1960s in some European countries (apparently also to a large extent in eastern Europe and the USSR regions, although that information did not emerge until many years later). The affected structures and buildings were very visible, and the damages revealed unexpected early public and private depreciation expenses and inconveniences. In many ways, it was a sociological paradox that while "throw away" habits dominated public attitudes to commodities in the rich countries, at the same time there developed exaggerated expectations that buildings, highways, etc., especially those made of concrete, ought to be durable without repair or maintenance costs. Hence, the concrete "durability crisis" became a broad, populistic feature and caused inexorable, long-lasting disparagement of concrete in the service of social welfare and human culture.

The most serious evidence of field concrete deterioration in the eyes of the ordinary civil engineer was corrosion of the reinforcement associated with cracking of ambient concrete. This was reasonable because the civil engineering education generally emphasized the structural aspects and the load-bearing function of reinforced concrete, while technology courses primarily dealt with compliance with standard specifications and quality control testing, except for a minority of specialist post-graduate courses. Consequently, loss of reinforcement by corrosion was seen as a safety hazard, and the volume increase of iron by corrosive conversion was an obvious, visible evidence of damage in field concrete.

The extents of cracking associated with reinforcement corrosion in field concrete of one or a few decades of age in western Europe and North America were truly impressive, if one may use that term, and almost equal to the extents of similar damage in the Middle Eastern region. The difference was that the rates of the deleterious reactions were significantly higher in the hot countries, so that the general decay occurred earlier and was more irreparable than in the northern-temperate regions. Hence, in the Middle East there soon appeared contract clauses of a minimum 20 years' guaranteed service life for concrete structures in airports, highways and industrial plant constructions. But even this modest requirement for concrete durability proved unpleasantly difficult to comply with for many conscientious and competent European and American civil engineers who won jobs in the area.

The magnitudes of damages worldwide spurred a tremendous boom of international "corrosion research". The basic properties of hardened concrete, porosity and permeability, and the thickness of the cover of the reinforcement were related to the rate of corrosion initiation and progress once initiated. Carbonation and chloride ingress were emphasized as the primary causes of the loss of the protective alkaline environment adjacent to reinforcement bars. The increase of the volume of solid corrosion products, iron oxides and hydroxides relative to pure iron, was assumed to be the vehicle of the crack-creating, expansion mechanism. Carbonation appeared to be the cause of corrosion of field concrete exposed to ordinary weathering, due to sloppy post World War II design and construction practice, and ingress of chloride was found to be an accelerating factor for concrete exposed to sea water.

The increase in the standard of living in North America and western Europe had made the automobile and aircraft the vehicles for the ever-expanding inland mass transportation of people and cargo. The consequence was inevitable demands on free (and safe) highway, road and air traffic all year around. That entailed unrestricted application of de-icing salts, predominantly as NaCl, on road and highway pavements, bridges and airfield service areas and runways in the colder tracts of the industrialized continents. The ingress of the salt brines into the concrete caused heterogeneous soaking intensity of the salt solutions within the concrete, and increasing spring temperatures engendered powerful anodic/cathodic cell creations in reinforcement bars.

In mid-continental States in the USA and Canada, summer temperatures on concrete surfaces probably equal those in the Orient (with higher relative humidity in the air as the only difference), and hence with high external heat as activation energy for accelerated corrosion. Western European inland and marine exposures are, in every respect, somewhat less aggressive than continental America on the one side and, on the other side, the subtropical sunbelt of the Middle East.

The fact that gradual increase of the C_3S contents and the fineness of Portland cements caused higher temperatures in concrete during early curing, and therefore lower ultimate strength and microcracking, was widely neglected. These debilitating effects of the higher strength yield were not disclosed by the authorized quality control and test method systems in any country (except where our Danish curing monitoring technology was introduced).

In the sunbelt regions, the effects of the aggravating environmental impact were:

- initial high temperature of fresh concrete and ambient air, affecting the setting and early hydration of concrete
- initial evaporation of free water in fresh concrete and during curing, inhibiting the progress of hydration

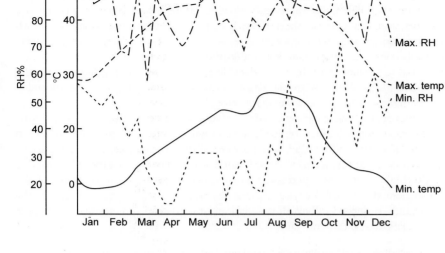

Fig. 64. Climatological records from Abu Dhabi, at the Arabian Gulf coast, 1974

☐ excessive early drying out of all elevated structural elements where wet curing could not be made and protection against evaporation such as applications of curing compounds was ineffective

☐ excessive daily drying during the service life of concrete, counteracted, but not balanced by condensation on concrete surfaces during nightly cooling.

Figures 64 and 65 are meteorological records of air temperatures and relative humidity from two localities at the United Arab Emirates' (new) coastal cities. Such statistical information, with supplementary data for the concentrations of airborne salt, the salinity of the coastal waters, and the salt concentrations in the soils, is indispensable for specification writing and construction works. If

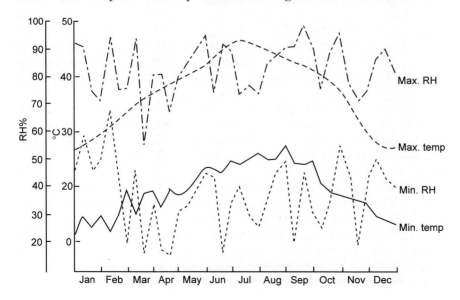

Fig. 65. Climatological records from Dubai at the Arabian Gulf coast, 1974

273

available at the commencement of the Middle Eastern construction boom in the early 1970s, it would have supported a concrete technology strategy to match the deleterious effects of the severe environments. But there were no such data banks available. Neither were there cutting-edge trained specification writers and construction managers in the remote European and American company head-quarters, so the required competence on which the crowds of resident engineers and job construction managers at these outposts should have been able to rely was also unavailable. (I had the data sheets shown in the figures especially procured for a failure case investigation in the early 1980s, in which the unheeded hot climatic exposure was an essential issue.)

Typically, the general practice of specifying the use of sulphate-resistant Port-land cement (with limited or negligent contents of C_3A) for marine concrete in western Europe and the USA was transferred to Middle Eastern concrete speci-fications without further ado – the elevated sulphate content of the sea water due to the high salinity was perceived as an obvious reason. In the course of the subsequent decade of decaying marine concrete structures, the research in the homelands observed, albeit during laboratory experimental testing, that these types of Portland cement:

☐ were less capable than ordinary Portland cement of absorbing and binding chloride ions in the hardened paste, and
☐ caused higher porosity/permeability than did ordinary Portland cement (which again was found to be inferior to pozzolanic cements, and in parti-cular to blast-furnace slag cements).

Such empirical "testing research" caused controversial stipulations and special research funding in failure cases where contractual warranty clauses became litigation issues.

I happened, in one case, to be asked to claim that the use of ordinary Portland cement was the cause of decay in about $50\,000$ m^3 concrete at a coastal, industrial plant in the region in the course of 5–10 years. The basis for this idea was a coin-cident belief among consulting British civil engineers that the national cement industry had inadvertently caused the common post World War II precast house dilapidation by having increased the burning efficiency and the C_3S contents of Portland cement. My general knowledge and the case investigation made me insist that Portland cements in Britain, as elsewhere over many years, had continuously been improved in order to satisfy the demands for structural innovations by higher and earlier concrete strength development for given w/c ratios. It was the civil engineering profession which had failed to observe the unavoidable, increased early and total heat of hydration development, which was further aggravated by the general increase of the cement contents in struc-tural concrete.

In the failure cases in the Middle East, it was repeatedly disclosed, where records of concrete production and environmental data existed, that with the direct transfer of north European or American concrete composition and produc-tion practice without due regard to the hot environments, the concrete was doomed to acquire invalidating, excessive cracking during its processing and thereby, so to say, "lose its immunity" for its subsequent service life.

Whenever my insistence on the importance of proper harnessing of the effects of heat on concrete was presented,[238–240] and referred to in failure case investigations, it was, at best, met by raised eyebrows. More often, it was contested, even by engineers and legal experts in diagnostic case studies. This happened not least when field engineers and responsible companies believed that they had done their duty by conscientious compliance with given specifications, unaware of the defects of these specifications under the given circumstances. (My alternative perception also happened to be a legal complication when warranty issues were believed to be best defended by reliance on the conventional cold-region specifications.)

The common utilization of low C_3A cements for sulphate resistance of marine concrete, at least throughout the 1970s, provided unwittingly, in cases in which I was involved, the information that this cement actually did inhibit the formation of ettringite in the concrete. Consequently, the concrete deterioration could not be due to sulphate attack. Since ASR was also excluded, initial microcracking and depressed strength development was incontestably due to the excess heating of the concrete during processing and performance, the implications of which could be calculated where sufficient input data were retrievable.

Figure 66 is a sketch illustrating the mechanism of deterioration in a pier wall, partly submerged, partly positioned in air, in the Arabian coastal regions. It was a common feature, also in inland concrete, that structural elements such as basements, pier foundations, etc. buried below ground were undamaged. (This was

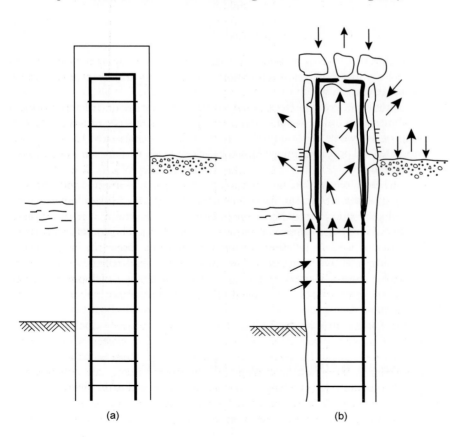

(a)   (b)

Fig. 66. Configuration of the exposure conditions and the deleterious effects on a concrete wall in the Arabian Gulf coast area — the heat induced evaporation increases the chloride concentration in the concrete and aggravates the corrosion of reinforcement

275

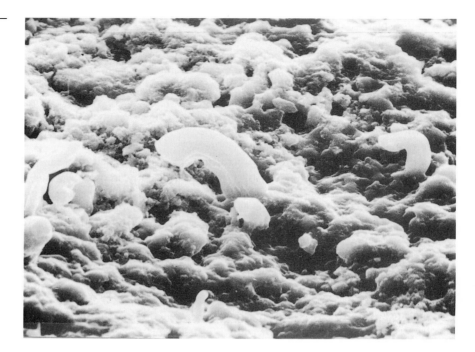

Fig. 67. Sodium chloride crystallizing in crumbling concrete surface under severe drying/wetting exposure in a hot, marine environment (SEM, 2000 × magnification)

also the case where such concrete was buried in soils with a mixture of large and small aggregations or particles of pure gypsum which made the sulphate content of the soil 20–30% by weight, but where the salts of the soil were dried up above the level of the groundwater and therefore also harmless to the concrete.)

The failure cases in which I was involved in the Middle East also revealed that severe scaling in concrete surfaces often occurred where structural members were partly submerged in saline water or in saline-saturated, wet soils, or where severe splashing of sea water continuously or frequently super-saturated the pores of cement paste (and porous aggregate particles) close to the surface with solidifying salt concentrations.

Figure 67 from reference [240] is a SEM micrograph showing pure NaCl crystals growing on the broken surface of a concrete core from a Middle East marine structure. In the laboratory it was placed with the lower end in a strong NaCl brine, while the upper end was exposed to severe drying. The continuous drive of transport of NaCl in solution towards evaporation above the water level created scaling fractures in the surface and the exudations of crystalline NaCl.

Figure 68 shows a concrete dolos in a breakwater slope with such severe scaling, and Figure 69 the same phenomenon in a concrete column, partly buried in salt-contaminated soil at another marine/coastal construction. This concrete was less than ten years old.

Heat as an issue of research transfer

The failure cases referred to above from the late 1970s and early 1980s showed that *heat in concrete is a prominent activator of early deterioration* under the given, described circumstances. The factual background was the increasing yield

Fig. 68. *Scaling in surface of concrete dolos made with sulphate-resistant cement and exposed over 5–10 years to a hot, saline environment*

values of Portland cement and the increasing use of richer concrete mix proportions. Civil engineering had taken advantage of these developments by remarkable structural design developments, along with rationalization of site and precast concrete production. The market situation imposed further production acceleration by application of external heat as steam injection and curing, and acceptance

Fig. 69. *Scaling in surface of concrete column made with Portland cement and exposed over about eight years to a hot, humid environment with saline groundwater reaching up to 0–50 cm below the soil surface*

277

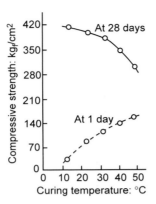

Fig. 70. (Left) Effects of curing temperature on compressive strength of concrete

Fig. 71. (Right) Relationship between the permeability of hardened cement paste and the w/c ratio, with curing temperatures 27°C and 60°C

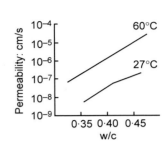

of natural heat in hot climates. Altogether, these achievements were great feats of industrial/engineering innovation. The snag in this phase of progressive service by concrete construction in the general societal development was the concurrent decline of concrete technology research, such as, for instance, in Denmark and the USA.[65]

My consultancy reports were thorough documentations of how engineering practice, including job specifications, quality control methods and management, etc. failed to respond to the changed conditions. This led to corresponding revelations of how the contemporary concrete technology research had omitted to extract suitable new guidelines for changes of concrete production methodology based on available science-based new knowledge. The situations in the USA and the UK were essential for analysis in these cases because the clients were primarily American and British companies, and our Danish research and research transfer had always drawn on the scientific research in these countries.

The application of the Arrhenius equation by G. Verbeck in 1960,[94] for calculation of the activation of hydration, was in fact the fundamental basis for our development of the maturity concept.

Figure 70, from reference [241], 1968, and Figure 71, from reference [242], 1981, are two later, evocative displays of accomplishments from the inherited capability of scientific American concrete research. Figure 70 shows the remarkable, accelerating impact of elevated temperatures on the early compressive strengths of concrete versus the distinct reducing effect on later concrete strength. Figure 71 correspondingly shows the higher levels of permeability of hardened cement paste which results from elevated curing temperatures.

Figure 72, after reference [243], 1964, illustrates further why excessive heat development during cement hydration may cause the inherent, mechanical deterioration of the microstructure and strength of hardening cement paste. Classic concrete manufacture was a low-energy conversion process in which coarse cements of low C_3S content, moderate cement content, and slow processing gave concrete which hydrated in a harmonious way over many years and converted the chemical energy in the cement minerals to binding forces and heat during low temperature rises and gradual exchange of heat with the

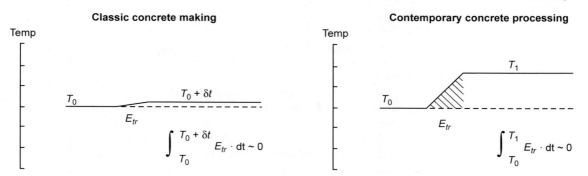

Fig. 72. Illustration of excessive heat development during cement hydration potentially causing mechanical deterioration of microstructure and strength of hardening cement paste

environments. Modern concrete manufacture causes an initially accelerated energy conversion at temperature levels which result in greater loss of heat, i.e. the development of binding forces of permanence is prevented, the energy is, so to say, rejected and lost.

In addition to these clarifications of the nature and effects of the hardening of cement paste in concrete at elevated temperatures, there was available for proper transfer of the research:

(a) the classical calculation methods of the mechanical effects of uneven temperature distributions and changes over cross-sections of structural elements, and

(b) scrutiny of the failure cases.

However, this approach to a conceptual utilization of research was not what I found as a mainstream technology axiom when I prepared the required bibliographic reviews for the clients.

The most broadly recognized engineering guidelines were the ACI committee reports on hot weather concreting.

The ACI committee 605, 1958 edition,[244] cautions that *"strength is reduced"* and *"the tendency to crack, either before or after hardening, is increased"*. No contemporary research or new curing technology abroad is referred to.

The ACI committee 305, 1977 edition,[245] contains the above Figure 68 with comments, but no further transfer of the research for adoption of a technology for curing at elevated temperatures.

The ACI 305 R, 1991 edition,[246] makes no mention whatsoever of the scientific background knowledge about the advantageous vis-à-vis the deleterious impact of heat on the curing of concrete and no references to past and contemporary development abroad of a science-based curing monitoring technology.

N. J. Carino and H. S. Lew were the first in American concrete research literature to introduce, in 1983,[247] the maturity principle as a measure of

279

strength development under different time-temperature developments. They referred to Saul's original adoption of the simplified Arrhenius perception,[77] and Bergström's following studies,[248] but did not imply that their principal approach was paving the way for an updated curing technology development.

N. J. Carino continued the presentation of the maturity method in 1984,[249] now basing his description on P. Freiesleben Hansen's application of the Arrhenius equation,[250] and the alternative approach by T. Knudsen.[251] There was also recognition of the pioneering introductions by R. W. Nurse in 1949,[252] A. G. A. Saul in 1951 and S. G. Bergström in 1953, and E. Rastrup's complementary study in 1954.[78] But there was still no indication in the paper that the previous scientific research in America, combined with the European studies and Freiesleben Hansen's transfer to a maturity-based curing monitoring system, could provide an eminent basis for the creation of an American updating of guidelines and methods for curing at elevated temperatures.

In the UK, the need for solutions to the housing problems in the wake of World War II caused the rise of the precast concrete industry. The surviving scientific cement and concrete research saw a corresponding opportunity for application of the maturity concept such as suggested by Nurse, Saul and others. The Cement and Concrete Association (C&CA) followed suit with a seven-page advisory leaflet: *Concreting in hot weather*,[253] in 1966, and shortly thereafter, in 1971, the more thorough: *Review of accelerating curing procedures*,[254] with guidelines for application of elevated temperature curing. Four phase curing cycles were recommended:

- a delay period of 0–4 hours without external heating
- a heating period with maximum 20°C per hour temperature rise in the concrete to an 80°C peak temperature
- an isothermal period with monitored switch off and on of external heat until attainment of a calculated maturity
- a cooling period with maximum 20°C per hour temperature drop in the concrete down to ambient temperature.

The basis for the maturity calculations was the Saul formula (which, incidentally, we had at that time found to be unreliable at temperatures higher than about +40°C,[87] but for which we had not yet managed to find a replacement).

The C&CA guideline was exclusively directed towards the precast concrete industry. It did not, as did the American ACI documents, deal with "hot weather concreting", or like the earlier Danish maturity application, with "winter concreting", in 1953,[79] and E. Rastrup in 1956.[82] Neither of these climatic conditions were of importance in the British Isles, and the construction boom in the Middle East had not yet begun to attract the British engineering firms and cement suppliers.

Then came the 1980s with depressed economies and stagnating investments in housing and construction. The heyday of precast concrete was over. Visible degradation of the concrete now began to appear, and general dilapidation in many of the 20–30 year old concrete-element housing schemes. The major part of the Middle Eastern structures from the early 1970s also began to show severe and widespread deterioration in the course of five years or less.[255] The vituperative news campaign pinpointed changes in the cement properties as the scapegoat in England more than elsewhere, and caused grave concern in the job-hungry civil engineering professions.

The Construction Industry Research and Information Association (CIRIA) approached the issue of concrete curing in two review studies, in 1981.[256, 257] However, the first of these did not comprise the issues of curing at elevated temperatures. The second recognized these conditions and referred also to applications of the maturity principle, incidentally with reference to the Rastrup formula from 1954.[78] But neither of the two reports referred to the early British introduction of maturity in the 1950s, or to C&CA's elaborate guideline from 1971.[254] And neither of the studies referred to elevated temperature conditions during hardening of concrete as related to the massive concrete deterioration in the Middle East.

In 1984, the Concrete Society felt it necessary to appoint a Working Party which, in 1984, produced a study report: *Changes in cement properties and their effects on concrete – design implications*.[258] The report was, in effect, a response to the populistic assertion that the cause of the concrete durability problem in England was that the cement industry had "*increased the C_3S contents in the Portland cement types considerably at the expense of C_2S over the last 50 years*".[259] The BRE enumerated this development with a figure showing the increase of C_3S to have augmented "*by a factor of approximately three the rate of heat liberation, as well as approximately 17% the peak temperature*". The Working Party report[258] made no mention of the maturity principle and neither reference to the early British work by Saul and Nurse, nor to the C&CA description in 1971 of a practical maturity-based curing technology for precast concrete.

A commentary article about the Working Party report, by D. Beckett, Sir Frederick Snow and Partners[260] contains the following concluding remarks:

"*Adequate curing is a key factor to achieving low permeability as there is evidence to suggest that concrete, uncured after striking formwork at one day will be permeable and hence prone to high rates of carbonation. Finally, it could be argued that today's concretes using cements of high heat of hydration, high cement contents and possibly low tensile strain capacity have characteristics which increase the risk of cracking at early age. This is a matter for further investigation*".

The last sentence confirms how loss of communication creates barriers between concrete research and engineering practice when the latter has to function under new, adverse conditions, very different from which education has prepared it to cope.

Summary on heat in concrete

As a special consulting service, I prepared the following summary statement of experience with several failure cases in the Middle Eastern region in which I had been engaged as chief investigator, made anonymous for this publication. The summary was for use by clients who had been forced to accept available European, primarily British, standards and ACI guidelines for hot weather concreting, curing, etc. for their operations. The situations, also in view of legal aspects, required that my investigation reports, and therefore also the summary, responded to the misconceptions in the contemporary British and

American professional constituencies and the news media about the issues of the properties of cement vis-à-vis the durability of concrete.

(a) No basis of knowledge exists on Portland cement which supports an opinion that general increases of the C_3S content and of the $C_3S : C_2S$ ratio over the last few decades have played any part in the damages to the concrete in the Middle East, or, for that matter, are a cause of poor durability of concrete anywhere in the world. There are no methods by which the original C_3S content in cement in deteriorating field concrete can be measured by examination of existing concrete.

(b) Evidence now increasingly confirms that numerous younger reinforced concrete structures along the Arabian Gulf coast are generally failing within 5–10 years' performance. Most of the deteriorating contemporary and younger structures are made according to, what is generally acknowledged, concrete technology state-of-the-art knowledge from North America and western Europe, and most likely they have all been made with fresh water as mixing water. Consequently, it is the applied engineering practice, which was believed to be adequate by many conscientious consulting engineers and contractors and which was authorized by standards and guidelines, that is in fact inadequate.

(c) It is increasingly acknowledged that the applied state-of-the-art knowledge has failed to take the excessively aggressive environmental conditions along the Gulf coast into consideration and, in particular, has failed to identify adequate precautions against the effects of high temperatures (during the concrete making and the entire service life), the humidity, and the salinity of the environment.

(d) It is increasingly sustained by my investigations that the inadequate specifications have resulted in initial thermal and shrinkage micro- and macro-cracking in concrete during the curing. This cracking has enabled the further progress of deleterious reactions, which are also aggravated by the permanent impact of the external heat. Hence: the cause of the damages is the aggressive environment, in which the applied specifications did not ensure the anticipated durability.

(e) The structural aspects of the damages in the affected concrete need to be examined. The need for such complementary investigations is enhanced by the threatening collapse of certain structures in 1986.

(f) Concrete strength control data from the construction works ought to be processed and presented as documentary evidence where work quality in compliance with the given specifications was observed.

(g) The scarcity of documentary data regarding the concrete materials and processing, the environments, and the defects of structures and samples at the time of investigation, necessitates the evaluation of the cases by inference. The means are the field inspection observations and the laboratory examination of the aged and altered concrete, coupled with critical analyses and application of contemporary knowledge and of more recent explanatory research.

(h) It is particularly surprising to me that the engineering profession and its research still hesitates to appreciate the enormous impact of heat as chemical activation energy combined with water as mass transport media as the major and continuously acting driving force in the aggravated deterioration of reinforced concrete in the Arabian Gulf region and where similar conditions predominate in other parts of the world, including in precast concrete plants with steam curing in colder countries.

Alkali-silica reaction

A case of ASR in Norway

In 1978, A. Kjennerud at the Norwegian Building Research Institute in Oslo had identified and described the occurrence of harmful ASR in concrete structures belonging to the famous Rjukan hydroelectric power complex.[190] Consulting engineers and public research professionals contested his findings, and Norsk Hydro approached me, as an unbiased foreign specialist, for a supplementary investigation, *inter alia* because expansions causing deformations of the concrete of the turbine encasements had repeatedly required machinery adjustments and repairs. The investigation substantiated Kjennerud's observations and made the case the first acknowledged occurrence of harmful ASR in Norway.[191] Polymineralic, volcanic and metamorphic rock types with susceptible silica were the reactive aggregates.

The reactivity had previously remained unnoticed despite the known high alkali contents of Norwegian Portland cement, because no one had previously identified harmful ASR in field concrete in the country. The available, national resources for concrete research had concentrated on the issues of freezing and thawing, site quality control, and a special, severe kind of sulphate attack in building foundations in Oslo, ascribed to oxidation in alumshale rocks, when excavated for new construction operations.[261] Later on, high priority had been given to research on corrosion of reinforcement as related to the new, spectacular development of offshore, deep-water concrete platforms.[262] ASR did not receive its justified general recognition by the public research in Norway before the 9th ICAAR in London 1992.[263]

The Kiambere project in Kenya

Soon after occupation with the Norwegian ASR problem, I was engaged for a study of the possible development of ASR in the new Kiambere hydropower plant of the Tana River complex in Kenya.

The Kiambere project[264] was financially supported by the World Bank, and designed and supervised by the British consulting engineering company Knight, Piesold & Partners. A major part of the coarse aggregate was a gneissic-granitic rock, excavated by blasting for the underground tunnels and turbine station. A Canadian consultant for the World Bank had suggested that the undulatory extinction angle (UEA) of the macro-crystalline quartz in the rocks might indicate alkali reactivity, referring to contemporary Canadian stipulations. Concurrently, harmful ASR had been identified in the previously built Kamburu dam upstream on the river.[265]

The circumstances of the project — its early stage of construction and the conscientious attitude of the engineering firm — made it possible to undertake a thorough documentary investigation showing that both the coarse aggregates and the sand (local river sediment) were non-reactive. (These investigations sustained, incidentally, that the Canadian method relying on the UEA of quartz in different rock types as a measure of alkali reactivity was unreliable.)

My examination of cores from the ASR-affected Kamburu dam concurred with the results referred to in the two above mentioned publications. However, a visit which I made to the aggregate quarry for this construction job showed that it had been an exposed rock outcrop. There was visible devitri-fication of the gneissic-granitic rock with apparent secondary silicification by dissolution of the silicate minerals in the rock complex. This geological process had left a soft, sticky silica-rich phase, akin to opal, in cracks and crevices in the rock. It was reasonable to conclude that this opaline material had been incorporated in the aggregates when retrieved at and closely below the outcrop surface. An analogy was justified with the earlier Australian reference[121] to the phenomenon of secondary silicification in igneous and volcanic rocks (and creation of opal in the desert regions), under hot, climatic and geological conditions akin to those at the Tana river region.

The available cement from the local ATHI cement plant was high-alkali, and an available pozzolan was also high-alkali (the alkali content of the pozzolan was incorporated in the mineral structure of the volcanic tuff, and hence only in the long term a possible alkali resource for ASR, whether harmless or harmful). Testing showed that the use of the ATHI cement with and without the pozzolan still showed no aggregate reactivity.

The thorough risk analysis, which the consulting engineering firm undertook when the investigations were accomplished, concluded that the blasted and river-deposited aggregates were non-reactive and could be used with the ATHI cement and, if desired, also with the local pozzolan interground. For completeness, special precautions were taken as insurance against possible, albeit unlikely problems with deformation of concrete in turbine basements, etc.

For once, it was exciting to be an "ASR consultant" at an early stage at which assistance was required with testing and studies for elimination of the risk of harmful reaction during the later service life of a structure in a country which could ill afford unreasonable maintenance and repair occasioned by a low-performance concrete. These circumstances meant that the concern on the part of the World Bank and the consulting engineering firm was well motivated, and that made it a pleasant job to compile available information, organize the investigation and supply the accomplished knowledge base for the client's decision making.

ASR turbulence in the UK

While the Kiambere investigations were in progress, a tempestuous debate emerged in the UK about ASR, and the national cement and concrete industries

285

and civil engineering profession were drawn into a vortex of attacks in the news media for neglect and ignorance. The hegemony of public and political management of social housing, health care and the infrastructure sectors made the cement industry and civil engineering professions easy and convenient targets in the sometimes vitriolic quest for scapegoats.

The previous British ASR investigation by the BRS in the 1950s (see Part II) had virtually persuaded the cement and concrete communities to make dismissal of harmful ASR a creed of permanent validity. Therefore in 1976 – incidentally while the third ICAAR was being held at Wexham Springs and in London – when harmful ASR was found to occur undeniably in some buildings in the south-west of England, all concerned appeared unprepared to handle the situation with a reasonable overview. (A case of severe ASR damage to a dam on the Channel Island Jersey had actually been revealed a few years earlier,[174, 266] but that had conveniently been considered to be "outside the mainland".)

For many years there had only been sporadic research in the UK on ASR.[207, 267] The general attitude that public silence about the issues was preferable, had resulted in the British standard specifications failing to mention ASR with precautionary measures in terms of:

☐   requirements of cement, aggregates and concrete
☐   test methods with acceptance and rejection criteria.

(In conjunction with the prevailing attitude, the proceedings of the 3rd ICAAR were not offered for public sale by the Cement and Concrete Association.)

The tabloid news made ASR infamous as "concrete cancer" and photographs appeared of affected concrete buildings with "dark-room enhanced cracking", implying risk of collapse beyond engineering control. In response, ASR expertise emerged, all of a sudden, as special service departments in large engineering and construction firms, and also in public research institutes and universities.

In a period when signs of declining public and commercial interest in cement and concrete research loomed on the horizon, this new basis for defensive research (like the contemporary interest in research about corrosion) promised to be prosperous and a help to commercializing the research itself as expert consulting services. These services emerged, very opportunely, when the situation inexorably made the responsibility for harmful ASR in existing field concrete a much-debated legal case issue.

The Royal Devon and Exeter Hospital case

The British Health Authority launched a long-term arbitration against the major construction firm Higgs & Hill Ltd. about harmful ASR in the precast and site-cast concrete of a major, twelve-year old, district hospital – The Royal Devon and Exeter Hospital (RDEH) – at Exeter, south-west England.

The susceptible aggregate component was a porous, light type of flint. The aggregate had been dredged off the British Channel coast near the Isle of Wight. The flint type was akin to light, white flint in aggregates dredged off the opposite French Channel coast (and some years later rejected as aggregates for the Channel Tunnel), and to the Danish type of porous, opaline flint, which had been known since our research in the 1950s to be a cause of severe, harmful ASR in Denmark.

I was engaged by the defendant as a foreign specialist, together with British researchers. The plaintiff engaged a special service department of a major consulting engineering company. In the course of the case investigations and the arbitration some heavy-weight legal implications emerged.

- The BS specifications were, without direct mentioning of ASR, ambiguous in terms of the case-relevant responsibility issues.
- The job specifications were correspondingly lacking specific requirements for the cement and aggregates with regard to potential alkali reactivity.
- The presentations of available ASR information to the arbitrators by the two groups of specialists became very different and dependent upon the relatively new concern in British research about ASR and its international knowledge base.
- New British investigation and test methods were introduced as the basis for the expert opinions and interpretations.
- The news media's implication of a collapse risk for the hospital's main building (housing about 500 patients) had no precedence in the known world history of ASR.

It was my impression, as the independent foreign expert, that the authoritative BRS dismissal of ASR as possibly occurring in Great Britain some twenty years earlier had left a general and lasting vacuum of unconcern, with cement industry interests in support of that view. Nevertheless, the BRS had, in fact, related their concluding view to the contemporary materials and technology knowledge base with the cautionary remark: "If new materials . . ." (see Part II). And the porous, light flint which, since the late 1970s, had been dredged off the south-west English coast, was undoubtedly such a new material, different from any of the types of potentially reactive flint which the BRS had referred to as concrete aggregate materials. No authorities or consulting engineers had previously examined the potential reactivity of this particular flint type and proposed corresponding revisions of the British Standards. Neither had any of the parties in the case at hand – or in other public projects using the particular aggregates – made special investigations for alkali reactivity of the new material. But there was a British common law stipulating that a vendor is responsible for the suitability of sold products for their intended use.

After more than five years of specialist investigations and prolonged direct and cross-examinations before the arbitrators, the case was closed in 1988 by an economic settlement between the two parties, including the clause that the special investigation reports for the case were to be kept permanently unavailable for publication. It was an omen that the litigation had been able to attract funding of several million pounds sterling for concrete research which, for the vast majority of relevant professionals in Great Britain, represented new knowledge, but of which the public and the professions were thereafter denied the output. It was another unfortunate coincidence that the young British ASR research collided with development initiatives, spurred by the general interest in energy savings for increasing utilization of the industrial, recycling materials fly ash (from the coal-fired power plants) and blast-furnace slag as GGBS (from the steel mills). Both materials had acquired international recognition as potential preventive measures against harmful ASR and were identified as actually representing beneficial fashions of ASR if used in adequate quantities.[177, 268] Nevertheless, much of the British research was directed to establish caution about the possible contribution to harmful ASR of alkali contents in the two materials, relying exclusively on empirical testing of room temperature cured laboratory specimens without supplementary studies of the energetics or means to optimize the reactivity beneficially. The resulting, vigorous debates in the technical press and at conferences apparently absorbed much R & D energy, which scrutiny of the international knowledge base could have shown to be superfluous.

Prestressed railway sleepers in Canada and Lucinda jetty in North Queensland, Australia

The RDEH case was in progress and two new consulting projects were about to be activated when, late in 1985, I negotiated the transfer of G. M. Idorn Consult ApS to the new G. M. Idorn Consult A/S with the major Danish consulting company Rambøll and Hannemann A/S as the owner. The two new cases comprised:

□ ASR in about 350 000 prestressed concrete railway sleepers in Canada, and
□ deterioration assumed to be caused by ASR of about 300 prestressed I-profile concrete beams, each of 20 m length, at the Lucinda sugar loading jetty near Ingham, North Queensland, Australia.

The major part of these investigations was subsequently made by the new G. M. Idorn Consult A/S, and descriptions of them are beyond the scope of this narrative. There are, however, some aspects of a principal nature in the cases which belong to my present conceptual analyses of the nature and effects of ASR in our "world of concrete":

□ the severe, albeit very different, climatic exposure conditions
□ the structural liability issues, and the investigation aims and methods
□ the aggregates
□ the legal situations
□ the constraints on desirable, related research.

The climatic exposure

The cross-continental Canadian railway was in the northern temperate/subarctic region between 45° and 55°N with long winters of heavy snowfalls and temperatures down towards −40°C, and long, hot summers with above +30°C maxima and relative humidity periodically as high as 80–90%.

The Lucinda jetty was in a tropical, marine environment at about 18° S with maximum temperatures about +30–35°C and minima about +15°C, torrential rains with about 2000–3000 mm precipitation annually in the winter season and constant dry weather at moderate relative humidity during the summer season. The weather also includes several cyclones annually with waves rising towards the jetty beams and splashing of the warm, highly saline estuary water over the concrete.

None of the cases offered my colleagues and myself the opportunity to incorporate studies of the impact of the exposure conditions on the development of the damages, despite the attractive circumstances for such research. I did, however, comparatively observe that the ASR under tropical temperature/humidity/salinity exposure developed at high rates. In contrast, about 80 000 Canadian sleepers, removed by the railway authority from service in the tracks, and stockpiled at a location some 100 km north of Toronto, exhibited very slow and moderate to slight development of surface cracking, suggesting ASR (but no scaling, incidentally, to indicate frost attack). Obviously, the winter seasons were hibernation periods for ASR, albeit with severe exposure to freezing, while the Lucinda exposure approached the acceleration procedures applied in many laboratory studies of ASR. And there were factors other than the exposure, potentially influential on the rate and severity of the deterioration, which only special research undertakings beyond the scopes of the cases could have enlightened.

Structural liability issues

The Canadian case was a litigation. The public, transcontinental railway company was suing the producer and vendor of the concrete sleepers due to damage (cracking) alleged to be caused by ASR. I was engaged late in the course of several years of legal trial preparations. I was granted access to the plaintiff's technical expert reports, previous reports made by other specialists for my client, the defendant, and obtained a few sleepers for macro- and microscopic examinations. I was commissioned to elucidate the cause(s) and effects of the observed cracking, the technical implications thereof and their possibly related legal aspects in view of the specifications, standards, quality control, etc. used.

The exceptional number of approximately identical sleepers under practically identical exposure during field service could have been an unusual opportunity for in depth examination of the exposed sleepers as a magnificent collection of "enlarged mortar bars" with ASR developing under natural climatic influence. Unfortunately, the railway authorities had, soon after the first observed cracking, summarily replaced all concrete sleepers with wooden ones (the use of the prestressed concrete sleepers had been a pioneering introduction in Canada, with imported design and manufacturing technology). The plaintiff's experts had ample opportunity to make some field inspections and petrography on selected sleepers. But there were no overall field inspection records with documented ratings of the extents of damage, their distributions and relations to manufacturing recording of aggregates, cement analyses, production time, etc.

There was, however, information about rated degrees of cracking for selected groups of sleepers. These showed the usual variations, with the larger amount of affected sleepers only negligibly or moderately cracked. The plaintiff also had on record that a substantial amount of sleepers with ASR which were tested for the effects on the strength, did not prove that there had been any impending safety issue. Neither were investigations presented by the plaintiff about the safety issues with wooden sleepers vis-à-vis those with prestressed concrete sleepers, and no fracture mechanics research appeared about the, probably negligible, effects of cracking in the concrete sleepers on their serviceability. Hence, the plaintiff's case seemed to me to be based more on conjecture than on the actual situation of the defective state of the sleepers.

In the case of the Lucinda jetty in North Queensland, the owner and user of the 6 km loading conveyor and access jetty "bridge" was primarily asking for assessments of whether the structure could safely be used for its purpose until the end of its 40-year depreciation period. In order to answer this question it was agreed that we should:

☐ establish the cause(s) of the visible, and in some places, serious cracking and expansion of the prestressed beams
☐ assess the reliability or risk by continued use of the construction and propose means which might impede the further progress of the deterioration
☐ examine whether the owner had reason for litigation over the responsibility for the damage to the structure.

The subsequent investigations and the assurance that the structural reliability was not affected even where the ASR was advanced, are reported in references [269] and [270].

The aggregates

In the Canadian case, the defendant had used aggregates retrieved from a quarry of limestone formations which had been a primary source of concrete aggregates during about fifty years of building and construction development in the area. The investigation confirmed that the layered limestone was of varying mineralogical composition, with "impurities" in the calcareous rock type. Occasional minor occurrences of rare minerals and rocks had been found by scientific, explorative studies. These findings included a very rare dawsonite rock which had proved to be able to release alkalis in water. (Its presence and characteristics were not known to the aggregate producer.) The petrographic investigations by the two parties identified dawsonite in ASR-affected sleepers with silica-containing, coarse limestone aggregates. It was not possible to assess, but appeared likely, that strata in the prevailing horizontal bedding of the limestone in the quarry with such "impurities" had been reached at the depth of operating coinciding with the sleeper production period (the late 1970s) and therefore been a contributing factor to the limited severity and the varied extents of ASR-conditioned cracking in the sleepers. (At the time of the investigation the quarry had been abandoned, and follow-up investigations of the rock-faces were not possible.)

In the Australian case, the coarse aggregates were crushed material from outcrops of volcanic, syenitic and basaltic rocks which, over the course of millions of years, had been exposed to the seasonal changes of half a year's excessive hot, dry weather alternating with half a year of continuous, warm rain. Zones of weak, secondary silica would therefore be present in such rock formations along with harder phases of residual, more stable mineral complexes.[121]

The blasting and screening processing of the materials would then have caused removal of most of the weaker material as dust (presumably of pozzolanic composition), whereas the screened aggregate fractions would consist of rock compositions of very variable glassy silica contents and alkali reactivity. My inference that such was the situation was substantiated by visits to the primary aggregate producing quarry. In the operating outcrop faces there were deep crevices of soft, white material down through harder, dark rock masses and corresponding heaps of light, powdery waste material.

Hence, the year-long production of the prestressed concrete beams had apparently been made with extremely reactive, alternating with moderately or negligibly reactive, coarse aggregates. This corresponded to the varying extents of cracking and expansions in the concrete on the jetty.[271]

We made the same observations at supplementary visits to concrete bridges up and down the North Queensland coastal highways and harbour structures.

Incidentally, my inference that we were dealing with secondary silicification in the aggregates was also based on former experience with the Kiambere/Kamburu case in Kenya and related to Australian descriptions of the geological process leading to the extensive occurrences of opal at certain depths below the ground surface in the Australian desert. Moreover, a later visit to aboriginal rock paintings in the Northern Territory disclosed that the painted surfaces of these ancient monuments were threatened by downward-seeping silica in solution in the soft, warm rainwater. (Tourist information about the Nourlangic rock paintings, Kakadu National Park.)

Legal situations

I examined two primary reasons for juridical considerations and engagements in the Canadian and the Australian cases. First, a reasonable fear that spectacularly visible surface cracking in the concrete sleepers and beams might suggest corresponding risk of structural collapse. Neither the Canadian railway companies nor the Australian Sugar Industry could live with that. Next, a consequential desire to "pass the buck" to the vendors of the products on claims of defective performance quality of the deliveries.

In Canada, the railway authorities had apparently chosen first to remove all sleepers summarily and then to blame the vendor for the whole calamity. In Australia, our client was satisfied by our assessment that the performance reliability of the jetty was in order for the predicted 40 years and by our installation of a monitoring system to survey the future development and effects of ASR. Besides, we examined, on the client's behalf, whether there might be reasons to claim negligence by the main consulting/construction firms.

In both cases, our investigations illustrated that the applied job specifications and executed quality control had been insufficient with regard to prediction of the potential risk for development of harmful ASR in the concrete. In Canada, the proximity of the USA with its long-term research into ASR and reliance since the early 1950s on the ASTM system for testing and application of preventive measures, had not caused a similar consensus approach to ASR, but rather general neglect of its potential occurrence. A few tests of aggregates (using ASTM methods) had been made by the railway's technical staff and had passed. In Australia, nobody concerned seemed to have been aware of the outstanding CSIRO research on ASR, 1947–58.[272] A few "Mielenz" tests had been run by the contractor and had passed, after which nobody considered the probability that those few tests might have made with non-reactive materials.

In Canada, the ambiguity of the job specifications, the contents of the national standards, and the purchasers' own involvement in testing and acceptance of the aggregates and the cement for the sleepers, may have been decisive for the duration of the 7–8 year "volleyball game" of controversial legal disputes between the two parties through their legal advisers and the insurance companies concerned. The role of the technical expert assistance in these higher hierarchical undertakings was – and is – uncertain (as compared with the legal, economical and policy aspects); and the final, confidential settlement of the dispute eliminated the test in the courtroom of validity of the expert service for the two parties.

In Australia, our analyses of the specification and contract conditions as related to the general, Australian engineering neglect of ASR at the time, assisted the client in making the decision not to sue the engineering design and construction company.

Constraints on related, desirable research

Inevitably, the investigations in the two cases here discussed, disclosed that updating of and supplements to the existing knowledge base left unresolved issues of ASR, on which it would be beyond the scope of the clients' interests to incorporate work. In the two cases such issues were:

- the fracture mechanics issues of the structural reliability of concrete affected by ASR
- the impact of climatic exposure conditions on ASR
- the secondary silicification of minerals in rock formations
- the exploration of microstructure features of ASR-affected concrete
- the transfer of laboratory modelling test to field concrete behaviour.

Our calculated documentation that the Lucinda jetty was capable of serving its purpose suggested that similar approaches might save otherwise costly structural reinforcements or replacements, such as for instance realized by the Canadian railway authorities.

The remarkably different climatic exposure conditions for the concrete in the two cases made it a sore point to admit the astonishing neglect by concrete research in general of the impact of heat as a source of concrete deterioration. (Incidentally, the cases were similar in one respect. Both the precast, prestressed sleepers in Canada and the beams in North Queensland had been steam cured, albeit with no processing data available for the case investigations.) The range of climatic exposure reached from the inland, extreme cold to the tropical marine environment. This displayed, so to say, two perfect "end points" for research into external physico/chemical impact on the properties of field concrete. How much richer was this opportunity than the usual "room temperature" standards, or the simplistic $+80°C$ treatment in the ASTM C289 test!

The secondary silicification I observed as a geological phenomenon in Australia (and Kenya) was another obvious example that heat, as nature's external energy force, deserves close attention in planning and execution of scientific concrete research. The observations reminded me of previous acquaintance with the Ikaite mineral growth in a Greenland fjord – demonstrating "the cold end" of the temperature scale of relevant climatic exposure conditions (see Part I).

In both the investigated cases referred to, standard or special job-related specifications and generally acknowledged tests for selection of ASR safeguards (such as the ASTM C33 system) had only been rudimentarily applied. However, as the cases showed, even more systematic application of the available test methods and acceptance criteria would have given illusory results due to the heterogeneity of the aggregates, the complexity of the climatic exposure, the ignorance about the structural impact of ASR, and other factors. On the other hand, the large number of identical structural elements, the sleepers and the beams, could have served as interesting "model transfer" objectives if in both cases overall, national interest in such research had been applied to for funding.

Both cases offered ample opportunities for investigation of microstructural effects of ASR by thin section petrography on samples of affected concrete. However, these examinations went no further than requested for the given purposes of documentation. Studies of many issues which could have contributed knowledge related to the matters emphasized above could not be pursued.

ASR investigations in Denmark

My comprehensive international engagements as special consultant left limited time for occupation with the occurrence of ASR in Denmark. I initiated a cooperative research project for the Road Directory about the structural implications of harmful ASR in prestressed highway bridge slabs without shear reinforcement. The project was subsequently carried out without my participation.[192, 212] It showed, at that time, a surprisingly minor loss of structural reliability even though extensive ASR had caused internal cracking; and it pioneered the use of large structural concrete elements as models instead of the conventional mortar bars and concrete specimens.

I was also a co-investigator in cases of ASR and corrosion of reinforcement in public swimming pools.[273, 274] But, more importantly, I initiated and assumed a key position in the organization of the 6th ICAAR at the Technical University of Denmark, Lyngby, in 1983.[176] Very appropriately, the conference contributions sustained that harmful ASR in structural concrete did not entail a risk of sudden, unexpected structural collapse. The conference failed to strengthen my influence on the simultaneous work by the Academy of Technical Sciences (ATV), who sponsored a number of research projects on concrete durability including ASR. These initiated the triple preventive measures policy, disregarding the available optimization potentials which the conference demonstrated (see Part I).

ASR consulting experience in retrospect

I was pleasantly impressed by the professional competence with which the Kiambere project was managed by the client, who acquired special complementary ASR knowledge from selected consultants and agreed to thorough, budget-controlled investigations of the various issues beyond the constraints of the conventional standard laboratory test methods. They applied their own "holistic" synthesis and added a professional risk analysis as the basis for common sense engineering decisions. It was positively educational to be a vehicle in this realistic transfer of research knowledge to progressive engineering practice under rather extraordinary conditions.

In the cases with actual or implied legal implications, it was particularly important that the clients fully appreciated my integrity regarding the decided investigations and the technical/scientific evaluations and interpretations of observations and data. Conversely, it was an overall obligation and practice to plan and manage all invested consulting efforts so as to serve the given needs of the client's case in a truthful way. Hence, to escalate investigations into research beyond the actual case needs was out of the question.

It was an advantage as a consultant to remain actively engaged in the international ASR research, *inter alia* by participation in the ICAARs. This made it possible to contribute the most recent knowledge, albeit as critically as the purpose required, whether in advice for new constructions, diagnostic investigations, or state-of-the-art documents and research for litigation. In several cases, the possible duration of harmful ASR in field concrete and the structural implications were questioned. Dams were generally acknowledged to be structures suffering for the longest times from active progress and visible effects of ASR. Still, no incidents of collapse were known, and only partial repairs had been required. Incidentally, the American dams referred to in published studies were all in hot summer/cold winter regions, some of them with sun-heated, dry downstream dam faces during daytime, practically "dragging" pore liquid through the dam body for intense evaporation. This particular aggravation factor did not show up in publications as a subject of special investigations, despite the common observation that in more "ordinary" structures such as highway bridges, buildings, etc. with less intensive moisture/heating/cooling exposure the usual duration of ASR activity was about 20 years or less.

In many ways, dams as well as highway bridges, etc. represent complex, climatic exposure conditions within the overall framework of climatic regions, and highlight the want of a research discipline which seriously approaches the kinetics and thermodynamics of ASR in concrete.

In the individual case studies, I repeatedly found the general picture that the severity of ASR always varies from negligible to more or less severe. This corresponded to the fact that the reaction in field concrete since the early days of recognition in the USA and Denmark has most often been found to take a harmless course, i.e. causing no cracking whatsoever. It is understandable that owners of structures affected by harmful ASR are not interested in why other structures do not suffer. It is less understandable that so much of the research in later years has also omitted to search for the reasons why the harmless mode is the most common.

During my work with the cases of ASR where the revelation of the occurrence came as a surprise, the national standard concrete specifications and, therefore, also ordinary job specifications, were inevitably deficient with regard to regulatory requirements, test methods with evaluation criteria and descriptions of preventive measures. They were also qualitative and diffuse for interpretation of their general durability clauses. Where legal aspects were the predominating management basis for investigations, the deficiency or ambiguity of the relevant national standards made justice a matter of considerable technical uncertainty.

The expert investigations which I performed or managed were indispensable for incontestable clarification of the technical aspects of the cases. They required documentation which was as irrefutable as possible, even if the outcome was not apparently in support of the clients' most favourable position. The task of the lawyers on either side was to win the case for their client. This meant emphasizing everything in favour of the client's case, and suppressing or disproving everything against it. Sometimes this meant dilution or fragmentation of arguments which, in the expert's view, might distort the context of his findings. However, in the courtroom such was the lawyers privilege, while the expert was confined, to "tell the truth, the whole truth and nothing but the truth" when questioned under oath. These different obligations for experts and lawyers often led to extended communication work between the two parties during the preparations for and the course of the court and arbitration procedures.

Ground, granulated blast-furnace slag

As a juxtaposition to the predominant requests for consulting services regarding concrete deterioration, it was fruitful during the first half of the 1980s to be engaged in the creation and dissemination of knowledge regarding the effective use of ground, granulated blast-furnace slag (GGBS) along with Portland cement in concrete.

Since the beginning of the twentieth century, the so-called slag cements, consisting of interground blends of Portland cement and quenched, granulated blast-furnace slag from steel mills, had been widely used in the steel-producing, continental European countries, and also in the USSR and Japan. In the USA, only a few steel companies invested in granulation plants at their mills, while in the remainder the slowly cooled, crystalline blast-furnace slag was considered a waste product which was stored in large stockpiles and occasionally sold as a fill material for secondary road construction.

When the steel mills installed quenching plants for the blast-furnace slag, they obtained a granulated, cementitious product which, after fine grinding, hydrated in alkaline liquids. The hydration of the slag was, in blends with Portland cement and water, initiated by the alkali hydroxide solution which was provided by the initial hydration of the Portland cement. The slag hydration was further activated by the heat of hydration from the Portland cement reaction with water. Basically, the use of GGBS in concrete was beneficial for the following reasons:

☐ It represented considerable energy-saving potential. The melting process in the blast-furnace in effect stored up chemical energy in the GGBS for subsequent activation during the Portland cement hydration in concrete.
☐ The activation of the slag during the Portland cement hydration consumed some of its heat of hydration, and thereby reduced peak curing temperatures. Thus, the heat was made productive (and thermal heat-damage less likely).
☐ The alkali hydroxide activation made concrete with GGBS resistant to harmful ASR with reactive aggregates, and reduced the permeability of the hardened concrete, hence generally improving the durability of the material.

These obtainable merits were balanced by delayed rates of early strength development in blends with Portland cement, if made by intergrinding, in comparison with the early strength development of ordinary Portland cement (OPC) concrete. The new technology, in which I became involved, consisted of separate grinding of the two components and delivery of the GGBS (later also having the acronyms GGBF and GGBFS) as a special product (in England called Cemsave by the first producer, in South Africa Slagment, in the USA Newcem). The material was marketed with the purpose of being blended with Portland cement at ready mix concrete or precast concrete plants, or on construction sites, instead of blending the two materials in the cement works as had been the practice up to that time. The previous classical technology had meant inevitable over-grinding of the softer Portland cement in blends when a particular overall fineness was needed for compliance with a given rate of strength development requirements, whereas separate grinding meant that the GGBS could be ground "to order", thereby providing improved grinding economy and flexibility for making blends in accordance with different customers' needs under given circumstances. The separate delivery of the two blend components also offered the purchaser increased price-setting flexibility.

Prior to this happening, the steel and cement industries in the continental European countries had created a fruitful techno/economic *modus vivendi*. The steel mills delivered the granulated slag to the cement plants which interground the two components to provide different types and brands of slag cement. These were either sold as being price-competitive, or due to their being acknowledged as providing superior concrete resistance in aggressive environments, such as for marine concrete. From the early 1970s onwards, slag cements were also recognized as effective preventive measures against ASR in concrete with reactive aggregates.[177]

The steel industries in the UK and the USA had traditionally deposited slag as waste without investing in the quenching and granulation technology. In the 1970s, audacious entrepreneurs, in Great Britain Frodingham Cement Ltd and Civil & Marine Ltd, and in the USA Atlantic Cement Company Inc., began to recognize the national market potential for delivery of GGBS, as a result of which the material was supplied directly, in bulk or bag-packaged, to consumers such as ready mix concrete plants, precast plants and major construction projects. The situation in the UK meant that the new enterprises were intruding on the market for ordinary Portland cement, as a result of which the development was opposed by most of the major cement companies. In the USA, the introduction of GGBS entailed the investment of about 75 million US$ by Atlantic Cement in a combined granulation and grinding plant at Sparrows Point near Baltimore, MD. Its obligation was to sell about 800 000 tonnes of the Newcem, along with its 1.2 million tonnes of OPC, within its marketing area along the East Coast States of the USA. Thus, blending of the Newcem with OPC by the customers would increase the total sale of OPC and GGBS by about 65% when the granulation plant came on line.

In 1980 and 1981, the top managements of Civil & Marine Ltd and Atlantic Cement Inc. each selected their teams of external consultants. I happened to be independently engaged by the two companies at the same time, and later I became involved in intensive overseas cooperation. In the UK, the primary issue was to establish an adequate new standard specification for the GGBS, created and adopted against stiff resistance from the cement industry. In the

USA there was a broader scope. The Atlantic Cement's competent internal R & D efforts needed to be supplemented by external background research, with interactive transfer of service information to customers, *inter alia* by publication of acquired new knowledge.

This period of some five years' participation as a consultant in the American and British R & D programmes, made the experience unusually fruitful and educational for me. The decisive condition for the achievements was the outstanding commitment of the industrial leaderships. They had a strategic goal for the R & D investments: production and profitable sales of high quality products. They also participated in the realization and management of the work and contributed market insight and contacts for dissemination of the R & D accomplishments.

Figure 73, after reference [275], illustrates the EIRMA type of capability-demand analysis which was applied in the American programme when an explanatory research programme was assigned by Atlantic Cement Inc. to Professor D. M. Roy, Materials Research Laboratory (MRL) at Pennsylvania State University, regarding the introduction of GGBS for ready-mix and site blending with Portland cement. Workability and durability came out as the prime priorities on the "demand list". Industry's demands are confronted by the university capabilities (shown on the right of the figure). The extended research with European participation revealed many cross-linked interrelations between the topics considered. The analytical and conceptual basic knowledge for which MRL's scientific professionals were renowned, was confronted in a series of meetings by the customers' demands for concrete produced with the new GGBS. A substantial number of scientific papers from MRL about the impact of the slag on the rheology of fresh cement paste, the reaction kinetics during curing, the pore structure and permeability of hardened cement paste and

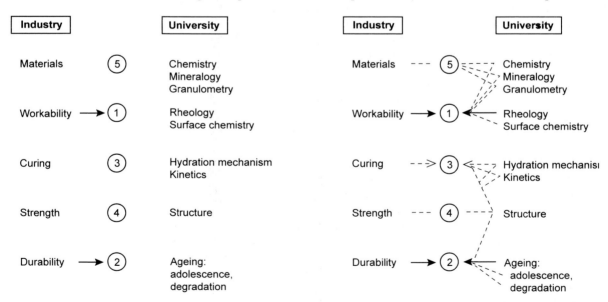

Fig. 73. Demand-capability analyses in cooperative research project for Atlantic Cement Inc., USA and Materials Research Laboratory, Pennsylvania State University. The numbers represent the research priorities which resulted from the analysis

concrete, etc. saw the light at conferences and in journals. I was co-author on three papers for engineering information,[237, 268, 279] and presented a concrete production orientated review[277] at the 1985 annual convention of the American Ready Mix Concrete Association. In the same year I gave the thorough review of the R & D programme realization[252] at the Engineering Foundation Conference in New Hampshire. Throughout the years of this service, thorough analyses of previous and contemporary research were made and referred to in our reports. Numerous old and newer studies, in the UK by Messrs. Sandberg, in France by M. Regourd, in Germany by H. G. Smolczyk and in the Netherlands by R. F. M. Bakker, were particularly helpful. Two workshops with selectively invited participation, at Pennsylvania State University in 1982 and in York and London, 1984, offered broader exchange opportunities. The sponsoring industries eventually supported participation in the implementation of the research accomplishments in new standard specifications, test methods and technical guidelines, such as in ACI reference [278].

To me, as an external participating consultant, there were many exciting aspects in the GGBS R & D cooperation epoch. When trial operating crews on sites in north-eastern USA commented, with regard to the effects on their fresh Newcem concrete, that "this stuff is good to work with", it brought past packing-rheology experience from Hanstholm to life (see Part I). The MRL research added electrochemical studies to explain the improvement by GGBS addition of the rheology/workability of concrete.

Figure 74, from reference [276] is the D. M. Roy/G. M. Idorn conceptual model of the two-phase hydration reactions of GGBS particles in Portland cement paste. Initially, the alkali hydroxide is the primary activator, whereas the Ca^{++} ions enters the reaction subsequently, when the heat of hydration of the Portland cement takes over as the primary activator of the hydration. (In principle, the reaction of fly ash in concrete is well described by the same model, which is also valid for other finely ground or naturally powdery, pozzolanic materials, rich in susceptible silica and of high specific surface.) At about the same time, research in Finland[279] substantiated this concept by producing concrete of GGBS solely with a strong alkali hydroxide solution as activator, and with a high-range water dispersion agent solution.

Hydration kinetics studies at MRL confirmed that heat of hydration of the Portland cement became utilized as activator of the GGBS fraction of cement in concrete, and that thereby the temperature rise was reduced in concrete during curing, an attractive benefit in much modern concrete production.

Figure 75, from reference [280], illustrates that the hydration of GGBS in Portland cement paste may have a considerable densifying effect on the hardened concrete paste. R. F. M. Bakker,[281] had earlier found the same effect. These and other similar findings explain why GGBS may be used to provide superb resistance to ingress of external moisture in field concrete, such as chloride-infected fresh water and sea water. Likewise, the migration of pore liquid within the cement paste of hardened concrete is inhibited by the improved density of the cement paste, a contributory factor for the prevention of harmful ASR in concrete.

Notwithstanding the unusually meritorious cost-benefit ratio of the R & D programmes, it is advisable to be aware that the decisive vehicles for the

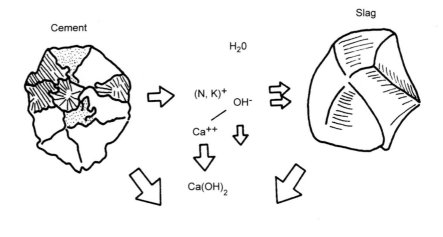

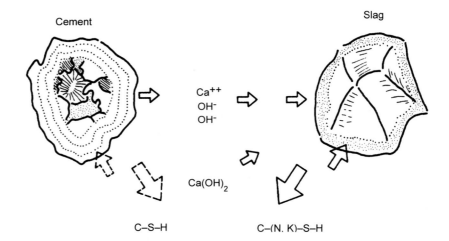

Fig. 74. Model of early and long-term hydration of blends of Portland cement and GGBS

subsequent commercial success of the new enterprises in the eastern USA and the UK were the effective production and marketing management efforts by the sponsoring companies. The R & D may be considered the essential "backing groups", as in modern pop music shows, for the front-line performer, the industry companies and their competent, technical and commercial staff members. But the holistic progress of the R & D work over the years was, at the same time, a comforting background knowledge base of lasting merit for the production and sale of the GGBS.

In my view, it emerged as a paradox during the course of our cooperative science/technology R & D work that most of the cement and concrete research professionals within our range of contacts took little notice of the frequent demonstrations of the holistic character of our project portfolio. I think that we consistently illustrated the interdependence of the abilities of the GGBS in blends with Portland cement: to improve the rheology of the fresh concrete, activate the slag fraction first by the alkali hydroxide and next by the released heat of hydration from the Portland cement and thereby reduce the peak

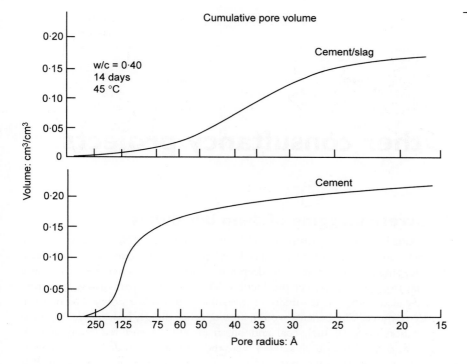

*Fig. 75. Pore size distribution
and cumulative pore volume in
cement paste made with pure
Portland cement and a 50/50
Portland cement slag blend: the
latter has the largest part of the
pores in the smallest pore size
diameters, and the total porosity
is the smallest*

curing temperature, and – dependent on these processing advantages – to densify the cement paste of the hardened concrete and inhibit harmful ASR. This practical and conceptual recognition of the cooperative system approach which we had adopted in our programmes and publications was not recognized in numerous contemporary and subsequent research projects from public and other institutional research programmes, especially in the UK and North America. The common denominator of this subsequent research was its prevailing philosophy of piecemeal planning and management.

A succession of conference proceedings from the mid-1980s, dealing with research on GGBS, fly ash, silica fume and concrete durability issues, is predominated by studies based exclusively on experimental laboratory testing of cement paste, mortar and concrete specimens, prepared and examined under sterile, room temperature conditions. Inevitably, such research disregards the real kinetics, thermodynamics and other relevant model transfer parameters, and therefore repeatedly presents insurmountable problems for realistic transfer of the results to engineering practice.

For GGBS, this conventional empiricism of the research inflicts further invalidity for application in practice because the applied "room temperature conditions" virtually obliterate the activation of the GGBS by the heat of hydration of the Portland cement fraction in the blend. The unconditional acceptance by conference organizers and peer-reviewers of this kind of reductional research philosophy only serves to delay the general comprehension within the research communities of the benefits of using GGBS in concrete.

Other consultancy projects

Concrete plugging of deep boreholes

The Danish power company ELSAM requested, in 1979, a study of how speciality concrete could be produced and placed to function as a long-term durable plugging material over deep-hole buried radioactive residual waste material from nuclear power production. The study was part of ongoing, preliminary analyses of the feasibility of investments in nuclear power as a national energy resource. The benefits would, among other things, be a reduction in the importation of fossil fuel, coal and oil, from abroad and reduction of CO_2 emission. Among the disadvantages were the common attitudes against nuclear technology. For effective performance of the study, it was arranged that through contact with professor D. M. Roy, Pennsylvania State University, I would obtain access to information from the coinciding, much larger and longer term research programme in the USA, which comprised different concepts and techniques for storing radioactive waste from the American nuclear power plants already in operation.

The study was, in principle, very interesting because its objective was to design for development a concrete performance quality which, over the millennia, would cause the concrete autogenically to converge towards the equilibrium state of a rocky conglomerate, corresponding to the physico/chemical environments at 2000 m depth in a salt dome.

I formulated a plan for the study, outlining the necessary requirements for:

☐ materials – cement, aggregates, admixtures, fly ash or GGBS
☐ mix compositions – *inter alia* resulting in excellent workability and controllable heat of hydration and monitoring of curing
☐ processing technology – with curing of the concrete in place on a preselected course engendering long-term conversion of the concrete to a solid-state, equilibrium rock conglomerate.

Before termination of negotiations for the execution of this programme (for which I would have needed several subcontractors) the Danish parliament, after an emotional debate involving public hearings, etc., voted against the establishment of nuclear power production in Denmark, and that abruptly brought the consulting service to an end.

Before the work was interrupted, I had taken the opportunity to review petrographic examinations of samples of Roman concrete made about 100–200 AD.

They were still in excellent condition and revealed evidence of the morphological conversions which had apparently brought about the longevity.[282] I also had thin sections left over from the BFL period of Danish medieval mortar samples,[36] and of excellently preserved marine concrete from the Danish west coast of close to seventy years of age. Hence, long-term durability could also be studied in relation to reality documentation.

Although interrupted before actually commenced in depth, the project was of lasting value for further consulting work, because it undeniably required a genuine holistic approach. In other words, the interdependent properties of the source materials, the fresh concrete, and the processing resulting in the "geological" performance quality, necessitated a superior, architectural panoply of planning systems even for the introductory phases of a full programme.

Iceland – industrial development

In the 1960s I had, on behalf of Aalborg Portland as a vendor of low-alkali cement and F. L. Smidth & Co. as a vendor of equipment to the national cement plant at Akranes, been consultant to the Building Research Institute and the cement company, and subsequently to a national committee for ASR research and policy. In the early 1980s I was, on several occasions, invited to follow the development of the successful research and its effective implementation.[283]

I was also engaged to advise on feasibility studies for the development of new industrial productions of high-technology materials, based on the inexhaustible resources of volcanic rocks and still unharnessed hydroelectric power. The strategic intentions were to reduce the monopolistic status of the fishing industry and related trades as the primary export commodity. One project of special interest was a feasibility study of the possibility of producing cement in a melting process based on the abundance of low-priced electricity. The study confirmed that there were interesting technical possibilities, whereas the economic conditions were prohibitive, because the cement consumption in the country was plunging and an incipient market for F. L. Smidth & Co. in developing countries failed to materialize.

Cement and Concrete Research Institute in Turkey

UNIDO was financing the creation of a new cement and concrete research institute in Ankara for the state-owned half of the Turkish cement industry and I was engaged by the Vienna branch of UNIDO as a consulting specialist for the concrete technology research – its facilities, planning and installation. At the time, the UNIDO office had ambitious promotion and planning projects for the erection of similar, large cement and concrete research institutes in other developing countries, such as Algeria and Nigeria, where the new oil field investments engendered enormous influx of capital. Turkey was less wealthy and the successive governments proved unable to secure the required financing for the running costs of the institute. Besides, the management of the cement industry was politically appointed and changed abruptly at each post-election government renewal. Unfortunately, therefore, purchase of equipment, engagement and education of staff and even completion of the building ran into deferments and termination of my UNIDO service arrangement, and not even a service department for transfer of know-how from abroad and arrangement of concrete technology education could be launched.

Consultant's service in its market-place

I never had an idle day without commissioned service agreements to work on during the eight years that I functioned as a private consultant. That was obviously a consequence of the current international decline of cement and concrete technology research and of its limited ability to transfer new knowledge to the industry and the civil engineering profession. Besides, my engagements merely represented one man's experience amid a boom of requests for special knowledge, in particular to stem the durability crisis in Europe, the Orient, North America and even farther afield. This crisis, in itself, illustrated the omnifarious character of the problems:

☐ Investments in research plunged, and therefore so did recruitment of young talent, and a concurrent brain drain of brilliant candidates to more prestigious and profitable career avenues took place.
☐ The decline of the research reduced the continuous updating of engineering education and the corresponding transfer to the operating professions.
☐ The slumping markets for cement and building and construction made cost-cutting a major element of business management, with exclusion of investments in new developments – even in areas where the conventional methods proved fatally inadequate, such as in the Middle Eastern construction boom.
☐ "Research" and "practice" became two increasingly different worlds with little mutual interaction, while the high technology sectors began to boom with accelerating rates of R & D based innovations.

Under the circumstances, it was exciting, but also exasperating, to become a lone "midwife" for the transfer of specialist knowledge to clients who saw their situation improved by its acquisition.

It was often an advantage to be a single consultant from a small country operating on personal goodwill and unquestioned integrity. Avoiding the temptation to create a staffed company, I remained able to engage qualified subcontractors and cooperators on an individual job basis, for instance for comprehensive testing, thin section petrography, chemical analyses, etc. I therefore offered jobs to former colleagues at home and to contacts abroad. I could also afford to keep close contact with the scientific research community and major "knowledge transfer" organizations such as ACI and RILEM.

Nevertheless, my small country origin was also sometimes a potential handicap. In particular, lawyers in litigation cases in the larger countries foresaw problems in acknowledging the expertise of an individual foreigner as opposed to the automatic authority possessed by their homeland's research institutes and university professors. The disparagement of foreign expertise was not uncommon when investigations showed that applied national standards and conventional test methods had adversely affected anticipated concrete performance quality, or would do so if not amended to suit new circumstances. Problems also arose when the best service to the client required introduction of know-how about the deleterious effects of excessive heating in concrete with the remedial curing technology, or the use of the long-term experience in Denmark with microstructure investigations by thin section petrography and scanning microscopy. This was cutting-edge expertise and unknown territory for most consulting and construction civil engineers and managements abroad, and even for many research professionals. Reliance on such new knowledge was like entering hazy legal situations, with authorized standards, test methods, etc., sometimes winning the courts' approval against more appropriate, yet not generally recognized, knowledge and methods. Now and then I had to insist that these were the lawyers' battlefields, not mine.

Throughout the work with the service projects, whether for litigation or development, the communication aspect was a great challenge. One issue was the often critical subtleties, in Danish eyes, of the English vocabulary and syntax, and the, in some respects, differing American ways of expression. Be that as it may, clients, professionals, and lawyers were usually effective tutors. It was a more serious problem that very few, if any, contemporary published research studies comprised mention of relevant boundary conditions, when conclusions were presented of empirical, experimental observations and measurements. Hence, the limitations for dependable interpretations and/or applications remained obscure. The prevailing attitudes among engineers meant that such "unlimited validity" papers were accepted as a matter of course, and often highly regarded by lawyers as suitable for legal game-playing. In contrast, it was the conscientious consultant's not always welcome task to expose limitations of the validity of published research results and consequently "to know better". This problem, which persistently appeared in analyses of available knowledge, was the fruit of the decline of contemporary research and of its increasing confinement to small-scale "normalized" laboratory studies. But there was also an element of salesmanship in communicating the research in such a way as to provide uncomplicated, "easy to read" accomplishments. Moreover, the larger part of the remaining cement and concrete technology research was kept alive by public funding and had no quality yardstick for transfer cost-effectiveness and reliability. That made its undeniable, legal applicability illusory and challenging to demonstrate.

My inherited holistic philosophy for concrete technology R & D became an asset for the consulting service, despite the fact that it was not saleable as such for improvements of the R & D management in the relevant industries and major concrete construction and consulting firms. I could, for instance, with no competition, calculate the defective impact of excessive heat on concrete and demonstrate its effects with microstructural investigations – based on many years of research and cooperation with concrete producers at home. This category of know-how was also applicable in studies of the effects of fly ash and GGBS in concrete and also in cases involving ASR. Likewise, I could elucidate the correspondence of cement and fly ash or GGBS hydration as akin to pozzolanic reaction and thereby characterize this kind of reaction as a beneficial mode of ASR.

Over the years, my close interaction on the one side with industry and the consulting and construction professions and, on the other side, with the research communities made the reasons for the difference between the industrial R & D management system and the prevailing makeshift transfer of concrete research to engineering technology clearer to me. One reason was the different commercial structure of commodity manufacturing companies and corporations, and the ways in which consulting engineering and contractors operated, illustrated in Figure 60 (page 264).

Process/product development in industries based on in-house research is designed to give attractive returns over future life cycles, and the passage from initial new idea through mass production to sales is managed as an integral element of the commercial system. Building and construction are one-off job enterprises. Project portfolios are each operated under specific conditions with negligible or no spare profit available to finance the introduction of new technology. Hence, the incentives for individual enterprises for enthusiastic investments in technology innovation are non-existent or, at best, rudimentary. Consequently, technology specialists are a rare species in what we term the concrete engineering practice, and therefore also the ability to follow the "news market" from research to job specific transfer is a rare commodity. Survival of the business is therefore ensured, especially in construction firms, by rigorous compliance with contractual specifications, and survival profits are earned by strong top-down planning and cost-cutting management. Within this system, incentives to develop also vanish for the ordinary civil engineer. Consequently, unexpected, adverse events arise, such as the severe, fast deterioration of structures in the Arabian Gulf states.

For the branch of consulting engineering firms, especially in the UK and Denmark, the situation is somewhat different. The simultaneous downturn in their home markets and the concrete durability crisis opened up a new market sector – failure case investigation, problem analyses and design of repair and renovation. Many companies suddenly created special service groups or departments which entered this new, lucrative market. Public research institutes, university departments and individual scientists did the same with investments in mobile testing equipment, field inspection facilities, etc. The market flourished until in the present decade when it became oversupplied by the service vendors.

Clashes are inevitable between different groups of such experts when operating as fact-finders and interpreters of facts for plaintiffs and defendants, respectively, in the British and American judicial systems. Profoundly disagreeing evaluations, for instance in cases of deterioration of field concrete, become a common feature, *inter alia* because the knowledge acquired by means of standardized laboratory testing and experiments with controlled parameters cannot simulate the immeasurable complexity of factors which create the history of field concrete performance.

The litigation cases I have referred to above concerned construction projects of about 70–80 million US$ investments. The expert services in the cases comprised:

- □ field and laboratory investigations with special, relevant research
- □ bibliographical and other documentary analyses
- □ preparation of expert reports for trial
- □ advisory consultations with clients and legal experts
- □ service at expert witness hearings.

The costs of the service efforts can reasonably be estimated at about 8–10 million US$ (total for both sides) which makes 10–15 million US$ for legal expenses a fair assessment. The clients obtained the assistance of operational staff and management for, probably, 1–2 million US$. Altogether, "my cases" therefore carried a total cost in the order of 20–25 million US$. This was small fry in comparison with the general state of affairs in these years, particularly in the UK and the USA, and engendered the profuse growth of the forensic engineering special brand of consulting engineering. Consequently, I found it fruitful in the course of 1985 to contemplate a future strategy for my consultancy.

It was evident that the litigation boom was far from over. Public departments as investors in building and construction could not politically accept carrying the costs of the durability crisis. Private investors, such as the Middle Eastern oil companies, were not inclined, after the first golden dollar influx, to accept the costs of renovations imposed by apparently unsuitable concrete technology and construction methods applied by renowned western firms. Construction companies could not, as in bygone days, assume the costs of modest "after termination" repairs. Their insurance companies, and those of consulting engineers, balked at the rapidly increasing penalty claims and the coinciding growth of the costs for legal and expert services. (They even, sometimes, became involved in secondary litigation about exemption clauses in insurance contracts.)

On the other hand, as I saw it, there would sooner or later appear a ceiling for investments in conflicts of this nature. I had experienced major settlements taking place just before, or during, the trial proceedings. Logically, settlements at earlier stages might save considerable costs. Besides, the commercial images of contractors and consulting engineers never gained by prolonged legal conflicts, even when they were acquitted.

But there were also the general public and professional interests in the litigation boom to consider. Major cases among those described above (and many others) were settled with the clause that all documentary studies (and legal investigations and process documents) were deemed permanently confidential. In Middle Eastern concrete deterioration cases this meant, for instance, that the comprehensive analyses which documented the urgent need for new standards and quality control methodology adaptable to the special environments, could not be communicated for general improvements of concrete technology and for new strategic research planning. In the RDEH case, the civil engineering structural design profession was not offered the benefit of new insight about the effects of harmful ASR on the structural reliability of high-rise buildings.

This had been a publicized issue in the case, concretized as a manifest collapse risk. Revelation of the adversary investigation reports and witness examinations was seen within the civil engineering profession as having broad public interest, but they were made unavailable by the confidentiality clause.

The overall consequences of the settlement policy were that:

☐ increasing concrete technology expertise, of which society urgently needed the benefits, was reserved for confidential investigations and research

☐ qualified concrete research personnel were concurrently made unavailable for progressive improvements of the general state-of-the-art knowledge

☐ the magnitude of the expert investigation investments began to exceed the general, public and private investments in concrete research, and replaced the technical output of the efforts by the movement of the spent capital from one party in the construction affairs to another

☐ the invested technical expertise was directed towards the specific, case-relevant objectives. General, unbiased analyses for progressive research priority selections were beyond the scope of the undertakings.

Updating of consultant strategy

In 1985, the pressure of work was growing to such an extent that I had to admit that I could not go on as a one-man enterprise, with repeated leasing of the basic analytical jobs such as petrographic and physico/chemical examinations, curing technology measurements and calculations, and not least the emergent field of structural design and performance risk analyses. I therefore took time to scrutinize the situation, the likely future market developments and suitable means to match them.

The forensic realm of service potential was definitely not yet fading away. I felt obliged to remain available for truth-finding in complicated cases of concrete deterioration, whether caused by incompetent use of up-to-date knowledge or ineluctable reliance on obsolete, albeit still widely applied and authorized knowledge.

Progressive concrete technology development would become the winning market area in the long term. The spiralling "waste" of service in concrete deterioration would tie up too much capital of no real future depreciation value, and my experience in these cases suggested that I had attainable alternative cutting-edge knowledge in my possession.

In-house possession of broader expertise became a requirement for effective response to the market demands. This was a promising situation for replacing subcontractors by recruitment of specialists with physico/chemical education and structural design expertise.

Personal international visibility was still desirable as a natural continuation of the many passed years' uncompensated services. I had preserved the common attitude in our profession of making new knowledge freely available to everybody, and there was now also a promotion value in article and conference presentations. Moreover, there was still the need to scan the news from the remaining public research and to search for potential partners and subcontractors abroad.

The association with Rambøll and Hannemann A/S came about as a rational consequence of these reflections. The company was one of the three "big" enterprises among Danish consulting civil engineering companies and, with a staff of about 1100 people, even big by international standards. It had a high reputation for integrity and structural design expertise. It had a growing position in international markets, and it was interested in the expertise and goodwill I could supply. We shared the conviction that integration of technology and structural expertise would prove to be a fruitful marketing asset. To transfer the personal, one-man G. M. Idorn Consult ApS to G. M. Idorn Consult A/S, 100% owned by Rambøll and Hannemann, and commence its further multi-expertise expansion was therefore easily accomplished by 31 March 1986.

CONCRETE IN THE MILLENNIUM'S TRANSITION

Concrete technology research now needs a renaissance in order to provide an effective service for the further development of cement and concrete production under profoundly changing conditions. The prevailing research has reached a gridlock situation through persistent reliance on the science-technology progress which was attained in the western world from the late 1930s to about 1960.

Fragmentary knowledge has, since then, been built on this foundation. At times this has provided improved clarification of the reactions in and the properties of concrete, and also benefits for construction practice.

But while structural engineering has made spectacular progress with design and construction of deep-water structures, high-rise buildings, bridges, monumental entertainment stadiums, etc., the technology research has lost its former power to anticipate and react to the concurrent changes in production methods and uses of concrete. In particular, the research has now become obsolete in the face of the tremendous needs for concrete production in developing countries in the warm regions of the globe. This is where the population growth is accelerating, while misery is still the standard of living for billions of people, who are aware through mass media communication that the means to provide them with better lives are available in the industrialized parts of the world.

The required renaissance of concrete technology research calls, above all, for a superior international leadership commitment for R & D planning and management, with a strategy which incorporates the capital and material resource issues and a holistic, materials science-based concept of the research itself.

15

The ageing decades of the twentieth century

When the National Academy of Engineering and the National Academy of Sciences in the USA held the joint symposium in April 1976: "Materials and the developments of nations: the role of technology"[284, 285] the world population was estimated to be about 6 billion at the turn of the millennium. The symposium, which covered the prospects for the global production and consumption of materials, was only marginally concerned with the demographic changes to follow in the wake of the population growth, and the natural resources which engendered most concern about exhausting consumption were oil and gas — in accordance with the simultaneous price rises and embargo policy by the OPEC countries. In an invited paper,[286] I pointed to the predictable future depletion of the source materials for concrete, in particular aggregates, but also reassured the audience that concrete technology had not yet explored innovative available solutions, such as:

- new technology for compaction of fresh concrete and curing monitoring methods
- high range water reducers which could provide excellent workability of fresh concrete with greatly reduced water contents
- extended utilization of fly ash, GGBS and synthetic lightweight aggregates
- fibre reinforcement
- impregnation of hardened concrete by polymerization of organic monomers, or by melted sulphur.

Notwithstanding that the global consumption of concrete was close to ten times greater than the production of the primary competitive building and construction materials, it was these and other, more sophisticated industrial source materials which were the predominant subjects at the symposium; an indication that concrete had begun to be downgraded in the broader materials research community and in the general, public perception of materials technology.

A quarter of a century after 1976, the demographic and socio-economic patterns in the world are changing profoundly, and the production and uses of cement, and therefore concrete, have more influence on people's lives than ever before. The corresponding upgrading of the general image of concrete as

Table 37. World population and cement production, production capacity and consumption in the developed and developing regions, respectively, 1995

	Population: millions	Cement: million tonnes		
		Production	Capacity	Consumption
Developed regions	850	385	419	382
Developing regions	4400	1004	1123	957
Total	5250	1389	1542	1339

the most widely used and available building material is a tremendous challenge to the industries concerned and the civil engineering professions in the new millennium.

In 1976, the global consumption of cement was about 750 million tonnes with about 400 million tonnes produced and used in the developed regions, and the other 47% in developing countries. In Denmark, the consumption in the peak year 1974 was 520 kg cement per capita vis-à-vis a world average of 172 kg per capita.

In 1995, the consumption in Denmark had plunged to 231 kg per capita, with no indication of a forthcoming upturn, while the global consumption had increased to 257 kg per capita.

Table 37 shows the changed world situation. In the developed regions, 16% of the world's population used only about 28% of the global consumption of cement in 1995, i.e. proportionally much less than in 1976, despite a 40% increase in total consumption since that time. The former leading regions: North America, western Europe and Japan are all now in stagnant situations, while the Indian subcontinent, south-east and north Asia are rapidly increasing their production and consumption, with China rising from 67 million tonnes in 1978 to 430 million tonnes in 1995 as the front runner. Latin America is moderately increasing its production and consumption, while the larger parts of Africa still lag far behind. The east European countries and the CIS region lost consumption capacity in the wake of the collapse of the USSR, but will regain their former capacity with the restructuring of their socio-economic development.

Concrete in the third millennium

The most challenging issues for concrete production and research at the threshold of the new millennium are caused by:

☐ the accelerating growth of the world's population in the developing regions, concentrating in the tropical/subtropical belt
☐ the increasing strain on the materials resources for concrete
☐ the changing preferences of capital investments to high-technology production and research, even in developing countries
☐ the reduction of international concrete research capacity during the later decades.

Global population growth

L. Brown *et al*.[284] suggests (UN and other sources) that the total population in the world will reach 8.9 billion in the year 2030, and peak at 11.5 billion in 2050.

Table 38 was my prediction in 1976 of the consumption of water and aggregates in the year 2000, corresponding to cement consumption of 300, 400 and 500 kg per capita per year, respectively, for a global population of 6 billion people. The 300 kg corresponds to the average standard of living in western European countries in about 1970 (although several countries at that time had reached 600–700 kg due to higher average wealth). It was the contention that the 300 kg was a reasonable commitment both from a humanitarian and a commercial viewpoint, and I saw two main obstacles ahead to be overcome before reaching the goal:

☐ would cement production be able to attain the $6 \times 300 = 1800$ million tonnes per year capacity in the year 2000 from a starting point in 1976 of 700 million tonnes?
☐ would the materials resources for cement, water and aggregates suffice for the suggested expansion?

I did not query whether the financial resources would be available for the corresponding expansions of the building and construction sectors. (The

Table 38. Projection to the year 2000 of cement production per capita and corresponding consumption of water and aggregates in concrete, from [283]

Cement: kg/capita*	Billion tonnes		
	Cement	Water	Aggregates
300	1.8	0.7	17
400	2.4	1.4	23
500	3.0	1.8	28

* Population assumed to be 6 billion.

prevailing philosophy at the time was that technology development was obliged and able to meet the challenges. The socio-economic and political issues were World Bank, UN, and governmental problems.)

Actually, the world population was 5.2 billion in 1990 and has been estimated to reach 7.0 billion in 2010 (US Bureau of Consensus, 1993). Cement production has reached 1500 million tonnes in 1995, and the corresponding concrete production has so far, at least until 1995, occurred without general short-term concern about exhaustion of the materials resources. But there are many millions of people in different parts of the developing regions who have not yet seen any urbanization, while elsewhere there are regions with a prosperous commercial/technical development where cement consumption has exceeded the European average. Moreover, a deliberately blinkered political attitude still seems to prevail towards the forthcoming problems, notwithstanding the fact that the world's socio-economic development is revealing more sinister aspects in the overall picture than most people, including those in materials research, anticipated in 1976. Brown et al.[287] referred to the fact that while the wealthiest 20% of the world's population possessed 70% of the total income in 1960, the poorest 20% possessed only 2.3%. In 1989, this was changed to 83% and 1.4%, respectively. This trend coincides with the transfer of population growth from the matured, industrial countries to the Third World.

Table 39 shows the present populations of some major metropolis in developing and semi-industrialized countries. The increasing overpopulation and

Table 39. Populations of major cities in developing and "semi-industrialized" countries, 1994 (World Bank, 1994; The Latin American city, A. Gilbert, 1994)

City	Million inhabitants
Mexico City	20.0
Sao Paulo	17.0
Rio de Janeiro	10.5
Buenos Aires	11.5
Shanghai	14.5
Beijing	12.5
Bombay	14.0
Calcutta	12.0
Jakarta	11.0

poverty in rural, agricultural societies have engendered immense slum habitations in and around the ever-growing cities, without proper urbanization planning. Many more cities in developing countries than those mentioned have several million inhabitants and are rapidly growing, incorporating overspill from the poor rural regions. Moreover, for comparison: Tokyo has 27 million and New York 17.5 million inhabitants. These and other big cities in the industrialized countries are also growing, many of them with increasingly large slum areas.

Materials resource issue

There are no easily procured statistical records which make it possible to analyse the needs versus the availability of the materials resources for projections of the cement and concrete production growth in the forthcoming decades. Nevertheless, piecemeal information shows that problems and solutions even at national/local levels deserve attention.

Many sources estimate, for instance, that the People's Republic of China presently has a population expansion of 13 million per year. This corresponds to a need for a 3.9 million tonnes increase in cement production per year, with a corresponding capital investment of 1.3 billion US$, plus the availability of water and aggregates, and investments for making these materials available. Many Chinese cities and rural areas already face water shortages, the agricultural production gains are slowing, and only 10% of China is considered cultivatable. But cropland is converted to other uses during urbanization, and industry and households lay claim to the scarce water resources. Much of the cement produced in China is high-alkali, vast resources of retrievable aggregates consist of alkali-reactive materials, and harmful ASR has appeared as a serious problem where the urbanization is now intense. Fragmentary information like this suggests that it is worthwhile looking at the concrete materials resource issues more generally.

Table 40 is an update of Table 37 with the currently predicted estimates of the global population in 2010, 2030 and 2050. The minimum 300 kg cement consumption per capita per year is preserved as a measure of how developing countries may make use of cement for concrete to attain reasonable social standards of living for their populations. Higher cement consumptions are likely in some countries at some times, and 400 and 500 kg cement per capita per year are therefore entered to illustrate the corresponding increase of consumption of the source materials. The mix proportions for simple purpose concrete may require less cement, the use of high range water reducers may save volumes of concrete and thereby the amounts of all materials. Be that as it may, the magnitude of the demands on the source materials is challenging enough to demand serious consideration.

The justification is amplified by the fact that no global and only scarce national records of the accessibility of the materials seem to exist. It seems as if concrete design engineers, contractors and authorities have generally assumed that since limestone, gypsum and natural rocks are inexpensive and commonly occurring all over the world they are also inexhaustibly available. Hence, mineral prospectors and national geological surveys have preferentially been directed to search for and map more precious materials.

Table 40. *Estimated global consumption of source materials for concrete, corresponding to predicted populations in 2010, 2030 and 2050*

2010 world population: 7 billion			
Consumption per capita per year	Cement	Water	Aggregates
	Production: billion t	Consumption: billion m^3	Consumption: billion t
300	2.1	0.8	20
400	2.8	1.6	27
500	3.4	2.1	33
2030 world population: 9 billion			
300	2.7	1.1	26
400	3.6	2.1	35
500	4.5	2.7	42
2050 world population: 11 billion			
300	3.3	1.3	31
400	4.4	2.6	42
500	5.5	3.3	51

Cement

The perspective regarding the raw materials for cement, limestone, clay (and argillaceous limestone), and gypsum, may appear to be the least bleak, although not without predictable problems. In the industrialized countries, the land prices are increasingly prohibitive for preservation of the land for the quarries where the cement plants are located. Environmental protection regulations impose additional expenses. Besides, technical restrictions on the chemical compositions of cement, in particular for sulphur and alkali contents, are tending to become incompatible with modern cement manufacturing technology. In the developing countries the quantities of pure, non-dolomitic limestone are not easily accessible everywhere.

Water

Various studies in recent years,[288] estimate the current consumption of fresh water in the world to be of the order of 7000 m^3 per capita per year, predict shortages already at this level of use, and suggest that strict precautions be imposed in all countries to reduce the consumption in order to prepare for increasing demands. The resources of fresh water are estimated to be only 3% of the total, global amount of H_2O, but not more than about 0.014% is retrievable from rivers and lakes. Deep underground reservoirs in some countries such as Israel/Palestine, the Arabic peninsula, and North Africa are now being exploited, but these deposits are not replenishable, and may be contaminated by salts through dissolution of minerals in the soils, when retrieved for agricultural or urbanization developments.

Table 40 shows that the demand for fresh water for concrete is a substantial part of the total consumption. To the 1250 million tonnes of cement produced in 1994 corresponds a water consumption of 625 million m³ (average w/c assumed to be 0.5), or about 8.5% of the 7400 m³ total consumption. This magnitude of water usage may gradually be reduced by increased utilization of water-reducing chemical admixtures, but that will not represent a great saving, since larger, unrecorded amounts of water are used for curing of concrete and for cleaning of site and plant equipment between work operations.

The presented figures are disturbing, in view of the global population growth in the warm belt. Israel and Palestine are already a region where the preference for agriculture over housing, roads and sanitation, plus competitive needs for the water resources in the northern neighbouring countries, makes the planning of water consumption a difficult technical and sensitive political issue. Circumstances in the Middle East have caused the Danish shipping giant, A. P. Møller (Mærsk), to announce that conversion of 300–400 000 tonnes supertankers from oil to water transporters is under consideration for loading in South-East Asia and delivery to the Arabian Gulf states.

Even regions with no immediate, or yet acknowledged, fresh water resource problems such as Denmark need to take the issues seriously. Over the past ten years, the price of water for private consumption has climbed from about 1 to 12–24 DKK per m³, and new price rises are likely as an environmental protection measure. Such new cost levels for water may prove threatening for the competitiveness of concrete vis-à-vis alternative materials. However, since any such competitor is unavailable in comparable quantities without its own corresponding price rises, the consequence of making concrete more expensive will probably result in a corresponding reduction of the average standard of living. In the longer term, and beyond Denmark, this perspective is also visible in the concomitant strain on the resources of aggregates for concrete.

Aggregates

The average person, who regards with awe tremendous mountains and plains, deserts, river and sea beds, with gravel and sand scattered all around them as debris, may feel confident that at least aggregates for concrete are available in sufficient amounts for centuries to come. Notwithstanding any such pictorial reassurance, a closer look at the world's geography and geology justifies concern for the strain on the available materials for aggregates vis-à-vis the projected increase of the consumption in Table 40.

In South-East Asia, the Pacific archipelagos and parts of Latin America and Africa, younger volcanic rock types and calcareous coral debris prevail as accessible aggregate resources. These materials are frequently porous, weak and brittle, and generally of inferior quality as aggregates. In large areas of South Asia and West Africa fat, lateritic and bauxitic clays predominate. These materials require calcination to be useable as lightweight aggregates. In the vast desert regions of all continents, the rocky outcrops comprise friable, weak materials due to the severe, permanently hot, arid or hot and cold, arid climates.

In the industrialized countries, such as North America, Japan and western Europe, the conventional resources, such as gravel and sandpits, are being emptied or, like solid rock outcrops, subject to environmental restrictions, or urbanization makes them inaccessible. North-west European countries with the adjacent shallow North Sea have still large retrievable quantities of sea-bed gravel and sand,[289] but restrictive regulations are certain to become a political EC issue, and also conflicting fishing interests are gaining inhibitory influence. This development is also likely to emerge everywhere else, and to make long-distance sea transportation of aggregates by bulk carriers a common feature in future concrete enterprises.

Alkali-silica reaction (ASR) constitutes a special problem. The scrutiny in Part II of the international research into this cause of damage in field concrete shows indefeasibly that:

- ASR is a globally occurring, potential cause of damage to field concrete
- most of the rock types in the world, which are retrievable as concrete aggregate resource, are alkali-reactive
- the available methods for classification of rock types with regard to their alkali reactivity are not predictive of whether their reaction in field concrete may engender damage or remain harmless.

The new "concrete construction demography" means that the major growth of aggregate consumption in the developing regions occurs where the least experience with harmless versus harmful ASR in field concrete exists, and where, in many cases, the utilization of alkali-reactive aggregates is unavoidable. The engineering choice would therefore there be calculated risk acceptance or reliance on the known preventive measures. Since low-alkali cement is scarcely available, the so-called supplementary cement materials, fly ash, GGBS and silica fume become important.

Fly ash, GGBS and silica fume

Davidovits in reference [290] estimates that in year the 2015 about 290 million tonnes of fly ash will be generated from coal-fired electricity utilities. Hitherto (1988) only 10–15% of this fly ash have been used in up to 25% (by weight) blends with Portland cement, whereas by far the largest amounts of fly ash have so far been used simply as a lower-price replacement material in earthfills, etc. Also, for other reasons, including quality problems and transportation costs, it is deemed reasonable to consider a maximum of 50 million tonnes of fly ash as being globally available as a preventive measure against ASR (the effects regarding ACR are uncertain) both now, in 2015 and further into the future.

Davidovits also mentions that from 290–560 million tonnes of GGBS might be available in the year 2015 for blending with Portland cement. GGBS is, in some contrast to fly ash, a high quality, industrial by-product, which may be used in up to 80% blends with Portland cement, or even as a cement alone in blends with a strong NaOH solution and a high range water-reducing agent.[279] Nevertheless, at present most blast-furnace slag in steel mills is left unquenched as a non-hydraulic, crystalline waste product. The quenching technology requires investments of about 80–100 million US$ per million tonnes GGBS. Such investments are only retrievable for steel producers if the complete productions are sold to concrete producers or to cement industries. Even the low 2015 prediction, of 290 million tonnes available for concrete, is therefore optimistic; 100–150 million tonnes seems more realistic.

The total production of silica fume in the world is about 2 million tonnes, and this is not increasing. In Iceland, the national production, 8000 tonnes per year, in 7% blends with the national high-alkali cement, serves as an effective preventive measure against harmful ASR. Elsewhere, in particular in the USA and Canada, the silica fume is used in special high-strength concrete formulae, and is not generally available to prevent harmful ASR.

Investment capital movements

During the first decades after World War II, the magnificent development of the precast industry in the USSR for industrial house building made it possible to rehouse the populations from devastated regions and renew obsolete housing all over the Union.

The contemporary investments in the two losing powers of the war, Germany and Japan, went further. In West Germany, the heavy industries of automobile manufacture, chemicals and construction attracted the investment capital, while the Japanese industries also focused aggressively on early creation of the high-technology electronics and assumed front-line positions in conjunction and competition with the same innovative industries in the USA. Subsequently, Taiwan, Singapore and South Korea have joined the high-technology race, which during the 1990s has spread with vigour to the entire South-East Asian subcontinent and, albeit still with strong modifications, also to the People's Republic of China.

This development is creating a new mass category of customers for commodity products. The low-salaried labour forces combined with the growing, new markets and favourable financial conditions is currently engendering, in 1997, investment opportunities promising 20–30% annual returns on pension funds, investment corporations and other sources of profit-seeking, idle capital in North America, western Europe and Japan. The concurrent development of flexibility within the financial markets is also making "kiss and run" speculation a preferable concept for such investors. They can – and do – move billion-dollar investments with brief or no notice from industry establishments in one continent to another, and from one production sector to another. Long-term, local or national loyalty towards socio-economic developments and strategies is not part of this picture, notwithstanding the fact that concrete construction is, indisputably, the fundamental necessity for the creation of broad, social welfare for developing countries. It is therefore a serious paradox that this sector of development is the least glamorous and investment-attractive, with only moderate or low annual returns on the available capital.

Table 41 (source: The global 1000, *Business Week*, 8 July 1997) shows the sales in 1996 of those private firms and corporations within the building materials and construction sectors, which qualify to figure among (*a*) the 1000 largest firms in the world, and (*b*) the 200 largest in the emerging markets (South-East Asia). It appears that the USA and Europe are lagging far behind Japan, which is closer to the emerging markets.

In the USA, only one building materials firm is among the 1000 global firms, and one construction company, while the USA, for all categories, has 422 listed companies and 46% of the total global market value, which is 11.2 trillion US$. It

Table 41. Sales in 1996 by companies in the building materials and construction sectors, ranking among the 1000 biggest in the world

	Total: billion US$
USA Europe Japan Emerging 200	2.127 25.923 120.625 18.787
	167.462

is a remarkable contrast that the four leading IT-companies, all in the USA, together reported sales of 125.598 billion US$, i.e. 75% of the sales of all ranking competitors in the world in the two building materials and construction sectors.

In western Europe, seven cement companies are among the global 1000, and one construction company (Skanska in Sweden).

Japan shows its supreme strength with five cement companies and eight construction companies listed. The cement industry reaches half of the European net sales, whereas the construction companies together reach about 20 times higher net sales than western European and USA companies together (Japan's total of the 1000 is 227 companies with 2.6 trillion US$ market value).

There are no companies of the two categories listed from eastern Europe, CIS countries, India (despite high growth rates of the cement industry), China, Africa omitting South Africa, South America or Canada. In western Europe, Germany, Italy and Spain are notable absentees.

Hence, even such a brief overview of the statistics shows how far the building and construction sector has plunged as a priority for economic investments by private enterprise. Closer analysis also reveals that banking and financial services, oil industry, pharmaceuticals, automobiles, airlines, commodities such as food and beverages, and entertainment are higher on the ranking list, even in the 200 emerging markets.

This predominant capital investment policy means that basic urbanization is left dependent on public capital creation through taxation of ordinary people as they gradually increase their income. This kind of capital growth is sensitive to the flood and ebb tides of political power changes and to the fluxes of stronger, external economies. In many developing countries, the rise of new, national building and construction enterprises for urbanization has therefore often hitherto been achieved at the expense of performance quality, while limited sectors of construction, such as high-rise commercial buildings in large cities, energy and heavy industry works, and selective infrastructure developments are those preferred by the foreign investment capital. Specifications for this kind of construction work inevitably favour transfer of conventional technology methods from the capital homelands in order to minimize design and construction costs.

Moreover, the new markets' growth by importation of foreign capital is primarily goaded towards the mass-produced commodity and service industries, including tourism, with massive news media support to vigorously promote the lifestyle and consumption drive in the matured, industrialized world. National, cultural heritage and identities are secondary, and, therefore, so are investments in education and in new science and research, *inter alia* for such basic development sectors as building and construction.

The forthcoming impact on concrete construction, and therefore on the needs for concrete research dependent on the trends of the demographic and socio-economic changes, deserves a full-time research study, far beyond the scope of the present narrative, and a few pragmatic data from news media confirm that this concern is justified. The Middle East and North African region with 270 million inhabitants (excluding Israel) exports today less manufactured products than Finland with a population of 5 million, and since 1986 real capital income in the region has dropped 2% per year. By 2010, the Middle East will need to have created about 50 million new jobs (World Bank economist N. T. Shafik in reference [291]). Obviously, concrete building and construction is a basic necessity for making such a development possible, and the need for broad concrete technology education, with adaptation of new methods, is an urgent requirement.

The decline of concrete technology research

I mentioned in 1976,[286] as the main reason for the general procrastination in the transfer of the available means for improvement of the performance yield of concrete by a factor of 2–3, that cement and concrete research was reduced to a dismal position. While the Danish cement industry still, in 1975 (before the closure of the BFL), spent about 1% of its sales on concrete research, i.e. for their customers' benefit, the Danish concrete industry responded with a rudimentary 0.25% of sales. Comparable figures for the USA,[65] showed that research expenditure in the cement industry was less than 0.03% of sales, and for the concrete producers less than 0.01% of sales in 1978. The Portland Cement Association spent 3.0 million US$ on R & D (i.e. a purchase power of 74% of the same money in the peak year 1960). The basic research investment was negligible. Apparently, the purchase of American cement companies by European corporations, such as, for instance, Lafarge, Heidelberg Zement GmbH, and Blue Circle Inc., had caused cement technology research to be moved to the capital fatherlands.

The visibility of the reduction in research which occurred in many countries was enhanced in the USA by its preceding decades of outstanding science-engineering interactivity.

I also mentioned other barriers to the transfer of research, such as:

☐ fragmented business organization and politically sensitive markets
☐ energy-intensive production
☐ low-cost bulk materials
☐ handcraft methods and empirical engineering accumulation of experiences
☐ responsibility fragmented among consultants and designers, contractors, authorities and primary materials industries
☐ consistent demands for increased capacity

□ small research units, insufficient communication and cooperation within the R & D framework

□ limited coordination in university education between silica science and education.

It is fair to say that now, despite the dismal situation in 1976, there has, during the 1980s and early 1990s, been new developments in concrete technology with improved cement qualities and new admixtures, and also in processing technology. Structural design and construction has achieved higher concrete strength yields by the use of silica fume and water-reducing agents. Site blending of fly ash or GGBS and cement has reduced concrete production costs and ensured improved durability. In addition, cement industries have radically rationalized the manufacturing technology and thereby cut the energy consumption by about 50% per tonne cement. The general increase of the production capacity of cement plants to 4000 tonnes or more per day has made cement a global commodity, with cost-reducing competitiveness enhanced by the low cost of long-distance marine bulk transportation.

But meanwhile, other obstacles to the updating and further development of cement and concrete R & D in the world have materialized:

□ The tremendous growth of the high-technology industries, above all in the USA and Japan, which has attracted investments with high annual returns has also created new, prestigious career potentials for the top intellectual grades of research professionals and students.

□ Public, political campaigns have made environmental protection, energy savings and the health care sectors high-priority categories for governmental funding of research.

□ Convenience appliances for the household market and short-term consumption products have been made widely available due to tremendous innovations in mass-fabrication technology, which also came to include the entertainment and travelling branches.

□ Building and construction has matured and become much more repair/maintenance orientated, not least as a result of the durability crisis in the 1970s and 1980s.

Hence, there were many factors in the ordinary citizen's environment in the leading industrial countries which combined to give the word *concrete* disparaging overtones of fossilized conservatism. And nowhere had cement and concrete research been able to maintain the image of the front-line servant for the users of concrete buildings and structures. So the challenges of restoration facing the concrete research communities in the forthcoming decades of the new millennium are formidable.

Industrial R & D management

Through the European Industrial Research Management Association (EIRMA) membership 1971—77 I became acquainted with the persistent drive of the manufacturing industries in the USA and western Europe towards systematic integration of their R & D investments and other operational functions within the company or corporation structure, and the striving of R & D for excellence in

323

Table 42. Synthesis of distribution of funding for the categories of R & D in research-intensive manufacturing industries

Category of R & D	Percentage of total R & D investment
Exploratory and explanatory scientific research	10
Innovative new process technology and products	25
Support to current production, sales efforts, etc.	65

performance and competitiveness. Much of the EIRMA experience was used in the work of the BFL until 1976; but planning and management of concrete technology research abroad did not develop towards application of this industrial approach. Instead, it lost coherence and systematic integration of research and transfer to technology innovations.

Table 42 is a synthesis of information collected during the EIRMA membership years about the proportional spending of R & D investments in research-intensive industries on the three categories of activity:

□ exploratory and explanatory research – the quest for new science-based knowledge with short- or long-term innovation potentials
□ innovation – the application of acquired, new science-based knowledge or independent creative ideas in process and product technology development
□ support to current production – research investigations for improvements or problem solutions within production programmes.

The system emerged in the 1960s among manufacturing industries with strong in-house R & D leadership at top-management levels. The R & D investments could be made cost-effective by the managed interaction of the three categories of efforts, and by close correspondence between the R & D and the other operating business departments: production, marketing, sales and administration.

In the cement and concrete sectors of industry, the cement manufacturing equipment companies in western Europe, the USA and Japan came closest to adapting industrial research management methods. The continuous drive after World War II towards higher worldwide cement production capacity and, from 1973, the energy crisis and new automation technology, made it possible to obtain high profitability of machinery developments. For the next level, the cement industry itself, the manufacturing technology was developed by the equipment makers and thus fixed per plant installation. The benefits of development belonged to the customers, the cement users, and returns on the R & D was only possible if competitive front-line positions increased the sales. With increasing overcapacity, normalized uniformity of cement properties, and the general development making cement a global commodity, the incentive for investment in R & D for the customers disappeared.

The concrete producers consisted predominantly of consulting, precast and construction companies, of which the majority were far too small to maintain in-house research, and the few who could, apparently found concrete technology research to be the least profitable to invest in. The strong impact of public investments in major building and construction projects, with more political pressure to keep project costs down than to finance innovations, and the buffer conservatism of the standard specification and test-based regulatory systems functioned in the same way. In other words, while the manufacturing industries intensified the professional development and utilization of R & D management and planning, the cement and concrete sector drifted backwards, away from its position of research-technology interaction into its reductional, fragmentary development.

The commercial depression of the cement and concrete R & D has further, in sharp contrast to the lessons from the general industrial development, made the academic research groups at universities the general caretakers of more than the exploratory and explanatory research, and, as they should, of the corresponding technology education. However, general, long-term funding of these basic activities also began to decline in the late 1970s. University faculties and professors had therefore to adopt bidding for public and private funding of their research in competition with public and private, institutional research and specialist groups in consulting companies.

Important public and private research institutes, under no less severe constraints than universities, were either closed, such as the BFL in Denmark, the C&CA in England, CERILH in France and others, or forced to compete for funding from the same sources as those above, and to explore the markets for consultancy services. Consulting companies in Europe and North America jumped on the bandwagon in periods of building and construction recessions. Finally, many individuals who lost their permanent appointments in institutional research and engineering companies established "mom and pop" consulting services, usually within narrow fields of personal expertise and goodwill, and often of limited business life. Evidently, the outlined degradation engenders repetitive "cosi van tutti" research funding for issues which enjoy much public attention, such as corrosion of reinforcement, the use of fly ash, GGBS and silica fume and ASR. But there is neither superior top-down management nor sufficiently powerful research groups to handle thorough demand-capability analyses with execution of planned research programmes, and to implement achievements effectively.

Table 43 presents, in some contrast, the titles of the published EIRMA conference papers from the 1990–1996 annual meetings of the association. The titles confirm that the major manufacturing industries in the uniting European countries are continuously sharpening their R & D management and planning professionalism in accordance with the general market and technology development (and lately also associating with the industrial aspects of the European Community developments). At present, in 1997, cement and concrete are represented in EIRMA by only one company, Lafarge in France, despite the fundamental importance of concrete for the membership companies' operations. Neither do the EIRMA publication titles suggest that the front-line European mass-production industries have yet recognized the indispensable nature of concrete for the broad socio-economic progress in the developing world as being an objective for EIRMA activity.

A recent, competent concrete professional leadership statement is worth quoting: The general director of the British construction research association,

Table 43. Annual conference papers published by EIRMA, 1990–96

Year	Venue	Title of annual conference paper
1990	Berlin	Mastering the growth of scientific and technological information
1991	Paris	From science to the market – 25 years of industrial R & D management in Europe
1992	London	Industrial R & D and the human resource
1993	Helsinki	Speeding up innovation
1994	Interlaken	Funding and financing industrial R & D
1995	Prague	Globalization of R & D
1995	Paris	The basis for long-term planning
1996	Amsterdam	Quality R & D

CIRIA, said in a speech at the British Institution of Civil Engineers (ICE) in April 1994 on the subject "towards a new industrial realism" that: "*Little progress seems to have been made in the last 30 years, raising serious questions about how important we judge construction research and whether the UK construction industry will continue to prosper*".[289] Since concrete construction has a large share of the entire construction production, the apparent disparaging evaluation of its own research should be considered a confirming omen for the concrete research community and the building and construction sectors that profound changes must be made early in the new millennium.

Progressive concrete research

The matching of sufficient concrete production to the service of social development in the developing regions of the world, and the threatening exhaustion of the materials resources, mean that short-term transfer of common sense technology knowledge on a grand scale is an urgent requirement for realization of urbanization, and for the education of new generations of indigenous professionals who want to serve in their own national progress. Concurrently, the foundations must be established for their access to new, progressive changes in concrete research.

The most fundamentally changing condition for the research is the transfer of the population growth to the warm belt of the globe. During the past two centuries, development of concrete technology was confined to the northern-temperate zone, with concrete produced under slow, gradual conversion of the hydraulic energy of cement at moderate to low temperature environments, with the "room temperature syndrome" a justifiable axiom for historical concrete research in the developed parts of the world. The consistently higher than "room" temperature levels of concrete during production and performance make the height and rate of energy conversion a prime factor in positive and adverse developments within its entire life cycle. Indeed, "energy conversion" might be an appropriate headline for elucidation of a holistic concrete research paradigm for the third millennium, and many years of personal activity in two particular fields of the research, the curing of concrete and ASR, make it pertinent for me to dwell on the choice of energy conversion as a general denominative title for the new era of research.

Curing of concrete

The pioneering exploratory research at the Portland Cement Association in the 1930s and 1940s by T. C. Powers and colleagues, which clarified the basic properties of hardened cement paste, was throughout based on room temperature experimental conditioning, i.e. in the USA 20°C (68°F), for the preparation and handling of laboratory specimens used in experiments and for testing purposes. The achievements of these long-term basic studies were so spectacular and widely acknowledged that "room temperature" became a ubiquitous, lasting standard condition in academic and most institutional, public research. This was also a consequence of the trend in the research towards concentrating on

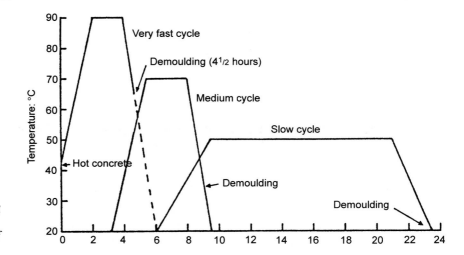

*Fig. 76. Survey of steam curing
procedures for concrete about
1974 showing different ranges of
temperature/time cycles*

laboratory experimental support for theoretical studies, and an unfortunate neglect of the concomitant, radical changes in the means and circumstances for concrete production in engineering practice – both with the precast and ready mix development and for site construction methods.

Figure 76, from reference [290], shows three different procedures for the curing of concrete, widely applied in the post World War II reconstruction decades in Europe and the USSR, in particular for site production in cold weather (winter concreting) and in precast concrete plants. The very fast cycle shown which applies external heating of the fresh concrete (except in hot countries), e.g. by steam injection in the mixer and steam curing, allowing peak temperatures of up to +90°C, made de-moulding possible after about 4½ hours, meaning that precast plants could operate three shifts per day. The medium cycle has a preheating period of several hours before steam is turned on and the peak temperature is reduced to +70°C. This procedure made two work shifts per day possible. The slow cycle, with a +15° peak temperature, would normally not require external heat supply (except in cold weather concreting). A specially controlled preheating period, as shown, is therefore fictitious. By use of the fast cycle as shown in the figure, the new industries were able to serve the societal needs by complying with the excessive demands of the new, governmental housing development plans in the 1950s and 1960s. The medium curing cycle sufficed, with corresponding cost savings and two shift operations, when the first major precast investment boom had passed, (when surplus production capacity had been reached). When the energy prices were raised exorbitantly in the 1970s and the major housing programmes in the industrialized countries had been completed, the slow cycle corresponding to one shift per day plant operations sufficed.

The decisive parameters for the choices of the processing procedures were:

☐ the demands on production capacity
☐ the production costs, primarily decided by:
— the price of fuel for external heating.

— the depreciation of the plant investments
— the labour wages.

The three "types" of curing temperature rise and fall courses shown are also displaying the development of circumstances for ordinary site production of concrete in the post World War II era:

▫ The slow cycle is archetypical of the earliest decades, with low-heat yielding ordinary Portland cement and generally less than 300 kg/m^3 cement content.
▫ The medium cycle represents the increased heat-yielding Portland cements (increasing C_3S and fineness) and increased cement content which were required by the concurrent structural design refinements.
▫ The very fast cycle represents the supplementary effects of external heat in the Middle Eastern construction boom in the 1970s.

The figure reflects a review of engineering practice at the time of representation (1974) with ubiquitous reliance on room temperature hardening in the cement hydration research, and for site and precast plant quality control of concrete strength development. Very few researchers queried the validity of the room temperature testing standards – or recognized the established gap between the real course of heat release in concrete and the room temperature removal of heat in the laboratory procedures.

Figure 77, from reference [294] is a summary presentation of safeguards which the precast industries in many countries introduced in the course of the 1980s as a delayed response to the intolerable numbers of failure cases caused by excessive heat release during early curing. It can be seen from the figure that the very fast cycles of Figure 76 seem to have been abandoned everywhere and peak temperatures of 60–70°C seem to be increasingly common. The advisory guidelines and specifications recommended:

▫ several hours' "pre-curing" without application of external heating
▫ limited rates of temperature rise during the early curing phase

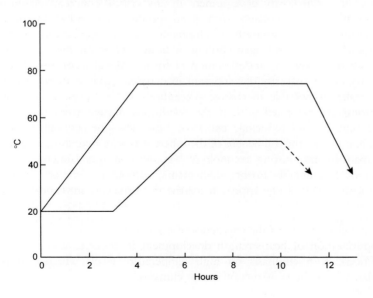

Fig. 77. Survey of range of temperature/time cycles for steam curing of precast concrete based on published guidelines and information from current practice (published and private communication)

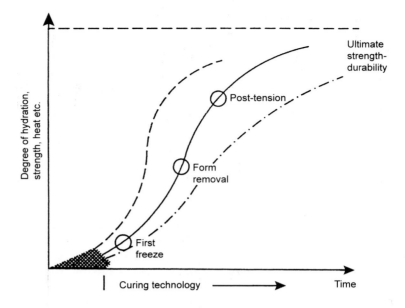

*Fig. 78. Model display of the
Danish curing technology
concept*

□ maximum soaking temperatures and duration of maintained top temperature level

□ limited rates of cooling down to ambient temperatures.

This kind of empirical, regulatory practice may help to avoid thermal cracking, but leaves no options for monitoring of the heat-strength development and thereby economizing on the cost-factors within given conditions.

Figure 78, also from reference [294], illustrates the principle of the previously described Danish curing technology method which enables the contractor to precalculate the maturity development in any critical concrete section at the planning phase, in compliance with given specifications, and to seek optimum temperature rise and strength development rates by application of required means such as liquid nitrogen cooling or heated water for the fresh concrete, insulation of formwork, and alteration of form removal times, etc. The direct recording of the maturity development in concrete sections during the curing phase makes it possible to change precautions so that prescribed courses of the curing are complied with if the conditions deviate from preset values. Hence, initial crack-inducing, excessive heat development can be avoided while, in contrast, the full benefit of the inherent heat of hydration is retrievable. This maturity monitoring technology has, since it was launched, been the subject of considerable further refinements, computerization and widespread implementation. It is one approach for the third millennium concrete research into:

□ basic clarification of the energetics of cement hydration

□ optimization of heat/strength development in concrete under given conditions, with emphasis on high temperature levels whether in precast plants or at site construction in hot climates.

Alkali-silica reaction

It is a fascinating thought that, although relevant knowledge about the chemical reaction and its mechanical effects in concrete has been established after six decades of ASR research, the reaction must, nevertheless, still be considered a potential threat to the durability of concrete in developing countries; and despite the fact that harmful ASR in field concrete is rare in comparison with harmless ASR, the research has no yardstick to offer for quantified transfer of the experience to the "new" developing regions.

The research has not managed to explore quantified geological/mineralogical survey mapping for the "new" continents, and not even made detailed advisory classification of aggregate resources available in more than a few "older" countries, despite the established reactivity of most of the rock types on the earth – igneous, metamorphic, volcanic and sedimentary.

Cement industries have access to the relevant knowledge about the dependence of the alkali content in cement on the raw materials and the manufacture technology, but they have no definite basis for strategies on how to apply that knowledge under different situations of raw materials resources, regulatory restrictions, and market issues.

Steel industries and coal-fired power plants have access to the extensive knowledge base on the preventive effects of their by-products on harmful ASR, but far too limited production capacity to supply the markets. No classification studies or even rough surveys exist of the undoubtedly enormous quantities of natural, acid pozzolans from passivated and active volcanoes in the world, especially in the "ring of fire", the several hundred active volcanoes encircling the Pacific Ocean.

The research on the testing of aggregate reactivity has, as was admitted in the keynote review at the 10th ICAAR, 1996, reached a dead end of laboratory modelling empiricism. The approximately 40 available test methods can ensure neither justified rejection nor acceptance of susceptible aggregates.

As described in Part II, Vivian's early contemplation of the conversion of chemical energy in ASR to the mechanical work of cracking and expansion passed into oblivion during the international dormancy of the ASR research in the 1960–70s. The fathers of the ASTM testing concept for ASR in the 1950s made it clear that their separated testing of the ASR chemistry (at 80°C) and the mechanical effect (linear expansion at room temperature) did not simulate the reality of the reaction in field concrete. This early comprehension of the holistic nature of energetics and mechanics of the reaction, and the transfer from increment to mega-scale also passed into oblivion.

The events of the 10th ICAAR signalled that the new activity regarding the basic chemistry and the fractal character of the cracking mechanism is paving the way to a new holistic concept of the "incremental" nature of the reaction and, with application of the chaos theory, also transfer from the increment to the mass effects in field concrete. With this concept, tremendous amounts of existing data from research previously undertaken in many countries may be used in new studies for realistic computer modelling.

Supplementary, direct-check records about harmless ASR in field concrete for realistic modelling input are reasonably accessible because investigated cases of harmful ASR on closer review inevitably reveal partial sections without signs of damage, i.e. harmless ASR.

The ubiquitous experience, substantiated by structural research, that ASR in field concrete does not cause structural collapse engenders general confidence that:

- □ available maintenance and rehabilitation methods for existing, deleteriously affected concrete are available and well described in the literature
- □ in new structures in the old world, harmful ASR can, with certainty, be made harmless, either by implementation at premium costs of combinations of available preventive means, or at a calculated risk by implementation of none or selected preventive measures.

In the developing continents the situation is different, owing to the lack of experience about the:

- □ reactivity of available aggregates
- □ uncertain cement perspectives
- □ availability and effectiveness of preventive measures, in particular natural pozzolans
- □ effects of warm, humid and arid, and marine environments.

Hence, there are great benefits to be harvested by thorough accumulation of information from all cases of harmful ASR in field concrete in the developing warm belt of the earth, in conjunction with new research and special civil engineering competence; and both the materials and the capital resource issues suggest that the research, the industries and the civil engineering professions concerned ought to interact internationally to establish long-term, cost-effective solutions.

The last issue concerning the ASR research to serve the third millennium is the cost-effectiveness of the research itself. The investments in the past six decades are indisputably of such magnitudes that the research in the "old" world must present extraordinary arguments for continuation of larger programmes. For the "new" continents, the situation is different. Without the many years' experience with ASR, they are developing under new circumstances for building and construction. For these continents continued ASR research is required, with its origins in the available knowledge base, the suggested new paradigm and determined leaderships.

Strategies and leadership

The reviews of the circumstances surrounding the development of the research on the curing of concrete and on ASR described above are chosen to illustrate the need for science-engineering based strategies − and of the absence of same. The two areas of research were chosen for this narrative due to my long-term involvement. In particular, the course and events of the ASR research since 1940 is a unique source of information about the interrelations between scientific and simplistic, empirical research and its technical-economic environments in industry and engineering.

Other fields of concrete research than curing and ASR could reasonably be analysed by their specialists for international coordinating leadership and absence of the same. Indeed, research regarding corrosion of reinforcement in concrete tells much the same story. It was activated in the 1970s when, simultaneously, the effects of the profuse application of de-icing salts to keep traffic moving throughout the winter seasons in North America and the construction boom in the Middle East disclosed the severe aggravation of reinforcement corrosion by chloride ingress. The fundamental common cause of the seriousness of the deterioration, namely the high-temperature activation level of energy conversion to the mechanical expansion and cracking, went largely unnoticed. This was despite the coincidence of the frequent initial thermal cracking in field concrete everywhere, of the high chemical activation temperatures in summer seasons in countries with de-icing practice, and of the all-seasons high activation in the Middle East, with high concentration of salts from the sea and in soils.

The intensity of research investments, which came when the "corrosion-durability crisis" surfaced, was undoubtedly related to the decisive function of the reinforcement in structural concrete, which for any civil engineer made severe corrosion a serious collapse risk. Nevertheless, also for civil engineers the limited industrial leadership interests left the research market open to much "cosi van tutti" research in one country after another with emphasis on the simplistic "linear-expansion" laboratory modelling. As a result, lessons from the past about how to make good impervious concrete and ensure adequate cover to reinforcement became the focal outputs of this research. The long-term, enduring effects of more refined innovations, such as epoxy-coating of reinforcement bars, remained questionable.

The civil engineering professions and funding public authorities have not attempted to interfere in planning and management of the corrosion research, but have rather chosen to apply average or "most acknowledged" accomplishments for regulatory requirements in the materials mix design and execution of concrete production for structural engineering. The cost-effectiveness of this kind of research policy is not accessible, because publication of research studies habitually do not include reference to project investments or estimations of the benefits attainable by implementation of the accomplishments.

The fragmentation hegemony

The funding authorities in the industrialized, "old" world may remain satisfied by the hegemony of the conventional system of funding of concrete research with a strategy of "supportive fragmentation" corresponding to the current, low societal priority of the building and construction sector. The materials science research community seems to be equally satisfied by such a continuation of the pluralistic self-managerial system. That was highlighted when the Royal Society in the UK decided, in 1983, to celebrate a remarkable British R & D accomplishment by the ICI Industries Ltd, the so-called "macro-defect-free" (MDF) cement paste. This was done by selective invitation to the conference "Technology in the 1990's: developments in hydraulic cements". The proceedings from the conference,[295] show that the MDF invention was elegantly construed on basic fracture mechanics theory and could be used to produce exceptionally deformable cement paste, albeit without accompanying realistic analyses of the industrial applicability. The contemporary Danish development of the very high strength product Densit, with compressive strength up towards 250 MPa was presented at the conference with promising market potentials.

Beyond these two industrial innovations, the Royal Society conference comprised a diversity of high-profile information on the chemistry and mechanisms of the systems of fresh, hardening and hardened cement paste. Nevertheless, these selected front-line representations of cement and concrete research did not suggest or promise any forthcoming realization of a new strategy of holistic research related to the resource issues, or in anticipation of the world population explosion.

Renovating concrete research in the third millennium

Nowhere on earth are nations, or tribes within nations, left to preserve pristine rural survival conditions without the impact of civilization's blessings and perils. And the industrialized part of mankind is beginning to learn, partly by trial and error, but also by scientific explorations of nature and technology, that the world is an entity, and that technology which will not backfire is indispensable for general progress. To believe that the conventional concrete technology research should be able to preserve its fragmentary ways of funding and operations is a phantasmagorical creed. The basic needs for long-term urbanization in the Third World make the creation of quality research capable of matching the demands vis-à-vis the resource requirements an urgency. There are two ways by which a renaissance of concrete research may bring this about.

One is the serendipitous way; relying on the unpredictable emergence of the creative, gifted talents, dedicated to exploring how disparate components of basic knowledge merge in the light of science.

The other is the strategic R & D planning and management system used by manufacturing industries which must consistently be on the look out for innovations in order to develop their enterprises and remain competitive.

The serendipitous approach includes, in the history of concrete research in our time, the work of individuals such as P. A. Rehbinder (basic rheology science for fresh concrete and packing), T. C. Powers (the physical properties of hardened cement paste), H. E. Vivian (conversion of chemical energy to mechanical work, cracking and expansion, caused by ASR in concrete), E. Freysinnet (workability and compaction of fresh concrete for achieving high strength), P. E. Freiesleben (reaction kinetics of concrete during curing), and H. H. Bache (superior compaction of fresh concrete with silica fume and fibre reinforcement). An integrated study of their different works would reveal many personal holistic concepts of concrete technology research and development.

It was easier to attract talented people of this visionary kind to concrete research during the first post World War II decades, when national motivations to develop concrete technology were obvious to everybody and the high-technology industries had not yet begun to cream off the top science-minded innovators.

However, at the threshold of the new millennium, the pressure for socio-economic and cultural welfare in the developing countries is certain to engender the birth of numerous new centres of concrete research, with quests for national integrity and independence. There are correspondingly large numbers of unknown young talents to draw upon; many more than concrete research has previously been able to muster in the "old" world.

In contrast, the already industrialized parts of the world have the upper hand in professional planning and management of cost-effective research and development on industry terms. The merits of this kind of system are that:

- a holistic knowledge base is capable of continuous absorption of pragmatic, science-based novelties from both in-house and external sources
- its achievements have their market in-house, namely the intelligent, goal-orientated transfer of basic knowledge as the vehicle for technology innovations
- its effectiveness relies on cognition of the profound paradox that commercial success in the long term depends on sincere evaluation of human capital as a far more decisive resource than monetary equity and stocks – and insensitive to market fluctuations.

It requires the determined efforts of both an R & D management and a superior industry leadership to ensure that the R & D efforts add value to the business operations. Experience shows that such success is not merely a matter of development competence, but also that appropriate environments and opportunities for the serendipitous kind of talented researcher are essential.

Figure 79 after reference [296] is a graphic depiction of the approach to strategic planning and management of technology R & D described above. It was made for the public Danish Technology Council in 1987 as guidance for selection and evaluation of applications for supportive, public funding. In principle it is, with modifications, also useful for planning and evaluation of individual research studies, for university research and post-graduate education programmes, and for industrial R & D groups and institutes. (When used as guidance in public sectors, more subtle but demanding quality criteria for funding and management returns on investment must be identified and adopted.) The figure emphasizes the following:

- Long-range R & D strategic planning makes it possible to identify external available technology as an alternative to in-house research.
- Breakdown of an established long-term strategy by demand-capability analyses for the preparation of an R & D portfolio includes quantified estimations of the potential future returns to be retrieved from the R & D investments, vis-à-vis the costs of the operations and of the tied-up capital. (In academic and governmental, technological research measures of merit other than commercial profits, such as international recognition, are applicable.)
- The operating phase of R & D work includes, in private enterprises, the evaluation and closing down of unsuccessful research projects, for which the carried expenses must be written off. (Academic and governmental, institutional research may adopt criteria other than the commercial incentive to shelf projects which appear to be without merit for progressive development.)
- Final transfer of R & D accomplishments includes, in commercial enterprises, the implementation phase and its expenses. In academic and other public research, the implementation phase is, in principle, the dissemination

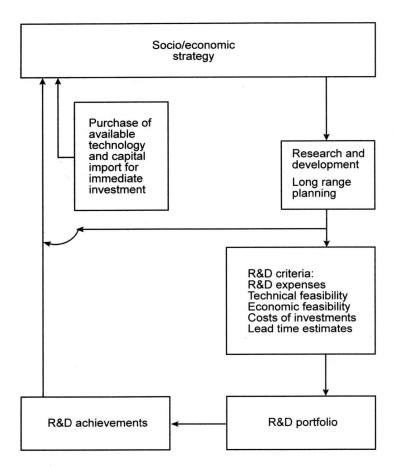

*Fig. 79. Strategic system for
socio-economic progress by
means of investment in research
and development*

of the acquired results and conclusions by publication and incorporation in
educational programmes. For special governmental research the dissemination of research accomplishments is, in principle, delivery for use in new
legislation, standard specifications, etc.

I am aware that the latter approach to a general concrete research renaissance is
the more promising of the two suggested above. The most urgent prerequisites
for ensuring that it takes place are, in my opinion, broad determination within
the industries, the technical professions and academia to advance new kinds of
interactive education of research workers and practising engineers, and to

create new international structures of committed R & D leadership. For these purposes, I suggest the following avenues for progress:

(a) For a period of several years, a large part of those currently employed as concrete researchers in the industrialized parts of the world shall be encouraged to undertake the thorough updating of concrete technology education and training of engineering students, professional engineers, and non-professional workers in developing countries, and be rewarded for doing so. Concurrent courses shall be arranged for the training of researchers in the developing countries in modern concrete engineering conditions, including general humanitarian subjects, such as demographic changes and resource problems.

(b) Academies of Science and Engineering shall be asked to arrange for the creation of an international leadership group of prominent materials scientists to update the available knowledge about the application of materials science in concrete technology research. A second objective for this group would be to create an award-offering evaluation system for universities which develop excellence in globally attractive, new approaches to interactive science/engineering concrete research.

(c) ACI, FIP, IABSE, CEB, RILEM, and national concrete associations shall be asked to cooperate in the appointment of an international leadership group of top executive cement and concrete producers and users. The first objective of this group will be to scrutinize the global concrete R & D needs vis-à-vis the available capability, including the human, materials and financial resources. The second objective for this group would be to prepare a "white paper" for a truly global concrete research strategy, and on that basis to make proposals for selected, most urgent R & D programmes to be internationally financed by public and commercial investments and to be awarded by tendering arrangements.

(d) An international academic and cement and concrete industry leadership group shall be established to manage a programme with modelling specialists with the objective of exploring how the present concrete modelling research may be refined so as to be transferable to technology circumstances.

(e) The three leadership groups described above shall be asked to convene for the creation of a *World Concrete Constitution* encompassing guidelines for its breakdown of the general concrete research and technology axioms into different operational undertakings. These would, for instance, be the preparations of standard specifications with the aim of ensuring that engineering concrete quality corresponds to relevant economic, technical and environmental circumstances.

Concluding remarks

It would be a quixotic venture to advertise a new holistic paradigm for concrete technology research as the panacea to resolve the demands on concrete for building and construction in the new millennium. Even to associate the concept of holism with such a paradigm would be an overstatement. In principle, that would need to incorporate also the research and development for concrete structural design, construction methods, standard regulatory systems and the increasingly popular performance life cycle axiom. Even the quest for progress of this logical larger entity of opportunities and problems encounters hindrances in the real world of basic economies and politics.

The huge amounts of instantaneously available investment capital in the current financial markets is one such hindrance; the different political cultures and the confrontation of conventional rural lifestyles with the overwhelming impact of modern urbanization is another, and sudden natural catastrophes occasionally overturn any man-made planning for rational socio-economic progress, including building and construction.

The rapidity of computerized international investment capital transfer is a highly complicating factor in the global socio-economic development. The capital holding investors, such as mutual savings corporations, pension funds, banks and individual speculators in the rich countries, and the nouveaux riches and governments in developing countries are prone to enter collision courses with long-term urbanization planning for the poorer people in the developing countries. The breaking down of general economic perspectives into gradual long-term urbanization with concrete building and construction is therefore made almost impossible to handle. The different political cultures among the people in the different continents of the new world may also, for some years ahead, mean less influence for progressive, social urbanization, especially where discovery of new oil fields and ore deposits turns the investment priorities of governments and private enterprises towards the floods of rapid, potential cash-flow. In the longer term, the pressures of population growth may reverse such situations and suddenly require overdue building and construction programmes to be massively advanced.

Unpredictable, major natural catastrophes, such as earthquakes and volcanic eruptions, are of much higher frequency and devastating energy release in many parts of the world with developing countries than generally experienced in most of our industrial countries with more benign geological conditions. Catastrophic events may thoroughly disrupt and even terminate major urbanization programmes, and may also effect changes in R & D priority strategies.

International Concrete Research Conference Overview 1997

The underlying, inexorably decisive conditions for concrete building and construction progress detailed above, and many years of declining societal priority for concrete research are reflected in current (1997) published programmes for international concrete research conferences. In contrast to the unavoidable request to modern manufacturing industries for identifiable cost-benefits of R & D investments, it is virtually impossible to make realistic accounts of the cost-effectiveness of the present-day international concrete research. The advance programmes of the international conferences make it possible to estimate the magnitude of the investments in the advertised research projects, but none of the announced programmes suggests that evaluations of the output of the investments are envisaged as being debated or audited post-conference, either as substantial additions to the basic scientific knowledge base, process or product innovation basis, or as significant savings in current engineering methodology.

On the expense side, records of international conferences to be held in 1997 appearing in concrete research journals, give some data for an estimate. Seventeen international conferences were announced in *Cement and Concrete Research*, December 1996.

Two of these:

- the 10th International Congress on the Chemistry of Cement (10th ICCC), Stockholm, 2–6 June 1997
- 5th CANMET/ACI International Conference on Superplastizers and other Chemical Admixtures in Concrete, Rome, 7–10 October 1997

are chosen together with the

- European Concrete Standards in Practice, Copenhagen, 22–24 May 1997

for comparative analyses of the cost-factors of the arrangements, made by experience based estimates as follows:

(a) The research investment which is required to justify presentation in an international, collegial forum is judged to be two years at 100 000 US$ per year including staff salary, cost of facilities and instrumentation, and communications.

(b) The conference expenses are estimated to be:

- conference fee   1000 US$ per delegate
- accommodation   100 US$ per delegate/day
- food, etc.   75 US$ per delegate/day
- travel   Europe: 1000 US$ per delegate
           overseas: 2500 US$ per delegate
- absence from work for delegates is averaged to about 1000 US$ per delegate/day.

Table 44 shows the estimated cost factors for the three selected conferences.

It is not possible to consider the total concrete research investments in the world by multiplying the 87 million and the 8.3 million US$ by 17:3, *inter alia* because much litigation and private industry research is not on record; but it is a reasonably modest estimation that the concrete research investments in the world for 1995–96 have been in the order of 200 million US$ or more, and the costs of the international conference communications at least 15–20 million US$.

The Copenhagen conference on the European Concrete Standards, May 1997, stands out as special among the common types of international concrete research gatherings. Its background is the recent creation of the cooperative organization ECSN (European Concrete Societies Network), and the two formidable civil engineering achievements of the Great Belt and the Øresund Link projects in Denmark. For the design and execution of these concrete works, international consulting and construction consortia have been engaged, and this has advanced integration of the different, national European standards and motivated further progress, incorporating also the EC development. The concrete specifications for the Link projects has also implemented new concrete construction monitoring methodology, rooted in our research in Denmark in the early post World War II decades (as described in Part I) besides much newer research aiming at achieving the requested 100-year service life of the structures. Hence,

Table 44. *Estimated cost factors for three selected concrete R & D conferences in 1997*

| Conference | Number of | | Research investment: × 1000 US$ | Conference expenses: × 1000 US$ | | | | | |
	Papers*	Delegates[†]		Fee	Accom-modation	Food, etc.	Travel	Absence	Total
European Standards – 3 days	38	50	3800[‡]	50	15	approx. 11	50	150	276
10th ICCC – 4 days	324	500	approx. 65 000	500	200	150	1250	2000	4000
SUPERPLAST – 4 days	90	500	18 000	500	200	150	1250	2000	4000
			approx. 87 000						approx. 8300

* According to final issued programmes.
[†] Estimations made prior to the event.
[‡] A "transfer conference", investment estimated to be half that of a research investment.

although not directly calculable, the conference has a visible output of (*a*) decisive research implementation, and (*b*) international, albeit in the first place European, integration of such implementation in common, regional standard specifications.

The two other conferences generally include many repetitive contributions, currently about such "hot topics" as high performance concrete, ASR, chloride ingress, fly ash, GGBS, and silica fume, without architectural strategies for the creation of progressive, holistic knowledge accumulation. Those who want "added value" information must search for relevant, reliable news in the voluminous series of the different conference proceedings. It is also significant that, for instance, the 10th ICCC is organized by a commercial conference organizing company, without participating cement-industry representation, while five conferences in 1997 (including the one referred to above) are organized by the Canadian Ministry of Energy and Mining which, for different conferences all over the world, co-organizes primarily with public and branch organizations. Hence, the archetypal international concrete research conference of today is primarily a collegial research community exchange forum with contributions chosen by the individual authors, but without coordinating leadership groups with top-level industry and science representation to sort out a progressive strategy, programme architecture, and quality criteria for acceptance selection. This is probably also why there are no specific conferences to discuss R & D management professionalism for concrete research, or research related to the conditions for socio-economic progress with concrete in the Third World.

Indications of progress

There are, however, some "rays of light" in the concrete research situation providing indications of progress which may concretize early in the new millennium.

ConREF Strategic Development Council (SDC) of the American Concrete Institute (ACI)

At the beginning of 1997, this new council was launched for the advance of cooperative, industry-led development of the concrete research and education foundation (ConREF), non-profit making and wholly owned by the ACI. Its mission statement says:

> "*As a council of ConREF, the SDC shall focus exclusively upon developing and directing collaborative private industry-led concrete research and development programmes leading directly to commercialisation. The thrust shall be in applied research (technology development), supported, as needed, by elements of basic (exploratory) research. The emphasis shall be on identifying and matching resources for research, executed directly or contracted by SDC member consortia under the umbrella of ConREF. SDC shall complement ConREF's mission to increase the understanding of concrete materials and to support programmes that improve concrete design and construction*".

The council shall, in other words, function as a legal forum for collaborative, pre-competitive R & D, involving both the producing enterprises and the user communities.

The council is the outcome of a 1995 approach to the American government for an earmarked 160 million US$ five-year funding of research for high performance concrete construction, which was axed by the congress budgeting majority (hence, confirming the declined status of concrete building and construction development in a leading, industrial society). The SDC does not include in its mission exploratory research *per se*, neither is it concerned about the professionalism of R & D management and planning. Its emphasis on applied research rather seems to imply preference for the fragmentary view of support for mutual investments by engaging parties, and it appears exclusively orientated towards the American concrete communities.

American Concrete Institute

The American Concrete Institute (ACI) launched a strategic plan in 1996, for action in ACI's second century. The plan concentrates on improving the service offered to the institute membership, of which 85% of about 16 000 members are Americans. Intensified efforts for the transfer of research to engineering practice are envisaged, but not the advance of exploratory, scientific research as the basis for the transfer and the foundation for materials engineering education. The plan designates the institute as an international leader of its kind, with the focus on American issues and conditions. The predominance in the forthcoming decades of investments in concrete uses in the developing continents rather than in the "old world", including North America, is not described in the document, which also does not mention the need for holistic planning and management of R & D.

European Concrete Societies Network

Turning to Europe, the new European Concrete Societies Network (ECSN), was launched in 1996 as a cooperation panoply for the:

> Belgian Concrete Group
> Czech Concrete Society
> German Concrete Association
> Danish Concrete Society
> Spanish Group for Concrete
> National Syndicate for Reinforced Concrete
> (UK) Concrete Society
> Irish Concrete Society
> (Dutch) Concrete Society
> Swedish Concrete Society
> Concrete Association of Finland.

The network will undertake exchange of information and joint advances of education and research cooperation defined as:

- working out the "partnersearch" concept
- collaboration under certain programmes such as CRAFT or Brite-Euram
- overview of research policies and programmes in different countries on concrete.

The opening network journal[297] does not mention any outreach activity towards concrete progress in the Third World, despite the intensive marketing efforts and investments in these continents by European cement and concrete enterprises. The creation of the European Community has stimulated efforts for cooperation and coordination within the member countries, although far from the extent of American federalism, in fact maybe, on the contrary, with benefits derived from the different inherited national customs and conditions.

International Congresses on the Chemistry of Cement

The 10th ICCC, Gothenburg, included two extra sessions:

- Dir. K. Hagan, UNIDO Vienna: "How to transfer modern technology to developing countries", Focus on Africa, with discussions
- Dir. M. Caocci, EC: "The thermic programme; European financial support for industrial investments in innovative technologies".

Indeed, these lectures suggest alertness on the part of the congress delegates towards the issues of Third World development by technology transfer, albeit especially to Africa, and towards means of subsidizing advances in industrial innovation. They present information for the gathered delegates about the concern in the international political world for progress in the developing countries. However, they do not appear specifically to deal with cement and concrete, and the announced 394 individual contributions to the congress represent the typical contemporaneous, fragmentary organization and structure of the international cement and concrete research. It is remarkable that the series of the ICCCs from the 1st in London, 1912, and the following including the 5th in Tokyo, 1968, were prestigious meetings of top-level cement chemistry scientists, cement and concrete technology specialists, and cement industry and research institute leaderships. With the 6th ICCC, Moscow 1974, the influx of second-order problems of cement production gained more influence.

The 8th ICCC in Rio de Janeiro and the 9th in New Delhi brought the Third World's issues to the fore, but the 10th ICCC diverts from this new policy, both by making Gothenburg in Sweden the venue and by having no cement industry representation in the congress leadership. Hence, the 10th ICCC evidences the still declining public appreciation of the private industrial leadership involvement, as well as the vanished importance of the series of ICCCs for private industries in the service of the building and construction sectors.

Breaking the waves; The "large scale engineering" concept will reshape the classical fundamental role of concrete for further societal development

It is a remarkable paradox of the indisputably fundamental position of concrete as the primary, global building and construction material versus the downgrading of concrete R & D in most countries that there is an increasing pressure of events in international political cooperation for strengthening of the global humanitarian/technology development.

The Council of the European Commission, EC, approved on 27 January 1997, an agreement for a ten-year cooperation for research and development in the

domain of Intelligent Manufacturing Systems (IMS) between the EC and
Australia, Japan, the USA, Norway and Switzerland.[298] The agreement will
function in coordination with the EC programmes for R & D adopted in
1994, including demonstrations in the fields of Industrial and Materials Technology (IMT) and Information Technology (IT). The programmes will adopt
the Large Scale Engineering (LSE) concept concerning the provision and use
of capital goods and characterized as:

- being of high monetary value
- being technically complex
- stretching the resources and know-how of involved participants to extremes
- requiring, for realization, an efficient, complex concerted effort of several
  companies, organizational units and professional disciplines
- representing a tight conceptual and physical integration of several technical
  systems
- usually undertaken on an urgent schedule:

These contingencies of the LSE concept[299] correspond in all aspects to the
conditions set out for the participants in the new IMS programmes which, being
further-reaching in scope and technical themes, must concern:

- total product life cycles
- manufacturing processes
- strategy planning and design
- human, organizational and social aspects
- extended or virtual enterprises.

It is striking that application of these LSE and IMS contingencies appears to be
100% self-explanatory and meritorious for international concrete R & D. This
narrative has emphasized the humanitarian/sociological importance of concrete
as a building material: first in Roman antiquity with its given circumstances,
next in Europe and North America in the Industrial Revolution, and in this
century for renovations after two World Wars. All of which leads up to the
current challenge of making housing, infrastructure and production facilities to
satisfy the demands of much larger populations than ever before, utilizing new
concrete technology which is

- cost- and resource effective
- suitable for global socio-economic progress, i.e. concentrating on Third
  World conditions.

Thus, the new IMS programmes ought to be made the panoply for cement and
concrete R & D, in the service of proper, international standard specifications
and engineering education in the domains of concrete technology, structural
design and construction practice. My narrative is meant to be an arsenal of
input information and motivation for such a renaissance of concrete progress.

References

Chapter 1

1 Efstathiadis, E.: *Greek concrete of three millenniums*. Public Works Research Centre, 31 pp. Athens, 1978.

2 Vitruvius, P.: *De architectura*. English translations by J. Gwilt, London 1826. I. Weale, London, 1860, M. H. Morgan, Cambridge Mass., 1914 and F. Granger, London, 1931.

3 McCann, A. M.: The Roman port of Cosa. *Scientific American*, pp. 84–91. March 1988.

4 Manzione, E: *The Colosseum (Amphitheatrum Flavium)*. 94 pp. Wage, Roma, 1982.

5 Gimpel, J.: *The cathedral builders*. Evergreen Profile Book 21. 192 pp. Evergreen Books Ltd, London, 1967.

6 Adams, F. D.: *The birth and development of the geological sciences*. Dover Publications New York, NY 1938 (new edition, unaltered, 1954).

7 Idorn, G. M.: *Die Geschichte der Betonteknik durch Mikroskop gesehen*. Sonderdruck aus *Zement und Beton*. Nr. 18, April 1960. Danish edition: *Beton-Teknik*, 4, 1959.

8 M. Faujas de Saint-Fond: *Recherches sur la puzzolanes sur la théorie de la chaux et sur la cause de la dureté du mortier*, 125 pp. Grenoble et Paris, 1778.

9 Smeaton, J.: *Narrative of the building and a description of the construction of the Eddystone Lighthouse*. London, 1813.

10 Stanley, C. S.: *Highlights in the history of concrete*. 44 pp. Cement and Concrete Association, Wexham Springs, Slough, 1979.

11 Blézard, R. G.: Technical aspects of Victorian cements. *Chemistry and Industry*, pp. 630–36, London, 1981.

12 Idorn, G. M. and Thaulow, N.: Examination of 136-year old Portland cement concrete. *Cem. Concr. Res.*, **13**, No. 5, 739–43, 1983.

13 Figg, J.: New light on the early history of reinforced concrete. *Chemistry and Industry*, pp. 793–95, November 1984.

14 Törnebohm, A. E.: *Ueber die Petrographie des Portland Cements*. Verein Skandinavische Portland-Cement-Fabrikanten. 34 pp. mit zwei Tafeln. Stockholm, 1897.

15 Childe, H. L.: Editorial notes from *Concrete and constructional engineering, including prestressed concrete*. 83 pp. Concrete Publication Ltd, London, 1958.

16 Billeskov Jansen, F. J.: *H. C. Ørsted som kulturpersonlighed*. Særtryk of Archiv for Pharmaci of chemi, 84. pp. 1273–88, 1977. (In Danish.)

17 *Durability of concrete*. G. M. Idorn International Symposium. Eds J. Holm, M. Geiker. ACI-SP 131, 425 pp. ACI, Detroit, 1992.

18 F. L. Smidth & Co.: *1922–1932*. 148 pp. Company edition. (In Danish).

19 Poulsen, A.: *Cement in sea water*. Report on the trials, commenced in 1896 on the Recommendation of the Society of Scandinavian Portland Cement Manufacturers. The International Association for Testing Materials 5th Congress. 59 pp. Also in French and German. Copenhagen, 1909.

References

20 Idorn, G. M.: *Concrete on the west coast of Jutland, Part I: Concrete technology*. Progress Report B1, 57 pp. Committee on Alkali Reactions in Concrete. Copenhagen, 1958.

21 Idorn, G. M.: *Concrete on the west coast of Jutland, Part II: Concrete durability*. Progress Report B2, 54 pp. Committee on Alkali Reactions in Concrete, Copenhagen, 1958.

22 Løventhal, J.: *Chemical value of the pozzolans and some experiments with hydraulic mortars*. Report I, pp. 5–22, and Poulsen, A.: *Hydraulic mortar in sea water*, Report II, pp. 23–36. IV International Congress of Navigation, Cairo, 1926. Reprint issued in Copenhagen, 1926.

23 Poulsen, A. and Lorenz, G.: *The use of concrete and reinforced concrete in maritime navigation works. Preservation of such works in salt water*. XV International Congress of Navigation. Venice 1931. Special report, 23 pp. Ex. Comm. General Secretary's office, Brussels, 1931.

24 Christiani & Nielsen: *Jernbetonens Pionerer*. Ved Chr. Ostenfeld. 246 pp. Polyteknisk Forlag, Lyngby, 1976. (In Danish.)

25 Ellehammer, J. C.: *Jeg fløj*. 118 pp. Drengebladet, København 1931. (In Danish.)

26 Blaser, W.: *Ludwig Mies van der Rohe*. 207 pp. Editorial Gustavo Gili, S.A. Barcelona. 1972 Verlag für Architecture Artemis, Zürich. Third Spanish/English edition, 1994.

27 Forgács, E.: *The Bauhaus idea and Bauhaus politics*. 237 pp. English translation. Central European University Press, Budapest, 1995.

28 Blake, P.: *Le Corbusier, Architecture and Form*. 159 pp. Pelican Books Ltd, Middlesex, New York, 1963.

29 First International Symposium on the Chemistry of Cement, 1918. *A general discussion on the setting of cements and plasters*. Transactions of the Faraday Society, Vol. XIV, 69 pp. 1918–19.

30 Second International Symposium on the Chemistry of Cement, 1938. *Symposium on the chemistry of cement*. Proceedings published by the Royal Swedish Institute for Engineering Research. 578 pp. 1939.

31 Carpocino, J.: *La vie quotidienne a Rome a l'apogée de l'empire*. Dansk oversættelse, 345 pp. Stig Vendelkærs forlag. Intet udgivelsesår.

Chapter 2

32 Pauly, H.: "Ikaite" a new mineral from Greenland. *ARCTIC, Journal of the Arctic Institute of North America*, **16**, No. 4, 263–64, December 1963.

33 Pauly, H.: Ikait, Nyt mineral der danner skær. *Naturens Verden*, pp. 3–12, June 1963. (In Danish.)

34 Malinowski, R.: Historical monuments in concrete. Concrete and mortars in ancient aquaducts. *Concrete International*, pp. 66–76, January 1976.

35 Roy, D. M. and Langton, C. A.: *Characterisation of cement-based ancient building materials in support of repository seal materials studies*. Technical report prepared for ONWI. Batelle Memorial Institute, Columbus, Ohio. 146 pp. December 1983.

36 Idorn, G. M.: *Durability of concrete structures in Denmark*. 208 pp. Teknisk Forlag. Copenhagen, 1967.

37 Gjørv, O. E.: *Durability of reinforced concrete wharves in Norwegian harbours*. Ingeniørforlaget A/S, 208 pp. Oslo, 1968.

38 Regourd, M.: L'action de l'eau de mer sur les ciments. Annales d l'Institut Technique du Bâtiment et des Travaux Publics. *Liants Hydrauliques*, No. 25, pp. 86–102, June 1975.

39 Idorn, G. M.: *Disintegration of field concrete*. Progress Report No. 1, Committee on Alkali Reactions in Concrete. 39 pp. Copenhagen, 1956.

40 Idorn, G. M.: *Studies of disintegrated concrete, Part I*. Progress Report No. 2, Committee on Alkali Reactions in Concrete. 77 pp. Copenhagen, 1961.

41 Idorn, G. M.: *Studies of disintegrated concrete, Part III*. Progress Report No. 4, Committee on Alkali Reactions in Concrete. 66 pp. Copenhagen, 1964.

42 Idorn, G. M.: *Studies of disintegrated concrete, Part IV*. Progress Report No. 5, Committee on Alkali Reactions in Concrete. 45 pp. Copenhagen, 1964.

43 Idorn, G. M.: *Studies of disintegrated concrete, Part V*. Progress Report No. 6, Committee on Alkali Reactions in Concrete. 81 pp. Copenhagen, 1964.

44 Idorn, G. M.: Concrete deterioration of a foundation. Acta Polytechnica. *Civil Engineering and Building Construction Series*, Vol. 4, No. 3. 48 pp. Copenhagen, 1957.

45 Nerenst, P.: *Alment om Alkalireaktioner i beton*. Progress Report A1. Committee on Alkali Reaction in Concrete. 47 pp. Copenhagen, 1957. (In Danish.)

46 Mather, B: Field and laboratory studies of the sulphate resistance of concrete. *Performance of concrete*. pp. 66–76. Ed. E. G. Swenson. University of Toronto Press, 243 pp. Toronto, 1968.

47 Verbeck, V. G.: Field and laboratory studies of the sulphate resistance of concrete. *Performance of concrete*. pp. 113–24. Ed. E. G. Swenson. University of Toronto Press, 243 pp. Toronto, 1968.

48 Mehta, P. K.: Durability of concrete in marine environment – a review. *Performance of concrete in marine environments*. pp. 1–20. ACI-SP 65. Ed. V. M. Malhotra. Detroit, 1980.

49 Stark, D.: Long-time study of concrete durability in sulfate soils. *George Verbeck Symposium, Sulphate Resistance of Concrete*, pp. 21–40. ACI-SP 77. Ed. D. Fletcher. Detroit, 1982.

50 Harboe, E. M.: *Long-time studies and field experience with sulfate attack*. pp. 1–20. ACI-SP 77. Ed. D. Fletcher. Detroit, 1982.

51 Swenson, E. G. and Mackenzie, C. J.: Contributions of Thorbergur Thorvaldson to cement and concrete research. *Performance of concrete*. pp. 3–17. Ed. E. G. Swenson. University of Toronto Press, 243 pp. Toronto, 1968.

52 Price, G. C. and Peterson, R.: Experience with sulphate environments in western Canada. *Performance of concrete*. pp. 93–112. Ed. E. G. Swenson. University of Toronto Press, 243 pp. Toronto, 1968.

53 Hurst, W. D.: Experience in the Winnipeg area with sulphate-resisting cement concrete. *Performance of concrete*. pp. 125–58. Ed. E. G. Swenson. University of Toronto Press, 243 pp. Toronto, 1968.

54 Hamilton, J. J. and Handegord, G. O.: The performance of ordinary Portland cement concrete in prairie soils of high sulphate contents. *Performance of concrete*. pp. 135–58. Ed. E. G. Swenson. University of Toronto Press, 243 pp. Toronto, 1968.

55 Thornton, H. T., Jr: Natural weather exposure station for concrete and concrete materials – Treat Island, Maine. *Performance of concrete in marine environment*. pp. 83–94. ACI-SP 65. Detroit, 1980.

56 Mather, K.: Concrete weathering at Treat Island, Maine. *Performance of concrete in marine environment*. pp. 101–12. ACI-SP 65. Detroit, 1980.

57 O'Neil, E. F.: Study of reinforced concrete beams exposed to marine environment. *Performance of concrete in marine environment*. pp. 113–32. ACI-SP 65. Detroit, 1980.

58 Schupack, M.: Behaviour of 20 post-tensioned beams subject to up to 2000 cycles of freezing and thawing in the tidal zone of Treat Island, Maine. *Performance of concrete in marine environment*. pp. 133–52. ACI-SP 65. Detroit, 1980.

59 Malhotra, V. M., Carette, G. G. and Bremner, T. W.: Durability of concrete in marine environment containing granulated blast-furnace slag, fly ash or both. *Performance of concrete in marine environment*. pp. 157–68. ACI-SP 65. Detroit, 1980.

60 Lamond, J. F. and Lee, M. K. Field exposure of concrete to severe natural weathering. *Paul Klieger Symposium on Performance of Concrete*. pp. 201–16. ACI-SP 122. Detroit, 1990.

61 Malhotra, V. M., Carette, G. G. and Bremner, T. W.: Canmet investigations dealing with the performance of concrete containing supplementary cementing materials at Treat Island, Maine. *Proceedings of the P. K. Mehta Symposium on Durability of Concrete*. pp. 291–335. Third Canmet/ACI International Conference on Concrete Durability, Eds K. H. Khayat and P. Aitcin. Nice, 1994.

347

References

62 *1992 Annual Book of ASTM Standards.* Section 4, Construction, Vol. 04.02. Concrete and aggregates. 828 pp. ASTM. Philadelphia, 1992.

63 USDA: *Plant hardiness zone map #814.* United States Government Printing Office, Washington DC.

64 Duvall D.: Snake, rattle and roll. *Natural history,* No. 11, pp. 66–72, 1986.

65 *The status of cement and concrete R & D in the United States.* Ed. D. M. Roy. 105 pp. National Materials Advisory Board, NMAB-361, Washington DC, 1980.

66 *Concrete durability – a multibillion-dollar opportunity.* Ed. J. Skalny, 93 pp. National Materials Advisory Board, NMAB-437. Washington DC, 1987.

67 Swenson, E. G.: Weather in relation to winter concreting. *Proceedings of the RILEM Symposium, Winter Concreting.* pp. A3–38. Danish National Institute of Building Research, Special Report, Copenhagen, 1956.

68 Vinberg, H. A.: Temperature variations in Sweden of importance for tests of freezing resistance. *Proceedings of the RILEM Symposium, Winter Concreting.* pp. A3–6. Danish National Institute of Building Research, Special Report, Copenhagen, 1956.

69 Jessing, J.: Influence of weather factors on heat energy level – a case of calculation. *Proceedings of the RILEM Symposium, Winter Concreting.* pp. A3–43. Danish National Institute of Building Research, Special Report, Copenhagen, 1956.

70 Poulsen, E. and Idorn, G. M.: Visual evidences of disintegration of concrete affected by freezing and thawing. Discussion to Session C, "Resistance of concrete to frost at early ages". *Proceedings of the RILEM Symposium, Winter Concreting.* pp. 7–16. Danish National Institute of Building Research, Special Report, Copenhagen, 1956.

71 Powers, T. C.: Resistance of concrete to frost at early ages. Session C. *Proceedings of the RILEM Symposium, Winter Concreting.* pp. 1–48. Danish National Institute of Building Research, Special Report, Copenhagen, 1956.

72 Nerenst, P. and Plum, N. M.: Freezing and thawing tests on green concrete. Session BI. *Proceedings of the RILEM Symposium, Winter Concreting.* pp. 3–28. Danish National Institute of Building Research, Special Report, Copenhagen, 1956.

73 Poulsen, E.: *Preparation of samples for microscopic investigation.* Progress Report M1, 46 pp. Committee on Alkali Reactions in Concrete. Copenhagen, 1958.

Chapter 3

74 *Pumpcrete practice.* Rex. 193 pp. Chain Belt Company, Milwaukee. Third edn. 1948.

75 Plum, N. M.: Denmark. *Concrete and Constructional Engineering,* pp. 123–40, Jan. 1956.

76 Powers, T. C. and Brownyard, T. L.: *Studies of the physical properties of hardened Portland cement paste.* Research Laboratories of the Portland Cement Association, Bulletin 22. (Reprint compilation.) Chicago, March 1948.

77 Saul, A. G. A.: Principles underlying the steam curing of concrete at atmospheric pressure. *Mag. Concr. Res.,* No. 6, pp. 127–35. London, March 1951.

78 Rastrup, E.: Heat of hydration in concrete. *Mag. Concr. Res.,* No. 17. pp. 79–82. London, 1954.

79 Nerenst, P., Rastrup, E., Idorn, G. M.: *Betonstøbning om vinteren.* SBI. Anvisning nr. 17. 108 pp. Copenhagen, 1953. (In Danish.)

80 *Proceedings of the RILEM Symposium, winter concreting, research and practice.* (Compilation of selectively paged sessions.) Danish National Institute of Building Research. Special Report. Copenhagen, 1956.

81 Rastrup, E.: The temperature function for heat of hydration of concrete. Session BII. *Proceedings of the RILEM Symposium, Winter Concreting.* pp. 3–20. Danish National Institute of Building Research, Special Report, Copenhagen, 1956.

82 Rastrup, E.: Discussion to reference 63. Session BII. *Proceedings of the RILEM Symposium, Winter Concreting.* pp. 35–50. Danish National Institute of Building Research, Special Report, Copenhagen, 1956.

83 Powers, T. C.: Discussion on "Resistance of concrete to frost at early ages". Session C. *Proceedings of the RILEM Symposium, Winter Concreting.* pp. 20–23. DNIBR. Special Report, Copenhagen, 1956.

Chapter 4

84 Nepper Christensen, P. og Kristensen, B. W.: *Trykstyrke og arbejdstimer for beton i afhængighed af vand/cement forhold og alder for 7 danske cementtyper.* BFL Internal Report No. 193, 1969.

85 Bache, H. H.: *Strength of structural lightweight concrete.* BFL Internal Report No. 155. 18 pp. 1967.

86 Bache, H. H., Nepper Christensen, P.: *Observations on the strength and rupture of structural lightweight concrete and ordinary concrete.* BFL Internal Report No. 106. 34 pp. Karlstrup, 1965.

87 Idorn, G. M.: Hydration of Portland cement paste at high temperature under atmospheric pressure. *Proceedings of the Fifth International Symposium on the Chemistry of Cement.* Session III–4.A. Tokyo, 1970. pp. 411–35. BFL Karlstrup Reprint No. 49, 1970.

88 *VIPRES.* Leaflet issued by VIPRES A/S, 10 pp. Undated. Published about 1976.

89 BFL. Internal Communication, 1974.

90 Idorn, G. M. and Fördös, Z.: *Cement – polymer materials.* Principal paper. *VI International Congress on the Chemistry of Cement*, Section 3, Topic 3-3, Moscow, 1974. Reprinted in *Il Cemento*, **72**, pp. 73–108, April–June 1975.

91 Thaulow, N.: Sulphur-impregnated concrete, SIC. *Cem. Concr. Res.*, **4**, No. 2, 269–77, 1974.

92 BFL. Internal Communication, 1975.

93 Bache, H. H. and Wibholm, O. M.: *Varmehærdning af Beton.* BFL Internal Report No. 102. 49 pp. 1965. (In Danish.)

94 Verbeck, G.: Energetics of the hydration of Portland cement. *Proceedings of the 4th International Symposium on the Chemistry of Cements*, Washington DC, USA. Vol. I, pp. 453–65. 1960.

95 Bache, H. H. and Dragsholt, P.: *Varmehærdning af Beton, Rapport Nr. 2.* BFL Internal Report No. 134. 58 pp. 1966. (In Danish.)

96 Alexandersson, J.: *Varmehärdningens Inverkan på Vidhäftningen mellan Ballast och Cementbruk.* BFL Internal Report No. 199. 1969. (In Swedish).

97 Alexandersson, J.: *Strength losses in heat cured concrete.* Swedish Cement and Concrete Research, Institute of Technology, Stockholm. Proceedings No. 43, 1972.

98 Freiesleben Hansen, P: *Hærdningsteknologi I. Portland Cement.* BKF-Centralen. 143 pp. 1978. (In Danish.)

99 Freiesleben Hansen, P.: *Hærdningsteknologi II. Dekrementmetoden.* BKF-Centralen. 133 pp. 1978. (In Danish.)

100 *The concrete of the Farø Bridges.* The Danish Ministry of Transport. The Road Directorate. Ed. G. M. Idorn. 156 pp. 1985.

101 Gotfredsen, H. H. and Idorn, G. M.: *Curing technology at the Farø Bridges.* ACI-SP 95, pp. 17–31, 1986.

102 Idorn, G. M.: *Concrete curing technology.* Conference on the United States Strategic Highway Research Programme "Sharing the Benefits". London 1990. R & D Consultants, Bulletin No. 19, 17 pp. 1990.

103 Idorn, G. M.: *The conflict between working for today and for the day after tomorrow.* Cembureau. 27 pp. 1973. (Also in French.)

104 Bache, H. H.: *Densified cement/ultrafine particle-based materials. 2nd International Conference on Superplasticizers in Concrete*, 33 pp. Ottawa. BFL Report No. 40. Aalborg Portland, 1981.

105 Bache, H. H.: *Introduction to compact reinforced composite.* Nordic Concrete Research,

Publication No. 6, pp. 1–33, 1987. Nordic Concrete Federation, Oslo, 1987. (Also CBL Reprint No. 17. Aalborg Portland, 1987.)

106 *Betonbogen.* Aalborg Portland, CtO. 719 pp. 1979. (In Danish.)

107 *Alssundbroen.* Vejdirektoratet. 65 pp. København. 65 pp. 1983. (In Danish.)

108 Monrad, T. & Meyer, F.: *Betonen til Guldborgsundtunnelen.* Vejdirektoratet. Broområdet. København. 116 pp. 1990. (In Danish.)

109 *Basic concrete specification, BCS.* Publication No. 89. Byggestyrelsen. Copenhagen, 1987.

110 SBI-årsberetning. 32 pp. 1988.

111 SBI-årsberetning. 17 pp. 1994.

Chapter 5

112 Stanton, T. E.: Expansion of concrete through reaction between cement and aggregate. *Trans. Am. Soc. Civ. Engrs*, **107**, Paper No. 2129, 53–126. Reprint. 1942.

113 *Aalborg Portland R & D seminar on alkali-silica reaction.* Summary of contributions. BFL Internal Report No. 342. 25 pp. Karlstrup, 1974. [1st ICAAR]

114 Bredsdorff, P., Idorn, G. M., Kjaer, A., Plum, N. M. and Poulsen, E.: Chemical reactions involving aggregate. *Proceedings of the 4th International Symposium on the Chemistry of Cement.* Session VI, Paper VI–1. pp. 749–83, with discussions pp. 783–806. Washington DC, 1962.

115 Powers, T. C. and Steinour, H. H.: An interpretation of some published researches on the alkali-aggregate reaction. Part 1: the chemical reactions and mechanism of expansion. *Proc. Am. Concrete Inst.*, **51**, 497–514, 1955.

116 Powers, T. C. and Steinour, H. H.: An interpretation of some published researches on the alkali-aggregate reaction. Part 2: a hypothesis concerning safe and unsafe reactions with reactive silica in concrete. *Proc. Am. Concrete Inst.*, **51**, 785–810, 1955. [2nd ICAAR]

117 Hobbs D. W.: *Alkali-silica reaction in concrete.* 183 pp. Thomas Telford, London. 1988.

118 *The alkali-silica reaction in concrete.* Ed. R. N. Swamy. 333 pp. Blackie Glasgow & London, V. Nostrand Reinhold, New York. 1992.

119 West, G.: *Alkali-aggregate reaction in concrete roads and bridges.* 163 pp. Thomas Telford, London. 1996.

120 Kennedy, T. B. and Mather, K.: Correlation between laboratory accelerated freezing and thawing and weathering at Treat Island, Maine. *Proc. Am. Concrete Inst.*, **50**, 141–72, 1953.

121 Alderman, A. R., Gaskin, A. J., Jones, R. H. and Vivian, H. E.: *Australian aggregates and cements.* Bulletin No. 229, Part I, pp. 1–46. CSIRO, Melbourne, 1947.

122 Blanks, R. F. and Meissner, H. S.: The expansion test as a measure of alkali-aggregate reaction. *Proc. Am. Concrete Inst.*, **42**, 517–39, 1946.

123 Meissner, H. S.: Cracking in concrete due to expansive reaction between aggregate and high-alkali cement as evidenced in Parker dam. *Proc. Am. Concrete Inst.*, **37**, 549–68, 1941.

124 McConnell, D., Mielenz, R. C., Holland, W. Y. and Greene, K. T.: Cement-aggregate reaction in concrete. *Proc. Am. Concrete Inst.*, **44**, 93–128, 1947.

125 Mather, B.: Petrographic identification of reactive constituents in concrete aggregate. *Am. Soc. Testing Materials, Proc.*, **48**, 1120–27, 1948.

126 Mather, B.: Cracking of concrete on the Tuscaloosa lock, Alabama. *Highway Research Abstrs.*, **21**, No. 11, 18, 1951.

127 Mather, K.: *Applications of light microscopy in concrete research, Symposium on Light Microscopy.* American Society of Testing Materials, Specification. Technical Publication No. 143. 1952.

128 Brown, L. S.: *Some observations on the mechanics of alkali-aggregate reaction.* American Society of Testing Materials, Bulletin No. 205, 40–44, 1955.

129 Davis, C. E. S.: Studies in cement-aggregate reaction XXV. Comparison of the expansions of mortar and concrete. *Australian J. Appl. Sci.*, **8**, No. 3, 222–34, 1957.

130 *Chemical reactions of aggregate in concrete. Identification of deleteriously reactive aggregates and recommended practices for their use in concrete.* Highway Research Board, Special Report 31,

National Acadamy of Science. National Research Council, Publication No. 549, Washington, 1958.

131 Lemish, J., Rush, E. F. and Hiltrop, C. L.: *Relationship of the physical properties of some Iowa carbonate aggregates to the durability of concrete*. Highway Research Board Bulletin 196, 1–16, 1958.

132 Svenson, E. G.: Cement-aggregate reaction in concrete of a Canadian bridge. National Research Council Canada (July 1958). Reprinted from *Am. Soc. Testing Materials, Proc.*, **57**, 1043–56, 1957.

133 Tovborg Jensen, S., Wøhlk, C. J., Drenck, K. and Krog Andersen, E.: *A classification of Danish flints etc. based on X-ray diffractometry*. Progress Report D 1, Committee on Alkali Reactions in Concrete, 37 pp. Copenhagen, 1957.

134 Woolf, D. O.: Reaction of aggregate with low-alkali cement. *Public Roads*, **27**, No. 3, 50, 1952.

135 Personal communication from G. M. Idorn, Senior Research Assistant, DNIBR, Copenhagen to F. N. Hveem, Department of Public Works, Division of Highways, Materials and Research Department, Sacramento, California. June 15, 1956.

136 Plum, N. M., Poulsen, E. and Idorn, G. M.: Preliminary survey of alkali reactions in concrete. DNIBR, Reprint No. 94 from *Ingeniøren* – International Edition, No. 1, Vol. 2. Copenhagen, Jan. 1959.

137 Vivian, H. E.: The effects on mortar expansions of the particle size of the reactive component in the aggregate. Studies in Cement-Aggregate Reaction, Part XIX. *Australian J. Appl. Sci.*, **2**, No. 4, 488–94, 1951.

138 Andreasen, A. H. M. and Christensen, K. E. Haulund: *Investigation of the effect of some pozzolans on alkali reactions in concrete*. Progress Report L 1, 88 pp. Committee on Alkali Reactions in Concrete, Copenhagen, 1957.

139 Bredsdorff P., Poulsen E. and Spohr H.: *Experiments on mortar bars prepared with selected Danish aggregates*. Progress Report I 2, 223 pp. Committee on Alkali Reactions in Concrete, Copenhagen, 1966.

140 Stanton, T. E.: Studies to develop an accelerated test procedure for the detection of adversely reactive cement-aggregate combinations. *Am. Soc. Testing Materials, Proc.*, **43**, 875–93, 1943.

141 Vivian, H. E.: The effect of storage conditions on expansion and tensile strength changes of mortar. Studies in cement-aggregate reaction, Part VII. *Journal of CSIRO*, **20**, No. 4, 587–94, Nov. 1947.

142 Vivian, H. E.: The effect of expansion on the tensile strengths of mortar. *Studies in cement-aggregate reaction, Part IV*. CSIRO Bulletin 229, pp. 67–73. Melbourne, 1947.

143 Jones, R. H. and Vivian, H. E.: Some observations on mortar containing reacting aggregates. *Studies in cement-aggregate reaction, Part IX*. CSIRO Bulletin 256, pp. 7–12. Melbourne, 1950.

144 Vivian, H. E. The effect of small amounts of reactive components in the aggregate in the tensile strength of mortar. *Studies in cement-aggregate reaction, Part XIV*. CSIRO Bulletin 256, pp. 53–59. Melbourne, 1950.

145 McGowan, J. K. and Vivian, H. E.: The correlation between crack development and expansion of mortar. Studies in cement-aggregate reaction, Part XX. *Australian J. Appl. Sci.*, **3**, No. 3, 228–32. Melbourne, 1952.

146 Idorn, G. M.: *Studies of disintegrated concrete, part II*. Progress Report N 3 Committee on Alkali Reactions in Concrete. 39pp, Copenhagen 1961.

147 Jones, F. E. and Tarleton, R. D.: *Reactions between aggregates and cement, Part VI: alkali-aggregate interaction: Experience with some forms of rapid and accelerated tests for alkali-aggregate reactivity: Recommended studies*. Research Paper No. 25. 31 pp. HMSO, London, 1958.

148 Idorn, G. M.: *Alkali-silica reactions 1975 and onwards. Proceedings of the 2nd ICAAR*. pp. 11–16. Icelandic Building Research Institute, Reykjavik, 1975.

351

References

149 *Performance of concrete. Resistance of concrete to sulphate and other environmental conditions.* Proceedings of a symposium in Honour of Thorbergur Thorvaldsen. Ed. E. G. Swansson. Canadian Building Series, No. 2. University of Toronto Press, 243 pp. 1968.

150 Alderman, A. R., Gaskin, A. J., Jones, R. H. and Vivian, H. .: Australian aggregates and cements in relation to cement-aggregate reactions. *J. Am. Concr. Inst.*, Proceedings V, 46, 613–16, April 1950.

151 Jones, F. E. and Tarleton, R. D.: *Reactions between aggregates and cement. Part IV: Alkali-aggregate interaction: The expansion bar test: Cements of high alkali content.* National Building Studies, Research Paper No. 20, Building Research Station, 1958.

152 Nerenst, P.: *Betonteknologiske studier i USA.* The Danish National Institute of Building Research, Studie (Study) No. 7. 1952. (In Danish. Summary in English.)

Chapter 6

153 *Proceedings of RILEM International Symposium, Durability of Concrete, Praha 1961.* 623 pp. Czechoslovak Academy of Sciences, Praha, 1962.

154 Biczók J.: *Betonkorrosion – Betonschutz.* 396 pp. VEG Verlag Berlin, 1960.

155 Plum, N. M.: Foreløbig Vejledning i Forebyggelse af Skadelige Alkalireaktioner i Beton. *Alkaliudvalgets Vejledning 1.* 60 pp. Statens Byggeforskningsinstitut, København, 1961. (In Danish.)

156 Jeppesen, A.: Vedligeholdelse og Istandsættelse af Beton- og Jernbeton-konstruktioner. *Alkaliudvalgets vejledning 2.* 151 pp. Statens Byggeforskningsinstitut. København, 1961. (In Danish.)

157 Mielenz, R. C. and Witte, L. P.: Tests used by Bureau of Reclamation for identifying reactive concrete aggregates. *Am. Soc. Testing Materials, Proc.*, **48**, 1071–103, 1948.

158 Idorn, G. M., Johansen, V. and Thaulow, N.: Assessment of causes of cracking in concrete. *Materials science of concrete III.* pp. 71–105. Ed. J. Skalny. The American Ceramic Society, Westerville, Ohio, USA, 1992.

159 Bache, H. H., Idorn, G. M., Nepper-Christensen, P. and Nielsen, J.: Morphology of calcium hydroxide in cement paste. *Proceedings of the Symposium on Structure of Portland Cement Paste and Concrete.* pp. 154–74. Highway Research Board Special Report 90, National Research Council, Washington DC, 1966.

160 Bache, H. H. and Isen, J. C.: Modal determination of concrete resistance to pop-out formation. *J. Am. Concr. Inst.*, **65**, No. 32. pp. 445–50. BFL Særtryk Nr. 44. 1968.

161 Svensson, S. E.: Eigenstresses generated by diffusion in a spherical particle embedded in an elastic medium. *Int. J. Mech. Science*, **33**, No. 3, 211–23, 1991.

162 Holm, J. and Golterman, P.: Fracture mechanics considerations in the assessment of deteriorating mechanisms in concrete. *Proceedings ACI International Conference, Hong Kong*, ACI-SP 128, pp. 323–38. December 1991.

163 Golterman, P.: Mechanical predictions on concrete deterioration, Part 1: Eigenstresses in concrete, Part 2: Classification of crack patterns. *Mat. J., Am. Concr. Inst.*, pp. 543–50, Nov.Dec. 1994 and pp. 58–63, Jan.–Feb. 1995

164 Nepper-Christensen, P. and Nielsen, T. P. H.: Modal determination of the effect of bond between coarse aggregate and mortar in the compressive strength of concrete. *J. Am. Concr. Inst.*, **66**, No. 1. pp. 59–62. BFL Særtryk Nr. 46. 1969.

Chapter 7

165 Idorn, G. M.: The relevance of research on alkali-aggregate reactions to precautions in contemporary engineering practice. *Proceedings of the 5th ICAAR.* Paper 252/16, 7 pp. National Building Research Institute of the CSIR, Cape Town, Pretoria, 1981.

166 *Symposium on alkali-aggregate reactions, preventive measures.* 269 pp. Building Research Institute, Icelandic Building Research Institute, Reykjavik, 1975.

167 Haulund Christensen, K. E.: *Evaluation of alkali reactions in concrete by the chemical test.*

Project Report H 1. Committee on Alkali Reactions in Concrete, 58 pp. Copenhagen, 1958.

168 Krogh, H.: Examination of synthetic alkali-silica gels. *Proceedings of the 2nd ICAAR.* pp. 131–63, Icelandic Building Research Institute, Reykjavik, 1975.

169 Grattan-Bellew, P. E.: Microcrystalline quartz, undulatory extinction and the alkali-silica reaction. *Proceedings of the 9th ICAAR.* pp. 383–94, Concrete Society Publications CS104, Wexham, Slough, 1992.

170 The effects of alkalis on the properties of concrete. *Proceedings of a Symposium held in London, September 1976.* Ed. A. B. Poole. 374 pp. Cement and Concrete Association, Wexham Springs, 1976. [3rd ICAAR]

171 Lawrence, C. D.: Changes in the composition of the aqueous phase during hydration of cement paste and suspensions. *Proceedings of a Symposium on Structure of Portland Cement and Concrete.* Highway Research Board. Special Report 90, pp. 378–391, 1966.

172 *Proceedings of the 4th International Conference on the Effects of Alkalis in Cement and Concrete.* 376 pp. Publication No. CE-MAT-1-78. Purdue University, Indiana, 1978.[4th ICAAR]

173 Verein Deutscher Zementwerke: *Vorbeugende Massnahmen gegen Alkalireaktion im Beton.* Schriftenreiche der Zementindustrie, Heft 40, 101 pp. Düsseldorf, 1973. (In German.)

174 Coombes, L. H.: Val de la Marc Dam, Jersey, Channel Islands. *Proceedings of the 3rd ICAAR.* pp. 357–70. Cement & Concrete Association, Wexham Springs, Slough. 1976.

175 *Proceedings of the 5th International conference on the Effects of Alkalis in Cement and Concrete.* National Building Research Institute of the CSIR, Cape Town, Pretoria, 1981. [5th ICAAR]

176 Alkalis in concrete, research and practice. *Proceedings of the 6th International Conference.* Eds G. M. Idorn, Steen Rostam. 532 pp. Danish Concrete Association, Copenhagen, 1983. [6th ICAAR]

177 Idorn, G. M.: Thirty years with alkalis in concrete. *Proceedings of the 6th ICAAR,* pp. 21–38. Eds G. M. Idorn, Steen Rostam. Danish Concrete Association, Copenhagen, 1983.

178 Concrete alkali-aggregate reactions. *Proceedings of the 7th International Conference.* Ed. P. E. Grattan-Bellew. NRC of Canada. Noyes Publications, Park Ridge, New Jersey, USA, 1987. [7th ICAAR]

179 Strauss, P. J. and Schnitter, O.: Rehabilitation of a Portland cement concrete pavement cracked by alkali-aggregate reaction. *Proceedings of the 7th ICAAR.* pp. 210–14. Ed. P. E. Grattan-Bellew. NRC of Canada. Noyes Publications, Park Ridge, New Jersey, USA, 1987.

180 Tang Ming-shu, Han Su-Fen and Zhen Shi-hua: A rapid method for identification of alkali-reactivity of aggregate. *Cem. Concr. Res.,* **13**, No. 3. 417–22, 1983.

181 Hirche, D.: IR-spectroscopy, a modern method to test the alkali-reactivity of silica aggregates. *Proceedings of the 2nd ICAAR.* pp. 205–12. Icelandic Building Research Institute, Reykjavik, 1975.

182 *Proceedings of the 8th International Conference on Alkali-Aggregate Reaction.* Eds K. Okada, S. Nishibayashi, M. Kawamura. 885 pp. 8th ICAAR Local Organizing Committee, The Society of Materials Science, Japan. Kyoto, 1989. [8th ICAAR]

183 Stark, D.: Osmotic cell test to identify potential for alkali-aggregate reactivity. *Proceedings of the 6th ICAAR.* pp. 351–58. Eds G. M. Idorn, Steen Rostam. Danish Concrete Association, Copenhagen, 1983.

184 *The 9th International Conference on Alkali-Aggregate Reaction in Concrete. Proceedings, Vols 1 and 2.* pp. 1128. Concrete Society Publication CS104. Wexham, Slough, 1992. [9th ICAAR]

185 The Institution of Structural Engineers: *Structural effects of alkali-silica reaction.* Technical guidance on the appraisal of existing structures. 45 pp. London, July 1992.

186 Palmer, D. (Chairman).: *The diagnosis of alkali-silica reaction.* Report of a Working Party, 2nd edn. British Cement Association, Slough, 1992.

187 Sorrentino, D., Ranc, R. and Carion, B.: Methodology of an industrial research laboratory to assess the reactivity of aggregates. Focus on reproductivity problems. *Proceedings*

of the 8th ICAAR. pp. 307–20. Eds K. Okada, S. Nishibayashi, M. Kawamura. 885 pp. 8th ICAAR Local Organizing Committee, The Society of Materials Science, Japan. Kyoto, 1989.

188 Bosschart, R. A. J.: Alkali-Reaktionen des Zuschlags im Beton. *Zement-Kalk-Gips,* **11**, 3, 100–108, 1958.

189 Museus, H. B.: *Alkali-kiselsyre-reaktioner i beton – En undersøkelse vedrørende fyllitters reaktivitet.* 96 pp. University of Oslo, 1962. (In Norwegian.)

190 Kjennerud, A.: *Skader på betonfundamenter (Såheim og Moflot Krafftstationer).* Norsk Byggeforskningsinstitut. 5 pp. Oslo 1982. (In Norwegian.)

191 Idorn, G. M. and Thaulow, N.: *Undersøgelse af alkali-kisel reaktioner i beton i Rjukan Kraftværker.* Private communications for Norsk Hydro. 1982. (In Danish.)

192 Thorsen, T. S.: Alkali-silica reactions in reinforced concrete beams with particular reference to bearing capacity. *Proceedings of the 7th ICAAR.* pp. 146–51. Ed. P. E. Grattan-Bellew. NRC of Canada. Noyes Publications, Park Ridge, NJ, USA, 1987.

193 Folk, R. L. and Weaver, C. E.: A study of the texture and compositions of chert. *Am. J. Science,* **250**, No. V, 498–510, 1952.

194 Braitsch, O.: *Über die natürlichen Faser in Aggregationstypen beim SiO_2, ihre Verwachsungsforum, Richtungsstatistik und Dobbelbrechung.* Heidelberger Beitrage zur Mineralogie und Petrographie. BD. 5. pp. 331–72, 1957.

195 Gry, H. and Søndergaard, B: *Flint-forekomster i Danmark.* 63 pp. Progress Report D 2. Committee on Alkali Reactions in Concrete. Copenhagen, 1958. (In Danish with an English summary.)

196 Micheelsen, H.: *The structure of dark flint from Stevns, Denmark.* (Dissertation.) Meddelelser fra Dansk Geologisk Forening, Bind 16, pp. 285–368. Copenhagen, 1966.

197 Alkali-aggregate reaction in concrete. *Proceedings of the 10th International Conference on Alkali-aggregate Reaction in Concrete.* Ed. A. Shayan. CSIRO Division of Building Construction and Engineering Melbourne, Australia. Melbourne, 1996. [10th ICAAR]

198 McCoy, W. J. and Caldwell, A. G.: New approach to inhibiting alkali-aggregate reaction. *Journal of ACI,* Proc. 47, pp. 693–706, 1951.

199 Kundsen, T.: A continuous, quick chemical method for the characterisation of the alkali-silica reactivity of aggregates. *Proceedings of the 7th ICAAR,* pp. 289–93. Ed. P. E. Grattan-Bellew. NRC of Canada. Noyes Publications, Park Ridge, NJ, USA, 1987.

200 Farrouto, R. J. and Haynes, W. L.: *Cement produced from glass powder by reaction with water.* American Ceramic Society, Bulletin 52: 3.276.1973.

201 Thaulow, N., and Knudsen, T.: Quantitative microanalyses of the reaction zone between cement paste and opal. *Proceedings of the 2nd ICAAR.* pp. 189–204. Icelandic Building Research Institute, Reykjavik, 1975.

202 Kawamura, M., Takamoto, K., and Hasaba, S.: Application of quantitative EDXA analyses and microhardness measurements to the study of alkali-silica reaction mechanisms. *Proceedings of the 6th ICAAR.* pp. 167–74. Eds G. M. Idorn, Steen Rostam. Danish Concrete Association, Copenhagen, 1983.

203 Thaulow, N., Holm, J. and Andersen, K. T.: Petrographic examination and chemical analyses of the Lucinda Jetty prestressed concrete roadway. *Proceedings of the 8th ICAAR.* pp. 573–82. Eds K. Okada, S. Nishibayashi, M. Kawamura. 885 pp. 8th ICAAR Local Organizing Committee, The Society of Materials Science, Japan. Kyoto, 1989.

204 Laing, S. V., Scrivener, K. L. and Pratt, P. L.: An investigation of alkali-silica reaction in seven-year old concretes using S.E.M. and E.D.S. *Proceedings of the 9th ICAAR.* pp. 579–86. London, 1992.

205 French, W. J.: Autoclave testing of concrete with respect to AAR. *Proceedings of the 10th ICAAR.* pp. 570–77. Ed. A. Shayan. CSIRO Division of Building Construction and Engineering Melbourne, Australia. Melbourne, 1996.

206 Katayama, T. and Bragg, D. J.: Alkali-aggregate reaction combined with freeze/thaw in

Newfoundland, Canada – petrography using EPMA. *Proceedings of the 10th ICAAR*. pp. 243–50. Ed. A. Shayan. CSIRO Division of Building Construction and Engineering Melbourne, Australia. Melbourne, 1996.

207 Dent Glasser, L. C., and Kataoka, N.: The chemistry of alkali-aggregate reaction. *Proceedings of the 5th ICAAR*. Paper No. S252/23. National Building Research Institute of the CSIR. Cape Town, SAR, 1981.

208 Geiker, M. and Knudsen, T.: *Chemical shrinkage*. Proceedings of the Engineering Foundation Conference: Research on the Manufacture and Use of Cements. Henniker, New Hampshire 1985. pp. 99–106. Ed. G. Frohnsdorff. pp. 244. United Engineering Trustees, Inc, New York, 1986.

209 Gleick, J.: *Chaos – making a new Science*. 314 pp. Viking Penguin Inc. 1987.

210 Cole, W. F., Lancucki, C. J. and Sandy, M. J.: Products formed in an old concrete. *Cem. Concr. Res.*, **11**, No. 3, 443–54, 1981.

211 Shayan, A. and Lancucki, C. J.: Alkali-aggregate reaction in the Causeway Bridge, Perth, Western Australia. *Proceedings of the 7th ICAAR*. pp. 342–97. Ed. P. E. Grattan-Bellew. NRC of Canada. Noyes Publications, Park Ridge, NJ, USA, 1987.

212 Bach, F., Thorsen, T., and Nielsen, M. P.: Load carrying capacity of structural members subjected to alkali-silica reactions. *Proceedings of the 9th ICAAR*. pp. 9–21.

213 Jawed, I.: Alkali-silica reactivity a highway perspective. *Proceedings of the 9th ICAAR*. pp. 471–76.

214 Mielenz, R. C., Highway Research Board Bulletin, 275: 39, 44, 1958.

215 Duncan, M. A. G., Swenson, E. G., Gillott, J. E. and Foran, M. R.: Alkali-aggregate reaction in Nova Scotia: I. Summary of a five year study. *Cem. Concr. Res.*, **3**, No. 1, 55–70, 1973.

216 Duncan, M. A. G., Swenson, E. G. and Gillott, J. E.: Alkali-aggregate reaction in Nova Scotia: II. Field and petrographic studies. *Cem. Concr. Res.*, **3**, No. 2, 119–28, 1973.

217 Duncan, M. A. G., Swenson, E. G. and Gillott, J. E.: Alkali-aggregate reaction in Nova Scotia: III. Laboratory study of volume changes. *Cem. Concr. Res.*, **3**, No. 3, 233–45, 1973.

218 Gillott, J. E., Duncan, M. A. G. and Swenson, E. G.: Alkali-aggregate reaction: IV. Character of the reaction. *Cem. Concr. Res.*, **3**, No. 5, 521–35, 1973.

219 Kennerley, R. A. and St. John, D. A.: Reactivity of aggregates with cement alkalis. *Proceedings of the National Conference on Concrete Aggregates, Hamilton, New Zealand*. 35–47, 200–204, 1969.

220 Worning, I. and Johansen, V.: Alkalis in cement and concrete manufacture. *Proceedings of the 6th ICAAR*, pp. 221–225, 1983.

221 Penkala, B.: Alkali-aggregate reactivity. Investigations in Poland – a review. *Proceedings of the 7th ICAAR*, pp. 221–225, 1986.

222 Wieker, W.: Personal communication to author, 1991.

223 Verbeck, G. and Gramlich, C.: Osmotic studies and hypotheses concerning alkali-aggregate reaction. *Am. Soc. Testing Materials, Proc.*, 55, 1110–28, 1955.

224 Chatterji, S., Jensen, A. D., Thaulow, N. and Christensen, P.: Studies of alkali-silica reaction. Part 3, mechanisms by which NaCl and $Ca(OH)_2$ affect the reaction. *Chem. Concr. Res.*, **16**, pp. 246–254, 1986.

225 Tang Ming-shu and Han Su-fen: Kinetics of alkali-silica reaction. *Proceedings of the 6th ICAAR*. pp. 261–67. Eds G. M. Idorn, Steen Rostam. Danish Concrete Association, Copenhagen, 1983.

226 Thaulow, N. and Olafsson, H.: Alkali-silica reactivity of sands, comparison of various test methods, Nordtest Project. *Proceedings of the 6th ICAAR*. pp. 359–64. Eds G. M. Idorn, Steen Rostam. Danish Concrete Association, Copenhagen, 1983.

227 *Concrete durability, Katharine and Bryant Mather International Conference*. Ed. J. Scanlon, Vols 1 and 2, pp. 2179. American Concrete Institute, SP100. Detroit, MI, USA, 1987.

355

228 *Canadian developments in testing concrete aggregates for alkali-aggregate reactivity.* 240 pp. Engineering Materials Office, Ministry of Transportation, Ontario, Canada. Report EM-92. March 1990.

Chapter 9

229 Idorn, G. M.: *Teknisk-videnskabelig Forskning og Udvikling i Danmark.* 7 pp. FRI-Bladet Nr. 6, 1969. (In Danish.)

230 *Possible contributions of cement and concrete technology to energy conservation.* 69 pp. US Department of Commerce/National Bureau of Standards, NBS Special Publication 542, Washington DC, 1979.

231 *Workshop Proceedings: Research and development needs for use of fly ash in cement and concrete.* 234 pp. EPRI CS-2616-SR Special Report. Palo Alto, 1982.

232 Idorn, G. M.: Modelling research for concrete engineering. Proceedings of the NATO/RILEM Workshop: The modelling of microstructure and its potential for studying transport properties and durability. pp. 3–27. Eds H. Jennings, J. Kropp, and K. Scrivener. *NATO's Advanced Science Institutes Series: E Applied Science.* Kluwer Academic Publishers. 558 pp. 1996.

233 Idorn, G. M. and Thaulow, N.: Effectiveness of research on fly ash in concrete. *Cem. Concr. Res.,* **15**, 535–44, 1985.

234 American Concrete Institute: *Use of fly ash in concrete.* Reported by ACI Committee 226. ACI 226. 3R-87. pp. 29. 1988.

235 Idorn, G. M.: *The concrete future.* Danish Concrete Institute, 37 pp. 1980.

236 Lew, H. S., Fattal, S. G., Shaver, J. R., Reinhold, T. A. and Hunt, B. J.: *Investigation of construction failure of reinforced concrete cooling tower at Willow Island, West Virginia.* Centre for Building Technology, National Engineering Laboratory, National Bureau of Standards, Washington DC. 73 pp. + tables, figures and appendices, 1978.

237 Idorn, G. M. and Roy, D. M.: Factors affecting the durability of concrete and the benefits of using blast-furnace cement. Reprint from *Cement, Concrete and Aggregates.* pp. 3–10. 1984.

Chapter 10

238 Idorn, G. M., Poulsen, E., Andersen, B. and Thaulow, N.: Contemporary concrete technology urgently needed for modern constructions. *Am. Soc. Civ. Engrs, Preprint 81-131.* 14 pp. 1981.

239 Idorn, G. M.: *Visions of the future – effective energy in concrete.* Invited lecture, 10th Annual Convention, Institute of Concrete Technology, England. 33 pages. 1982. (Private publication.)

240 Idorn, G. M.: Concrete energy and durability. Raymond E. Davis lecture. ACI 1983. *Concrete International,* pp. 13–20. February 1984.

241 Verbeck, G. J., and Helmuth, R. H.: Structure and physical properties of cement pastes. *Proceedings of the 5th International Symposium on the Chemistry of Cements.* VIII. pp. 1–32. Tokyo, 1968.

242 Goto, S. and Roy, D. M.: The effect of w/c ratio and curing temperature on the permeability of hardened cement paste. *Cem. Concr. Res.,* **11**, 575–79, 1981.

243 Brophy, J. H., Rose, R. M. and Wulff, J.: *The structure and properties of materials. Volume II. Thermodynamics of structure.* John Wiley and Sons, Inc. 216 pp. 1964.

244 Recommended practice for hot weather concreting. ACI Committee 605. *Journal of ACI,* Title No. 55-34. pp. 525–33, 1958.

245 Hot weather concreting. ACI Committee 305. *Journal of ACI,* Title No. 75-33. pp. 317–32, 1977.

246 Hot weather concreting. ACI Committee 305. *ACI Materials Journal,* Title No. 88-M49. pp. 417–36, 1991.

247 Carino, N. J. and Lew, H. S.: Temperature effects on strength – maturity relations of mortar. *ACI Journal*, Technical Paper, Title No. 80-17. pp. 177–82, 1983.

248 Bergström, S. G.: Curing temperature, age and strength of concrete. *Mag. Concr. Res.*, **5**, No. 14, 61–66, 1953.

249 Carino, N. J.: The maturity method: theory and application. *Cement, concrete and aggregates*, **6**, No. 2, 61–73, Winter 1984.

250 Freiesleben Hansen, P. and Pedersen, J.: Maturity computer for controlled curing and hardening of concrete. *Nordisk Betong*, **1**, 19–34, 1977.

251 Knudsen, T.: On particle size distribution in cement hydration. *Proceedings of the 7th ICCC.* Vol. I, pp. 170–175. Ed. Septima. Paris, 1980.

252 Nurse, R. W.: Steam curing of concrete. *Mag. Concr. Res.*, **1**, No. 2, 127–40, 1949.

253 Shirley, D. E.: *Concreting in hot weather.* C&CA Construction Guide. 7 pp. 1st edn. 1966.

254 Kirkbride, T.: Review of accelerated curing procedures. (*Precast Concrete*, Feb. 1971). C&CA reprint 2/80. pp. 1–12, 1971.

255 *Concrete in the Middle East.* Reprint of five articles from *Concrete.* A Viewpoint Publication. Cement and Concrete Association. 24 pp. 1977.

256 Birt, J. C.: *Curing concrete – an appraisal of attitudes, practices and knowledge.* CIRIA Report 43. (2nd edn) 33 pp. 1981.

257 Harrison, T. A.: *Early-age thermal crack control in concrete.* CIRIA Report 91. 48 pp. 1981. (Revised edn 57 pp. 1992.)

258 *Changes in cement properties and their effects on concrete.* Report of a Concrete Society Working Party. 22 pp. 1984. (Concrete Society circulation paper.)

259 Nixon, P. J.: *Changes in Portland cement properties and their effects on concrete.* BRE information leaflet. 2 pp. 1986.

260 Beckett, D.: Changes in cement properties and their effects on concrete – design implications. *Concrete*, July 1985.

Chapter 11

261 Bastiansen, R., Moum, J. and Rosenquist, I. Th.: *Bidrag til belysning av visse bygningstekniske problemer ved Oslo-områdets Alunskifre.* Norwegian Geotechnical Institute. 70 pp. Oslo. 1957. (In Norwegian, with English summary.)

262 Moksnes, J.: Oil and gas concrete platforms in the North Sea – reflections on two decades of experience. *Proceedings of a Symposium honouring Professor Ben. C. Gerwick, Jr.* pp. 127–46. Ed. P. K. Mehta. Dept of Civil Engineering, University of California, Berkley, 1989.

263 Jensen, V. and Danielsen, S. W.: Alkali-aggregate reaction in southern Norway. *Proceedings of the 9th ICAAR.* pp. 477–84. Concrete Society Publication CS 104. Vol. 1. London, 1992.

264 Anon. Kiambere hydroelectric project. *International Cement Review.* pp. 5258. March 1993.

265 Sims, G. P. and Evans, D. E .: Alkali-silica reaction: Kamburu spillway, Kenya case history. *Proc. Instn Civ. Engrs*, Part 1, 1988, 84, Dec., 1213–35.

266 Cole, R. G. and Horswill, P.: Alkali-silica reaction; Val de la Mare Dam, Jersey. *Proc. Instn Civ. Engrs*, 1989, Part 1, 1237–59.

267 Poole, A. B.: Alkali-silica reactivity in concrete from Dhekelia, Cyprus. *Proceedings of the 2nd ICAAR.* pp. 101–12. Icelandic Building Research Institute, Reykjavik, 1975.

268 Idorn, G. M. and Roy, D. M.: *Opportunities with alkalis in concrete testing, research and engineering practice.* ASTM, Special Technical Publication 930, pp. 5–15, 1986.

269 Braestrup, M. W. and Holm, Jens: *Structural effects of alkali-silica reaction in concrete.* Paper presented at DABI Symposium on Re-evaluation of Concrete Structures. 11 pp. Copenhagen 1988. (R & H Bulletin No. 2, April 1989.)

270 Holm, Jens, Idorn, G. M. and Braestrup, M. W.: *Investigation, re-evaluation and monitoring of the Lucinda jetty prestressed concrete roadway.* Paper presented at DABI Symposium on

Re-evaluation of Concrete Structures, 13 pp. Copenhagen 1988. (R & H Bulletin No. 2, April 1989.)

271 Thaulow, N., Holm, J. and Andersen, K. Th.: Petrographic examination and chemical analyses of the Lucinda jetty prestressed concrete roadway. *Proceedings of the 8th ICAAR.* pp. 573–81. Eds K. Okada, S. Nishibayashi, M. Kawamura. 885 pp. 8th ICAAR Local Organizing Committee, The Society of Materials Science, Japan. Kyoto, 1989.

272 Idorn, G. M.: Systematic ASR-expertise – Australian research 1940s to 1968. *Proceedings of the 10th ICAAR.* (Invited keynote paper submitted to conference.) Ed. A. Shayan. CSIRO Division of Building Construction and Engineering Melbourne, Australia. Melbourne, 1996.

273 Mørup, H.: A swimming pool deteriorated by alkali-aggregate reactivity. *Proceedings of the 6th ICAAR.* pp. 435–40. Eds G. M. Idorn, Steen Rostam. Danish Concrete Association, Copenhagen, 1983.

274 Petersen, Svend E.: Damages to swimming pools due to alkali-silica reaction. *Proceedings of the 6th ICAAR.* pp. 441–48. Eds G. M. Idorn, Steen Rostam. Danish Concrete Association, Copenhagen, 1983.

Chapter 12

275 Idorn, G. M.: University-industry cooperation in cement and concrete research – a case study. *Proceedings of the Engineering Foundation Conference: Research on the manufacture and use of cements.* Ed. G. Frohnsdorff, United Engineering Trustees, 1986.

276 Roy, D. M. and Idorn, G. M.: Hydration, structure and properties of blast-furnace slag cements, mortars and concrete. *ACI Journal.* Technical Paper. Title No. 79-43. pp. 444–57. December 1982.

277 Idorn, G. M.: *The effect of slag in concrete.* National Ready Mix Concrete Association, Publication No. 167. 14 pp. April 1985.

278 *Ground granulated blast-furnace slag as a cementitious constituent in concrete.* ACI, Committee 226. 16 pp. ACI 226 IR-87. First printing Jan. 1988.

279 Forss, B.: Experiences from the use of F-cement – a binder based on alkali-activated blast-furnace slag. *Proceedings of the 6th ICAAR.* pp. 101–104. Eds G. M. Idorn, Steen Rostam. Danish Concrete Association, Copenhagen, 1983.

280 Roy, D. M. and Parker, K. M.: *Microstructures and properties of granulated slag-Portland cement blends at normal and elevated temperatures.* ACI-SP 79. pp. 397–414, 1983.

281 Bakker, R. F. M.: About the cause of resistance of blast-furnace cement concrete to the alkali-silica reaction. *Proceedings of the 5th ICAAR.* Paper S252/29. National Building Research Institute of the CSIR. Cape Town, SAR, 1981.

Chapter 13

282 Idorn, G. M.: Microskopiske glimt af betonteknikkens historie. (The history of concrete technology through a microscope.) *Beton-Teknik,* 4, 119–41, 1959. (In Danish.)

283 Idorn, G. M.: Concrete durability in Iceland. *Concrete International,* pp. 41–43. November 1988.

Chapter 15

284 Materials and the development of nations: the role of technology. Proceedings of a Joint Symposium of the National Academy of Engineering and National Academy of Sciences. Part 1; 71 pp. Washington DC. 28–29 April 1976. *Materials and society,* Vol. I, No. 1, May 1977.

285 Ibid. Part 2, pp. 72–202, No. 2, May 1977.

286 Idorn, G. M.: Cement use innovations: necessary and possible. Proceedings of a Joint Symposium of the National Academy of Engineering and National Academy of Sciences. pp. 119–124. *Materials and society,* Vol. I, No. 2, May 1977.

Chapter 16

287 Brown, L. R. *et al.*: *State of the world, 1994*. 252 pp. World Watch Institute, 1994.

288 Reference to studies by Sandra Postel, World Watch Institute, USA, referred to in Berlingske Tidende 24 August 1995 and 7 April 1996.

289 Marine sand and gravel in the EC seas. Report 93/01 Central Dredging Association. 31 pp. with appendices. Bounded by EC seas. (Unpublished.) Oct. 1993.

290 Davidovits, J.: High-alkali cements for 21st century concretes. Concrete technology past, present, and future. *Proceedings of the V. Mohan Malhotra Symposium*. Ed. P. Kumar Mehta. pp. 383–98. ACI SP-144. 1994.

291 Reference to World Bank by N. T. Shafik in Business Week, 6 Nov. 1995.

292 CIRIA Spectrum. *Innovation – the key to industry survival*. Construction Industry Research and Information Association, London, Issue 3, 1994.

Chapter 17

293 Venuat, M.: The effect of elevated temperatures and pressures on the hydration and hardening of cement. Principal paper. *Proceedings of the 6th ICCC*, Moscow, 1974.

294 Idorn, G. M.: Concrete in a state of nature. *Proceedings of New Concrete Technology, Robert E. Philleo Symposium*. pp. 11–37. ACI SP-141. 1993.

295 *Technology in the 1990s: developments in hydraulic cements*. Proceedings of a Royal Society discussion meeting held on 16 and 17 February, 1983. Eds Sir Peter Hirsh, J. D. Birchall, D. D. Double, A. Kelly, G. K. Moir and C. D. Pomeroy. 207 pp. The Royal Society, London, 1983.

296 G. M. Idorn Consult A/S: *The strategy and updating of the procedures for the management of support to concrete technology research and development via the Council of Technology*. 18 pp. With appendices 1–9, 53 pp. G. M. Idorn Consult A/S, May 1989.

297 *ECSN Journal*. European Concrete Societies Network, Edition 1996/1; 2 pp. Secretarial ECSN, Goudas, Netherlands, 1996.

298 Nyhedsbrev: *Intelligent Manufacturing Systems (IMS)*. Eurocenter, Erhvervsfremmesty-relsen, 4 pp. 30 April 1997. (In Danish.)

299 Personal information. J. Rubek Hansen, Rambøll.